₁ ₂
H He

₅ ₆ ₇ ₈ ₉ ₁₀
B C N O F Ne

₁₃ ₁₄ ₁₅ ₁₆ ₁₇ ₁₈
Al Si P S Cl Ar

₂₂ ₂₃ ₂₄ ₂₅ ₂₆ ₂₇ ₂₈ ₂₉ ₃₀ ₃₁ ₃₂ ₃₃ ₃₄ ₃₅ ₃₆
Ti V Cr Mn Fe Co Ni Cu Zn Ga Ge As Se Br Kr

₄₀ ₄₁ ₄₂ ₄₃ ₄₄ ₄₅ ₄₆ ₄₇ ₄₈ ₄₉ ₅₀ ₅₁ ₅₂ ₅₃ ₅₄
Zr Nb Mo Tc Ru Rh Pd Ag Cd In Sn Sb Te I Xe

₇₂ ₇₃ ₇₄ ₇₅ ₇₆ ₇₇ ₇₈ ₇₉ ₈₀ ₈₁ ₈₂ ₈₃ ₈₄ ₈₅ ₈₆
Hf Ta W Re Os Ir Pt Au Hg Tl Pb Bi Po At Rn

Penguin Education X50
The Penguin Library of Physical Sciences

Modern Physical Chemistry: an Introduction

M. F. C. Ladd and W. H. Lee

Advisory Editor
V. S. Griffiths

General Editors
Physics: N. Feather, F.R.S.
Physical Chemistry: W. H. Lee
Inorganic Chemistry: A. K. Holliday
Organic Chemistry: G. H. Williams

Modern Physical Chemistry: an Introduction

M. F. C. Ladd and W. H. Lee

Penguin Books

Penguin Books Ltd, Harmondsworth
Middlesex, England
Penguin Books Inc., 7110 Ambassador Road,
Baltimore, Md 21207, U.S.A.
Penguin Books Australia Ltd, Ringwood,
Victoria, Australia

First published 1969
Copyright © M. F. C. Ladd and W. H. Lee, 1969

Filmset in Monophoto Times
by J. W. Arrowsmith Ltd, Bristol
and made and printed in Great Britain
by Gilmour & Dean Ltd, Hamilton

Contents

Editorial Foreword

This volume is the first of a series of degree texts in chemistry which are being produced by Penguin Education. The series is planned to cover the normal content of honours degree courses of British universities, and those of comparable standard – C.N.A.A, Royal Institute of Chemistry, etc. Most of the optional subjects, which are becoming a prominent feature of present-day courses, will be included.

It is customary, and indeed incumbent upon the general editor, to explain why a new series of chemistry books should be deemed necessary, in view of the many which are currently available. The arguments may be summarized as follows.

Firstly, the series has been planned as a whole; nomenclature, the enumeration of tables and diagrams, and their layout, have been standardized throughout, so that there is a minimum of duplication. Every student will agree that an appreciable part of almost any modern textbook of organic or inorganic chemistry includes an account of atomic structure, wave mechanics, atomic and molecular orbitals, hybridization, etc., before making use of these concepts. This kind of duplication may be eliminated, in a uniform series, by frequent cross-referencing.

Secondly, the subject has been subdivided so that students may buy the appropriate volumes as and when they become relevant to their course of study. Due to the introduction of optional subjects, and the advent of inter-disciplinary courses, not every student will require every volume. The outlay required, in any one year of the course, becomes realistic in present-day terms.

Each author has chosen to write upon the field of his special interest or study, and has been encouraged to make his contribution as up-to-date as possible, while remaining consistent with the scholastic level of the series.

It is editorial policy to include a large number of examples for solution by the reader. With the increasing introduction of a tutorial system into university teaching, these should be found valuable by tutors, for starting small-group discussion on either the correct answer, or the precision with which this answer may legitimately be quoted.

W. H. Lee
University of Surrey, 1968

Preface

In this volume we have tried to present the topics basic to a first course in physical chemistry. The subject matter is mainly conventional and should meet the requirements of the A-level and Scholarship syllabuses of most G.C.E. examining boards; we hope that it will also be useful for first-year students of chemistry, as a main or subsidiary subject, at universities and other institutes of higher education.

The treatment is intended to be modern, and to that extent is unconventional. To give three examples: we have dwelt at greater length on the solid and liquid states of matter than is usual at this level; we have replaced 'active mass' by 'activity'; and we combine Faraday's 'laws' of electrolysis into one equation.

Each chapter is followed by a number of problems, based largely upon the subject matter therein considered. Chapter 1 is, however, introductory; the problems on page 19 should be attempted after further chapters of the book have been studied.

We should like to point out one or two features of style in this volume. Headings to columns of data are aligned from the left; for example, in Table 18 the headings 'NaCl' and 'ZnS' should be taken to apply to columns 3–6, and columns 7–10, respectively. No significance (other than the introduction of variety) is to be attached to the different presentations of the phase diagrams in Figures 123 and 124.

We take this opportunity of gratefully acknowledging permission to reproduce the following figures:

67 and 68 A. Westgren, *Angewandte Chemie*, vol. 45 (1932), p. 33.
70   A. Westgren and G. Phragmén, *Metallwirtshaft*, vol. 7 (1928), p. 700.
89   H. Eyring, in *Physical Chemistry*, by Walter J. Moore, Prentice Hall, 3rd edn, 1962.
91 and 92 J. D. Bernal, in *Liquids: Structure, Properties, Solid Interactions*, ed. T. J. Hughel, Elsevier, 1965.
120   This apparatus is manufactured by Polymer Consultants Limited, High Church Street, New Basford, Nottingham.

Chapter 1
Introduction to modern chemistry

Modern chemistry investigates the structures of chemical compounds, the mechanisms by which these compounds react, and the energy changes which accompany their reactions.

1·1 Structure

The term 'structure' includes the lengths of all the bonds between atoms, the angles between these bonds, the distribution of electrons, the packing of molecules and the distances between molecules.

For example, in the water molecule, H_2O, each hydrogen atom is linked by a bond of about 0·96 Å. to the oxygen atom, the angle made by the O—H bonds (written H—Ô—H) being about 104·5°. The distance between the two hydrogen atoms, the interproton distance, is approximately 1·52 Å. The electron distribution in this molecule is such that the effective charges on the oxygen atom and on each of the two hydrogen atoms are about −0·32 and +0·16 respectively. The units here are of magnitude equal to the charge on the electron, $4·803 \times 10^{-10}$ e.s.u.

In the liquid state, the charges on the hydrogen and the oxygen atoms lead to association between neighbouring water molecules. Hydrogen bonds exist between the

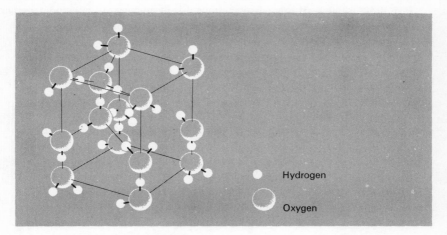

Hydrogen

Oxygen

Figure 1. The crystal structure of ice.

hydrogen atoms of any one water molecule and the oxygen atoms of adjacent water molecules, the average energy of these hydrogen bonds being approximately 4·5 kcal. mole^{-1}. In the solid at $-183°C$. there is nearly complete hydrogen-bond formation, leading to the four-coordinated structure for ice (fig. 1), but at 40°C. the average number of hydrogen bonds is about one-half of the total. The structure of ice is relatively 'open' and a volume contraction occurs upon melting; the distance apart of water molecules, the O—O distance, is about 2·76 Å.

A number of properties of water are summarized in table 1 and compared with the same properties of other hydrides of group VIB of the periodic table. Water is clearly anomalous in this comparison and we may consider that the important chemical and biological properties of water are related to its unique properties, which stem from the hydrogen-bonded structure.

Table 1 Properties of the Hydrides of Group VIB

	H_2O	H_2S	H_2Se	H_2Te
m.p., °C.	0	−83	−63	−48
b.p., °C.	100	−62	−43	−4
ΔH_f (gas), kcal. mole^{-1}	−57·8	5·3	−15·8	−33·9

Many chemical compounds, however, do not exist in the form of discrete molecules. For example, sodium chloride and other electrovalent compounds exist as ions in the solid state, but no two ions are particularly closely related although the formula NaCl tends to suggest that they may be. If sodium chloride is heated until it first melts, (at 801°C.) and then boils (at 1413°C.) some sodium chloride molecules NaCl then exist in the vapour. At lower temperatures it is meaningless to talk about sodium

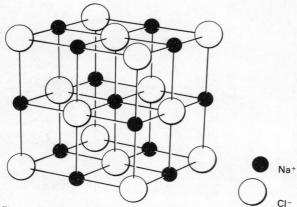

Figure 2. The rocksalt (NaCl) structure type.

chloride 'molecules' and only the structure of the crystal itself has to be considered.

The sodium chloride structure type is illustrated by fig. 2. Sodium ions, Na^+, and chloride ions, Cl^-, occupy special positions in a face-centred cubic lattice; there are four formula weights associated with the cubic unit cell of side $a = 5\cdot64\,Å$. The closest distances of ions are $2\cdot82\,Å$. for $Na^+ - Cl^-$ and $3\cdot99\,Å$. for $Na^+ - Na^+$ or for $Cl^- - Cl^-$.

In the crystal of calcium sulphate, anhydrite, the structural units are calcium ions, Ca^{2+} and sulphate ions, SO_4^{2-}. Electrical neutrality of the crystal requires equal numbers of calcium and of sulphate ions. The sulphate ion itself has a tetrahedral structure which is preserved, with very little change in size or shape, in all sulphate structures: there is no single unique distance $Ca^{2+} - SO_4^{2-}$ in anhydrite.

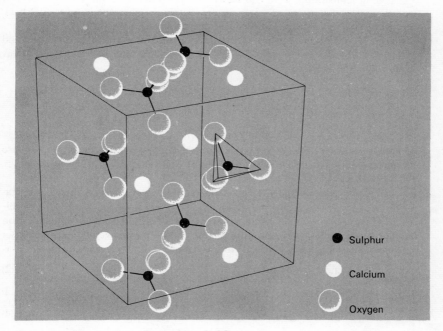

● Sulphur

Calcium

Oxygen

Figure 3.   The structure of anhydrite, $CaSO_4$.

1·2   Kinetics

The mechanisms of chemical reactions are often derived from a study of the rates at which they proceed and of the factors which control these rates. For example, the reaction between hydrogen molecules and iodine molecules occurs as a result of collisions between them. If the partial pressure of each gas is one atmosphere, only about one collision in 10^{13} is effective in bringing about the chemical reaction represented by equation (1.1); at $668°K.$, the frequency of collisions is about 1.2×10^{18} per second and so the extent of reaction soon becomes appreciable.

$$H_2 + I_2 \rightleftharpoons 2HI. \qquad\qquad (1.1)$$

In the collision process, the activated complex $\begin{smallmatrix} H{-}H \\ | \quad | \\ I{-}I \end{smallmatrix}$ is produced, which can then break down either to give the products, two molecules of hydrogen iodide, or to re-form the reactants, one molecule of hydrogen and one molecule of iodine.

The reaction is described as bimolecular, and the rate of production of hydrogen iodide at $668°K.$ is about 2.9×10^{-2} mole $1.^{-1}$ sec.$^{-1}$ The rate of this reaction is markedly increased by a rise in temperature, the rate increasing by a factor of 70 for a change in temperature from $600°K.$ to $700°K.$ From this fact, it may be deduced that the molecules must overcome an energy barrier corresponding to 39.5 kcal. before collisions produce two moles of hydrogen iodide.

(Recently it has been shown that the reaction between elementary hydrogen and iodine, in the temperature range $633–738°K.$, is not the bimolecular process (1.1) but the termolecular reaction

$$H_2 + 2I \rightarrow HI$$

which is kinetically equivalent. The iodine atoms are supplied by the equilibrium

$$I_2 \rightleftharpoons 2I.$$

Although reaction (1.1) does not occur in the above temperature range, we shall use the approximation in this introduction. See J. H. Sullivan, *Journal of chemical Physics*, 1967, vol. 46, p. 73.

The reaction between hydrogen and chlorine is very slow unless activated by ultra-violet light; the reaction then proceeds explosively and does not occur through collision between the reactant molecules. The first stage in the reaction is the dissociation of chlorine molecules into atoms which then react with hydrogen molecules and set up a chain mechanism (equations 1.2 to 1.4). The dissociation of chlorine molecules is

$$Cl_2 + energy \rightarrow Cl + Cl \qquad\qquad (1.2)$$

$$Cl + H_2 \rightarrow HCl + H \qquad\qquad (1.3)$$

$$H + Cl_2 \rightarrow HCl + Cl \quad etc. \qquad\qquad (1.4)$$

an easier process, energetically, than the dissociation of hydrogen molecules.

The main difference between the hydrogen–iodine reaction and the hydrogen–chlorine reaction is therefore the way in which the molecules acquire the energy needed for reaction: in the first-named case the energy is obtained by a collision process whereas in the hydrogen–chlorine reaction the energy of activation is acquired by irradiation. If the latter reaction were initiated by collision we would expect the ratio of the rates,

$$\frac{d[HCl]}{dt} \div \frac{d[HI]}{dt},$$

to be about 10^{-8} (from the relative bond-strengths of HCl and HI), but light of wavelength less than about 4969 Å. supplies quanta of sufficient energy to break the Cl—Cl bond and the remaining stages of the reaction are extremely rapid. If uncontrolled, the reaction becomes explosive with a relative rate of about 10^6.

The reaction between nitric acid and an organic molecule such as toluene is usually written as in equation (**1.5**), the *ortho* and the *para* derivatives predominating in the products. If this reaction proceeded by collision between toluene molecules and nitric

$$C_6H_5CH_3 + HNO_3 \rightarrow C_6H_4CH_3NO_2 + H_2O \qquad (\textbf{1.5})$$

acid molecules, we would expect the reaction to be bimolecular, and first order with respect to each component:

$$\frac{d}{dt}[C_6H_4CH_3NO_2] = k[HNO_3][C_6H_5CH_3]. \qquad (\textbf{1.6})$$

Under certain conditions (excess of nitric acid and with glacial acetic acid as a solvent) the rate is independent of the concentration of toluene even though this is not present in excess and the reaction is now of zero order with respect to toluene. This tells us that the reaction must occur in stages, and that the nitration stage is rapid: the slow step, or rate-determining step, is the production of the actual nitrating agent, the nitronium ion, NO_2^+. The reaction may thus be written in two stages, equations (**1.7**) and (**1.8**), with the organic molecule effectively 'waiting' for the nitronium ion to be formed.

$$2\,HNO_3 \xrightarrow{\text{slow}} H_2O + NO_2^+ + NO_3^- \qquad (\textbf{1.7})$$

$$NO_2^+ + C_6H_5CH_3 \xrightarrow{\text{rapid}} C_6H_4CH_3NO_2 + H^+ \qquad (\textbf{1.8})$$

If we consider the decay of radioactive isotopes we find that the kinetics are first order. The elements of atomic number greater than 83 (bismuth) decay spontaneously emitting energy in the form of α or of β radiations (fig. 4). Radioactive decay is a true first order process, the rate of decay depending only upon the number, or concentration, of radioactive atoms to the power unity.

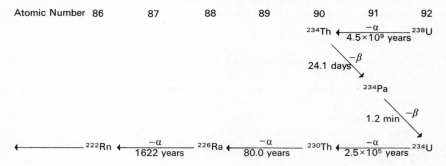

Figure 4. Part of the ^{238}U decay series: $-\alpha$, $-\beta$ refer to the emission of the corresponding radiation; the times are the half-lives of the parent species in each case.

No change in pressure or temperature has any effect upon the rate of the decay process. The activation energy of this process arises from the redistribution of energy within the nucleus of a single atom.

1·3 Energetics

Chemical reactions, such as that between hydrogen and iodine for example, do not in general proceed to completion. At 668°K. the reaction between equal volumes of hydrogen and of iodine reaches an equilibrium state when about 78 per cent of the reactants have been converted to hydrogen iodide, 1·56 mole of hydrogen iodide having been formed for every two moles of reactants (one each of hydrogen and of iodine). In the process 6·2 kcal. of heat are absorbed by the reacting system, so that in an isolated container the reaction mixture would become colder than its surroundings as reaction proceeded. However, the driving force of chemical reaction is not solely the change in heat content, or enthalpy (ΔH), but includes also an entropy term (ΔS); together these functions determine the free energy change (ΔG) for the reaction and are related by equation (1.9), ΔG for the hydrogen–iodine reaction at 668°K. being $-5·2$ kcal. mole^{-1} HI.

$$\Delta G = \Delta H - T\Delta S. \tag{1.9}$$

A spontaneous reaction is accompanied by a decrease in the free energy of the system. Thus although the hydrogen–iodine reaction is endothermic, favouring a positive value for ΔG, it occurs at 668°K. because it is accompanied by a decrease in the free energy of the system. Evidently the entropy change is a controlling factor in this reaction, and at this stage we should note that the entropy change ΔS is a measure of the probability that the atoms are arranged in the form 2HI as compared with H_2 and I_2. The term $T\Delta S$ is an energy term, and in the present example has the value of $+11·4$ kcal. mole^{-1} HI. Hence from equation (1.9), $\Delta G = -5·2$ kcal. mole^{-1} HI, as already stated.

At 25°C., the standard free energy change, $\Delta G°$, for the same reaction is $+0·3$ kcal. mole^{-1} HI. The relationship between the standard free energy change and the equilibrium constant is given, without proof here, by equation (1.10), so at 25°C., $K = 0·6$.

$$-\Delta G° = RT \ln K. \tag{1.10}$$

From energetic considerations the mixing of one mole each of hydrogen and iodine therefore leads to the attainment of equilibrium at 25°C. when 0·56 mole of hydrogen iodide has been formed, but the rate of reaction at 25°C. is about 10^{-5} times the rate at 668°K. and is consequently so slow as to be inappreciable.

Many chemical reactions which are thermodynamically spontaneous do not take place to any extent unless sufficient energy (the energy of activation) is supplied to the system to initiate the reaction, as will be seen in the discussion of chemical kinetics.

1·4   Bohr's atomic theory

In chapter 2 we shall examine some current ideas on valence theory and interatomic bonds. It is appropriate at this point to review the more important tenets (and the contributions to atomic theory) of the Bohr–Sommerfeld theory, which was developed during the period 1913 to 1923 and is now largely of historical interest but nevertheless shows the first application of Planck's quantum theory to chemistry and illustrates the calculation of the energy changes that result from transitions between atomic energy levels.

The Bohr–Sommerfeld theory suggested that atoms could not exist with arbitrary energies, but only with certain discrete values of energy. An atom with such energy occupied a stationary state and electrons were assumed to move in elliptical orbits around the atomic nucleus. Only those orbits having certain well-defined values for the major and minor axes of the ellipses were permitted so that the occupation of several such orbits by all the electrons in the atom constituted a stationary state.

Each elliptical orbit was specified by two integers, n and l, the first of which was the principal quantum number whilst the second was the azimuthal quantum number. The allowed values of n were $1, 2, 3, \ldots$; l was assigned the values $0, 1, 2, \ldots (n-1)$, corresponding to a given value of n.

It was a fundamental postulate of Bohr that an electron rotating in an allowed orbit neither radiated energy nor absorbed energy thus overcoming objections to the atom models of Thomson and Rutherford. Only when an electron 'jumped' from one allowed orbit to another was the difference in energy between the two orbits made apparent. We express this idea now in a rather different way by saying that the state of an electron in an atom or molecule is characterized, not by its distance from a nucleus, but by which of a quantized set of energy levels it occupies. Quantization is introduced because only discrete values of energy are permitted : if an electron jumps from the orbit of energy E_1 to the orbit of energy E_2, where E_2 is considered to be greater than E_1, it absorbs energy equal to $(E_2 - E_1)$. A jump in the reverse direction gives rise to the emission of energy equal to $(E_2 - E_1)$. The energy absorbed or emitted is also quantized, its value is fixed by E_1 and E_2, and it is transferred as a packet (or quantum) of energy which manifests itself as electromagnetic radiation either in the form of light or of radiant heat. It will be characterized by a frequency v and a wavelength λ, so that $v\lambda = c$, the velocity of light. The energy difference is related to the frequency by a constant known as Planck's constant, h, in equation (**1.11**).

$$(E_2 - E_1) = hv = \frac{hc}{\lambda}. \tag{1.11}$$

If the energy is measured in ergs, h has the value $6{\cdot}626 \times 10^{-27}$ erg sec.$^{-1}$

The simplest kinds of atom or ion contain just one electron, for example H, He^+, Li^{2+}, and are known as 'hydrogen-like' species. The energies of their electron orbits depend upon the principal quantum number n and upon the nuclear charge Z, but are independent of l. The lowest energy state is that for the orbit closest to the nucleus of the atom, i.e. $n = 1$, which is the ground state of the hydrogen atom ; the next highest energy level corresponds to the value $n = 2$, and so on. In the Bohr theory these levels were denoted by the letters K, L, M, N, $\ldots$, and could accommodate

2, 8, 18, 32, ... electrons respectively. For the hydrogen atom, there is the following series of energy levels:

$10^{12}\,E$ erg	n
0	∞
$-1\cdot362$	4
$-2\cdot411$	3
$-5\cdot447$	2
$-21\cdot79$	1

The zero of energy corresponds to the ionized atom, $(H^+ + e^-)$. If the electron changes from the orbit $n = 3$ to the orbit $n = 2$, the energy emitted is $(5\cdot447 - 2\cdot411) \times 10^{-12}$ erg and from equation (**1.11**) we can determine that the wave-length of the emitted radiation is 6522 Å., corresponding to the red region of the visible spectrum. We can likewise calculate that the electron jump from the level $n = 3$ to the level $n = 1$ is accompanied by emission of radiation of wavelength 1021 Å., which lies in the ultra-violet region of the electromagnetic spectrum.

For atoms or ions which contain more than one electron, the energy of an electron is no longer specified uniquely by n, the principal quantum number of its orbit, and by Z, the atomic number. For a given value of n, a number of energy levels are possible, according to the allowed values of the azimuthal quantum number, l. For $n = 4$, the values of l are 0, 1, 2 and 3:

$$n = 4 : l = 0 \quad (s)$$
$$n = 4 : l = 1 \quad (p)$$
$$n = 4 : l = 2 \quad (d)$$
$$n = 4 : l = 3 \quad (f)$$

In modern nomenclature, the various values of l are described by the letters s, p, d and f. Originally, these letters were used to denote the spectral series described as 'sharp', 'principal', 'diffuse' and 'fundamental', respectively.

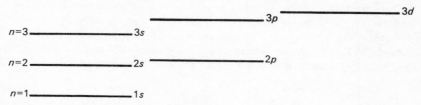

Figure 5. Some energy levels for atoms of atomic numbers less than about 20.

These energy levels are still considered to be correct numerically and to be defined by the quantum numbers n and l, but it is no longer considered that electrons are restricted to particular circular or elliptical orbits. The Bohr theory has been replaced by quantum mechanics.

There are two main reasons for this development. Firstly, Bohr's theory is of limited application: it cannot explain the shapes of molecules (for example, the tetrahedral carbon atom of organic chemistry) nor account for the spectroscopist's empirical selection rules which predict which of all the possible transitions between energy levels will in fact give rise to observed spectral lines or bands. Secondly, according to Heisenberg's uncertainty principle we cannot determine precisely both the radius and the energy of an electron within an atom; it turns out, for example, that the uncertainty in the first Bohr radius for hydrogen ($n = 1$) is about 1 Å. – twice the radius itself (0·51 Å.)! Clearly the idea of sharply defined orbits must be abandoned.

Problems

1. Write a short account of modern chemistry.
2. Write an essay on 'Water, its Structure and Properties'.

Chapter 2
Chemical structure and valency

2·1   **Ionization energy**

The atom of an element is, in most cases, a stable structure. It is true that all the heavier elements (those of atomic number 84 and above) exhibit radioactivity due to the decomposition of the nucleus, but there is no example of an atom spontaneously ionizing because it requires energy to remove an electron from an atom. This energy is the *ionization energy* (*I*), and is the energy acquired by an electron which has been accelerated through a potential of *V* volt. For a given value of *V*, $e \times V = I$, the ionization energy in electron-volts (eV.), sometimes erroneously called the ionization potential.

If we measure the successive ionization energies of an atom, we find that they do not increase by equal steps, but in a manner which reflects the electron structure. Thus for the calcium atom, the first and second ionization energies have the relatively

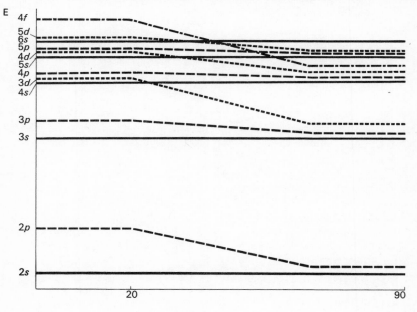

Figure 6.   The variation of energy levels with atomic number *(Z)*.

low values of $I_1 = 6.34$ eV., $I_2 = 11.9$ eV., after which there is a large increase to the value of I_3, 51.3 eV. In the case of the first four ionization energies of aluminium, a correspondingly large increase is shown between I_3 and $I_4 : I_1 = 5.85$ eV., $I_2 = 18.8$ eV., $I_3 = 28.4$ eV., $I_4 = 120$ eV. This suggests that all electrons in an atom are not attracted equally strongly by the nucleus, the deep-seated electrons being more firmly held than those further away. There are a number of *energy levels* occupied by electrons in the atom, and we shall now consider three series of energy levels of the type named in fig. 5. The s levels ($1s$, $2s$, $3s$, etc.) can each be occupied by a maximum of two electrons, the p levels ($2p$, $3p$, etc.) by a maximum of six electrons and the d levels ($3d$, $4d$, etc.) by a maximum of ten electrons.

We may imagine the ground states of atoms to be formed by feeding electrons into the system of energy levels $1s$, $2s$, $2p$, etc., the lowest level being filled first, followed by the filling of progressively higher levels, so that, for example, in the ground state of the nitrogen atom the seven electrons occupy the levels $1s$, $2s$ and $2p$ with two electrons on the $1s$ level (shown by writing $1s^2$). Similarly, the occupancy of the remaining electron levels is designated $2s^2$ and $2p^3$.

The energy levels do not continue to fill up in this way. After the $3s$ and $3p$ levels are filled, the next two electrons fill the $4s$ level, and successive electrons occupy the ten vacancies of the $3d$ level. The $4s$ level lies below the $3d$ level in energy (fig. 6) for the lighter elements, the order of the energy-levels changing as the atomic number increases; the electron structure of the vanadium atom may be represented by

$$\text{V}(Z = 23): 1s^2\, 2s^2\, 2p^6\, 3s^2\, 3p^6\, 4s^2\, 3d^3$$

and that of the arsenic atom by

$$\text{As}\,(Z = 33): 1s^2\, 2s^2\, 2p^6\, 3s^2\, 3p^6\, 4s^2\, 3d^{10}\, 4p^3.$$

The electron structures of the elements up to $Z = 38$ are shown in Appendix A.

2·2 Atomic orbitals

In the modern theory of atomic structure, electrons are no longer thought of as point charges situated on fixed orbits as Bohr believed them to be. Instead, the charge of each electron is considered to extend from the centre of the atom to infinity, although the electron charge is not evenly distributed throughout this space; for example, the centre of the atom is occupied by the positive nucleus so that the electron charge there is zero. However, the charge of each electron is mainly concentrated within a certain region of space, or alternatively there is a high probability that the electron may be found within this region. Taking the centre of the atom as origin, we may draw a *boundary surface* (or its section, in the plane of the paper) which shows the relative charge distribution in a given direction and encloses some definite percentage (e.g. 90 per cent) of the total charge for each electron. Such a boundary surface is often used to represent an *atomic orbital* and is an approximate representation of this mathematical function. The fall-off in electron charge with distance outside this boundary is so rapid that the electron may be thought of as effectively located within it.

Atomic orbitals are classified as s, p or d, in the same way as the energy levels considered previously. The first class, or s orbitals, show spherical symmetry of charge distribution about the nucleus and can contain a maximum of two electrons (the s electrons). The s orbital closest to the nucleus, analogous to the first Bohr orbit, is the $1s$ orbital; it contains one electron in the ground state of the hydrogen atom and two electrons in the ground state of helium. In lithium the $1s$ orbital is filled, and the third electron enters the orbital of next highest energy (the $2s$ orbital), which is filled in beryllium ($1s^2 2s^2$). It is apparent that the energies of the electrons depend upon the orbitals which they occupy, so that in lithium two electrons occupy the $1s$ energy level and the third occupies the $2s$ level.

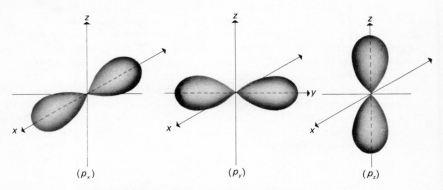

Figure 7. p orbitals (surfaces of constant ψ^2 for p electrons).

The charge distributions of electrons which occupy p orbitals show axial symmetry (fig. 7). Three p orbitals, the p_x, p_y and p_z, extend along the mutually perpendicular x-, y-, and z-axes respectively, and each orbital may contain a maximum of two electrons. These electrons, designated p_x, p_y, or p_z, may number up to six, and are of equal energy. The p electron of lowest energy occupies a $2p$ orbital, there being no $1p$ orbital and hence no $1p$ electron. Therefore in the carbon atom, which contains six electrons,

Figure 8. Atomic orbitals of F atom.

the structure may be envisaged in terms of the orbitals which are occupied. The $1s$ and $2s$ orbitals each contain two electrons, and two of the p orbitals (e.g. the p_x and p_y) are singly occupied, the $2p_z$ orbital remaining empty. In general, according to Hund's rule, orbitals are singly occupied by electrons as far as possible in order to minimize the repulsion between like charges. In neon, the three $2p$ orbitals are fully occupied $(1s^2\,2s^2\,2p^6)$: although this arrangement introduces considerable electron repulsion, it is of lower energy than one in which electrons are promoted to higher energy levels. Table 2 illustrates the electron structures for several atoms. The arrow ↑ or ↓ not only represents an electron but also possesses an added significance because an orbital will contain two electrons only if they differ in a property called spin. A vertical arrow ↑ represents one value $(+\frac{1}{2}$ unit) of the spin whilst an inverted arrow represents the other possible value $(-\frac{1}{2}$ unit), these being the only two values for the spin. Two electrons in any one orbital will therefore have a resultant spin of zero and their spins are then said to be paired, but unless they pair in a common orbital, electron spins remain parallel, like those of carbon and nitrogen in table 2. We can simplify the

Table 2   The Electron Occupancy of Atoms in the First Period

	$1s$	$2s$	$2p_x$	$2p_y$	$2p_z$
Li	↑↓	↑			
Be	↑↓	↑↓			
B	↑↓	↑↓	↑		
C	↑↓	↑↓	↑	↑	
N	↑↓	↑↓	↑	↑	↑
O	↑↓	↑↓	↑↓	↑	↑
F	↑↓	↑↓	↑↓	↑↓	↑
Ne	↑↓	↑↓	↑↓	↑↓	↑↓

electron description of the atoms in table 2 by writing the number of electrons in a given orbital as a superscript to the letter designating the orbital type. Thus for Li, Be, C, and Ne we have

Li $1s^2\,2s$
Be $1s^2\,2s^2$
C $1s^2\,2s^2\,2p^2$
Ne $1s^2\,2s^2\,2p^6$

We drop the distinction between the p_x, p_y and p_z electrons because they have the same energies, but we can always reintroduce the description if necessary – we know that $2p^4$ is, for example, $2p_x^2\,2p_y\,2p_z$ (fig. 8).

The energy levels $1s$, $2s$, $2p$, $3s$ and $3p$ are a set that steadily increase in energy and are followed by two sets of very similar energy levels, the $4s$ and the $3d$. There are certain variations in the building up of the electron shells for the next group of elements, the first transition series. We note firstly that as there were three equivalent p orbitals, so there are five equivalent d orbitals, each capable of holding a maximum of two electrons having opposite spins. Using the symbol [Ar] (argon) to represent the configuration $1s^2\,2s^2\,2p^6\,3s^2\,3p^6$, the electron arrangement for the atoms $Ca\,(Z = 20)$ to $Zn\,(Z = 30)$ is illustrated in table 3.

Table 3   The Electron Configuration of Elements of the
First Transition Series

Ca	$[Ar]4s^2$	Fe	$[Ar]4s^2\,3d^6$
Sc	$[Ar]4s^2\,3d$	Co	$[Ar]4s^2\,3d^7$
Ti	$[Ar]4s^2\,3d^2$	Ni	$[Ar]4s^2\,3d^8$
V	$[Ar]4s^2\,3d^3$	Cu	$[Ar]4s\,\,3d^{10}$
Cr	$[Ar]4s\,\,3d^5$	Zn	$[Ar]4s^2\,3d^{10}$
Mn	$[Ar]4s^2\,3d^5$		

The five d orbitals are designated d_{z^2}, $d_{x^2-y^2}$, d_{xy}, d_{xz} and d_{yz}, the boundary surfaces enclosing a given fraction of the charge of an electron in each of these orbitals are illustrated in fig. 9. The five d orbitals are of equivalent energy, and are occupied singly as far as possible in order to reduce the repulsion between electrons. The d orbital of lowest energy is the $3d$, occupied by $3d$ electrons.

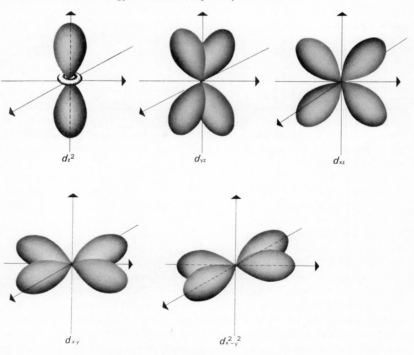

Figure 9. d orbitals (surfaces of constant ψ^2 for d electrons).

24   Modern Physical Chemistry: an Introduction

From table 3 it is apparent that the regular increase in the number of d electrons as the atomic number increases is interrupted at the elements chromium and copper, so the structures given in the table are evidently more stable than the arrangements $4s^2 3d^4$ and $4s^2 3d^9$ respectively.

The elements helium, neon, argon, krypton and xenon were known until recently as the inert gases, although they have now been shown to combine with the strongly electronegative elements such as oxygen or fluorine. They are still, as a class, by far the most inert of the elements and if we adopt the view that atoms and molecules undergo chemical changes in order to reduce their energies we must conclude that the inert gases are already in a relatively low energy state. Does their electron structure give any explanation for this fact?

The electron structures of the first four inert gases are:

$$\text{He} \quad 1s^2$$
$$\text{Ne} \quad 1s^2 2s^2 2p^6$$
$$\text{Ar} \quad 1s^2 2s^2 2p^6 3s^2 3p^6$$
$$\text{Kr} \quad 1s^2 2s^2 2p^6 3s^2 3p^6 4s^2 3d^{10} 4p^6$$

Notice that if we add a further electron to any of these atoms the new electron must enter an s orbital of higher principal quantum number. This involves an increase in energy of about 3 eV., so these atoms have no tendency to acquire an additional electron and so form an anion. On the other hand all the electrons are firmly bound by the nucleus (as shown by the high ionization energies of the inert gases) so that the removal of an electron to form a cation also involves a considerable increase in energy.

2·3 Lattice energy

Consider next the element sodium, with electron structure $1s^2 2s^2 2p^6 3s$. One of the electrons, that on the $3s$ level, is less firmly attached than the others, but to remove this electron from a single sodium atom requires 5·14 eV. If all the sodium atoms in the gram-atom of sodium, 23 g., were ionized in this way, the total energy required would be

$$I = 5\cdot140 \times N = 3\cdot09 \times 10^{24} \text{ eV. g-atom}^{-1})$$

where N is the Avogadro constant. To convert this to the usual energy units of kcal. g-atom^{-1}, the value of I is multiplied by $1\cdot602 \times 10^{-12}$ (to convert to erg g-atom^{-1}) and divided by $1000 J$ where J is the Joule equivalent ($4\cdot18 \times 10^7$ erg calorie^{-1}), giving $I = 118$ kcal. g-atom^{-1}. The heat of vaporization of sodium metal is 25·9 kcal. g-atom^{-1}, so that the total energy required to convert 23 g. of sodium metal to the gaseous ions is 144 kcal. Obviously it is incorrect to say that sodium 'has a tendency to ionize', or 'wants to lose an electron' because the process in isolation requires too large an increase in the energy of the system.

The element fluorine has the electron structure $1s^2 2s^2 2p^5$; the addition of an electron to a fluorine atom to produce a fluoride ion is a spontaneous process, liberating 83·5 kcal. g-atom^{-1}. If we consider a g-atom of fluorine, first dissociating the F_2 molecules into atoms (there will be $3\cdot01 \times 10^{23}$ F_2 molecules, giving rise to

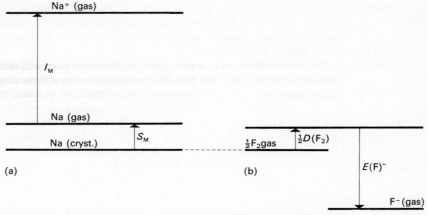

Figure 10. Energy changes involved in the processes: (a) Na → Na$^+$ + e (b) F + e → F$^-$.

$6\cdot02 \times 10^{23}$ atoms) and then adding one electron to each atom, the total energy liberated is $65\cdot2$ kcal. g-atom^{-1} (fig. 10). Thus the reaction

$$\text{Na (metal)} + \tfrac{1}{2}\text{F}_2 \text{ (gas)} \rightarrow \text{Na}^+ \text{ (gas)} + \text{F}^- \text{ (gas)}$$

would not be expected to occur because of the energy required: $144 - 65\cdot2 = 78\cdot8$ kcal. mole^{-1}.

Another source of energy is available, however. If these ions are brought together, they will pack under the influence of forces of attraction (between unlike ions) and repulsion (between like ions), the attractive forces predominating. A large quantity of energy, the *lattice energy*, is released, amounting in sodium fluoride to 219 kcal. g-mole^{-1}.

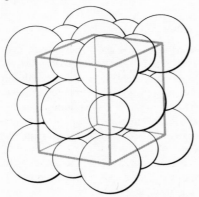

Figure 11. The crystal structure of NaF.

The arrangement of the ions in sodium fluoride is regular, with six F^- ions surrounding each Na^+ ion, and vice versa, arranged on or around the points of a *crystal lattice* or *space lattice* (fig. 11). The energy liberated in the formation of the ionic crystal drives the reaction

$$Na \text{ (metal)} + \tfrac{1}{2}F_2 \text{ (gas)} \rightarrow NaF \text{ (crystal)}$$

forwards. Sodium metal and gaseous fluorine are both stable substances if they are mixed they can produce an even more stable compound, NaF, as a result of this reaction, which occurs spontaneously.

Binding forces in chemistry are often discussed under the general heading of *valency*, and in sodium fluoride we have an example of one kind of valency, *electrovalency*. If instead of sodium we consider the metal magnesium, the changes occurring during the reaction with fluorine to form magnesium fluoride could be represented by:

$$Mg \text{ (metal)} + F_2 \text{ (gas)} \rightarrow Mg^{2+} \text{ (gas)} + 2F^- \text{ (gas)} \rightarrow MgF_2 \text{ (crystal)}.$$

Again, an overall decrease in energy of 264 kcal. $mole^{-1}$ produces spontaneous reaction between the elements.

2·3·1 *Born–Haber cycle*

Many of the metallic oxides and sulphides can be considered as formed in the same way, and it is convenient to introduce the Born–Haber cycle to represent the energy changes involved in the formation of ionic crystals.

In the formation of calcium oxide, the calcium atom loses two electrons in forming the Ca^{2+} ion which are then gained by an oxygen atom to form the O^{2-} ion. The ions pack into a crystal lattice

$$Ca^{2+} \text{ (gas)} + O^{2-} \text{ (gas)} \rightarrow CaO \text{ (crystal)}.$$

The enthalpy change of this process is -848 kcal. $mole^{-1}$. If we start from calcium metal and oxygen gas, we can imagine the formation of the calcium oxide crystal in a series of steps:

(i) The metal is volatilized, requiring enthalpy equal to the latent heat of vaporization, S_M.

(ii) The individual atoms of the gaseous metal are ionized to Ca^{2+}, requiring energy equal to the sum of the first two ionization energies for calcium, $(I_1 + I_2)_M$. Since this reaction occurs entirely in the gas phase, no distinction need be drawn between enthalpy and energy changes.

(iii) Oxygen gas is dissociated into atoms. Since the reaction

$$Ca + \tfrac{1}{2}O_2 \rightarrow CaO$$

takes place, we require to produce one g.-atom of oxygen from one-half mole; this absorbs heat $\tfrac{1}{2}D(O_2)$, where $D(O_2)$ is the dissociation enthalpy of oxygen per mole.

(iv) Two electrons are attached to each oxygen atom, forming an O^{2-} ion; the energy required for this process is called the electron affinity of oxygen atoms for two electrons, $E(O^{2-})$.

(v) The gaseous Ca^{2+} and O^{2-} ions are allowed to pack into the crystal lattice, releasing the *lattice enthalpy* of the crystal, ΔH_l.

Now if we burn calcium metal in oxygen gas, the same product, crystalline calcium oxide, is formed, with an enthalpy change called the heat of formation, ΔH_f, of calcium oxide. Since both this direct route and the series of changes (i) to (v) lead to the same product, the sum of the enthalpy changes must be the same in each case (Hess's law, page 58), i.e.

$$S_M + (I_1 + I_2)_M + \frac{D}{2} + E + \Delta H_l = \Delta H_f. \tag{2.1}$$

The enthalpy changes for these processes are shown in fig. 12. Equation (2.1) can be

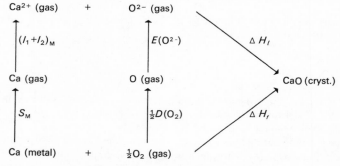

Figure 12.   The Born–Haber cycle for the formation of CaO.

used to find any one of the enthalpy terms involved, provided that the others are known; the lattice energies U of crystalline solids are often obtained in this way:

$$U = \Delta H_1 + nRT \tag{2.2}$$

where n is the number of ions per formula weight, R is the gas constant per mole and T is the absolute temperature (p. 76).

We may note that in the formation of calcium oxide the calcium atoms each lose two electrons and the oxygen atoms each gain two electrons; under normal conditions, no compounds are formed in which Ca^+ ions or O^- ions are present, so these atoms either form doubly charged ions or (in the case of oxygen) combine in some other way.

2·4 *d* electrons

The ions we have considered so far have either lost electrons from an outer *s* orbital or completed an outer *p* orbital; they have thus acquired a completed set of *s* and *p* orbitals of the same principal quantum number – the characteristic feature of the atoms of inert gases:

Na	$1s^2\,2s^2\,2p^6\,3s$	$\rightarrow$	Na^+	$1s^2\,2s^2\,2p^6$, as in Ne.
F	$1s^2\,2s^2\,2p^5$	$\rightarrow$	F^-	$1s^2\,2s^2\,2p^6$, as in Ne.
Mg	$1s^2\,2s^2\,2p^6\,3s^2$	$\rightarrow$	Mg^{2+}	$1s^2\,2s^2\,2p^6$, as in Ne.
Ca	$1s^2\,2s^2\,2p^6\,3s^2\,3p^6\,4s^2$	$\rightarrow$	Ca^{2+}	$1s^2\,2s^2\,2p^6\,3s^2\,3p^6$, as in Ar.
O	$1s^2\,2s^2\,2p^4$	$\rightarrow$	O^{2-}	$1s^2\,2s^2\,2p^6$, as in Ne.

Not all ions have this 'inert gas' type of structure however. Consider an iron atom, of electron structure $1s^2\,2s^2\,2p^6\,3s^2\,3p^6\,3d^6\,4s^2$. If the $4s$ electrons are lost, the ferrous ion is formed, Fe^{2+}, but the $3d$ and $4s$ levels are close together in energy so relatively little further energy is required to remove one more electron to form the ferric ion, Fe^{3+}:

$$Fe^{2+} \quad [Ar]3d^6$$
$$Fe^{3+} \quad [Ar]3d^5, \quad [Ar] \text{ representing the electron structure of argon.}$$

Thus the Fe^{2+} and Fe^{3+} ions do not have the inert gas type of structure. The cuprous ion Cu^+ and the cupric ion Cu^{2+} are formed in a similar manner:

$$Cu^+ \quad [Ar]3d^{10}$$
$$Cu^{2+} \quad [Ar]3d^9.$$

2·5 Interatomic bonds

Electrovalent compounds are formed between atoms of different types, one of which (typically a metal) can lose electrons, the other (typically a non-metal) gaining electrons. The 'donor' atoms which form cations are said to be *electropositive* whilst the 'acceptor' atoms are *electronegative*. The atoms so far considered are therefore classified as follows:

electropositive	*electronegative*
Na (Li, K)	F (Cl, Br, I)
Mg (Ca, Sr, Ba)	O (S, Se)
Fe, Cu	

2·5·1 *Electrovalent and covalent bonds*

The electropositive elements do not occur normally as small molecules of the type Na_2 or Fe_2, whereas the electronegative elements are often present as *diatomic* (two-atom) molecules; we must now seek the reason for this and determine what forces are responsible for holding together two identical atoms (as in F_2 or O_2). It has

29   Chemical structure and valency

already been shown that electrons are now considered to be spread out over the whole atom in a non-uniform manner rather than concentrated as point charges, and it can be demonstrated that if the electron is even less restricted (i.e. if it is spread out over two atoms) the energy of the two-atom system is lowered. In general, electrons are distributed in pairs between two atoms, the two electrons contributing to form a *molecular orbital* similar to the atomic orbitals already considered except that it encloses the nuclei and inner electrons of the two atoms. The two electrons must be *spin-paired* when they occupy a common molecular orbital.

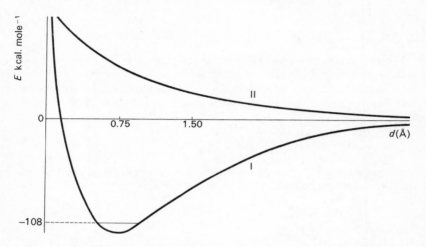

Figure 13. Interactions of two H atoms, distance d Å. apart.

If two hydrogen atoms each in the ground state with an electron in the $1s$ atomic orbital approach each other, there is a chance that the spins will become paired and a hydrogen molecule will be formed; the new molecular orbital is called a σ orbital. The potential energy curve of two hydrogen atoms which form an H_2 molecule is represented by I in fig. 13; curve II represents the potential energy of the two hydrogen atoms when the spins remain parallel (unpaired). When the σ molecular orbital is formed, the potential energy of the two hydrogen atoms is reduced by about 4·69 eV., which corresponds to an energy charge of -108 kcal. mole^{-1} H_2 formed (fig. 13). The energy difference between this level and the minimum of curve I is the *zero-point energy*, a residual vibrational energy which is possessed by the molecule even at 0°K.

The hydrogen molecule is rather a special case because there are no other electrons to screen those in the molecular orbital from the attraction of the nuclei. In lithium, for example, the bond energy of an Li(2s)—Li(2s) bond is only -26 kcal. mole^{-1}, and this molecule is not normally produced in chemical reactions. Generally speaking the molecular orbital which can be formed between two s-type atomic orbitals is not very strongly bonding because there is insufficient *overlap* of the atomic orbitals to allow the electrons of the orbitals to exchange, thereby reducing the energy of the system. It might appear that the overlap could be increased by bringing the two atoms closer together, but this would soon introduce strong internuclear repulsion. However, we considered earlier the directional character of the p- and d-type atomic orbitals and these can produce a far greater overlap than the non-directional s orbitals; the singly occupied $2p$ orbitals of two fluorine atoms produce a doubly occupied π molecular orbital which reduces the energy of the two atoms by 1·58 eV., or 36·6 kcal. mole^{-1} F_2 formed (fig. 14).

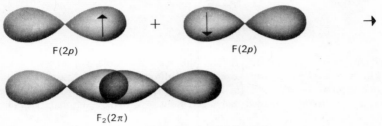

F(2p)   +   F(2p)   →

F$_2$(2π)

Figure 14.   The overlap of $2p$ orbitals in forming an F_2 molecule.

There is no obvious source of binding energy in the sharing of a pair of electrons (i.e. in the overlap of their atomic orbitals) comparable to the electrostatic attraction between oppositely charged ions of an electrovalent compound, but the covalent bond is nevertheless equally strong and is restricted to the two atoms concerned, which enables individual molecules to exist.

In the crystal of sodium fluoride each sodium ion is attracted equally by six equidistant fluoride ions, and each fluoride ion is surrounded by six equidistant sodium ions, whereas in a crystal of hydrogen, the atoms are firmly bound together in pairs and the attraction between this molecule and other hydrogen molecules in the crystal is very much weaker. For example, in a crystal of sodium fluoride weighing 1 g.

there are approximately $\dfrac{6 \times 10^{23}}{23 + 19}$ ions of each type, i.e. about 10^{22} Na$^+$ ions and 10^{22}

F$^-$ ions. The number of ions in the six crystal faces is about 10^{16}, so that only about one ion in 10^6 is at the surface and the great majority of ions are surrounded by six neighbouring ions of opposite charge. The total binding energy of the crystal is its lattice energy, 5·3 kcal. g.$^{-1}$.

In a crystal of hydrogen weighing 1 g., on the other hand, there are $\dfrac{6 \times 10^{23}}{2}$

(or 3×10^{23}) H$_2$ molecules and the total binding energy is 54 kcal. g.$^{-1}$, but the interactional energy between molecules is only about 14 cal. g.$^{-1}$.

We shall discuss the nature of these weaker intermolecular forces under the heading of van der Waals forces (page 44), but it may be noted here that electrovalency leads to an ionic crystal structure, with each ion attracted to its neighbouring ions, whilst covalency leads to discrete molecules.

In the hydrogen chloride molecule the overlap of the hydrogen $1s$ and the chlorine $3p$ atomic orbitals produces a molecular orbital. When two or more atomic orbitals

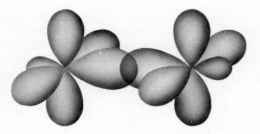

Figure 15. F_2 molecule.

of different shape combine together in this way, the molecular orbital formed differs in shape from either, and is usually more directional in the sense that it points from one atom to the other (fig. 15). The overlap is greater than it would have been had the atomic orbitals remained unchanged in shape, with the result that the binding

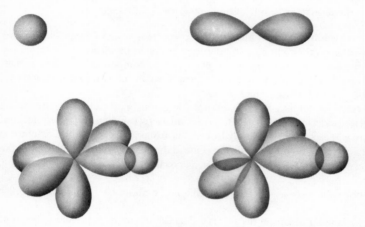

Figure 16. Orbital representation of the formation of the HCl molecule.

energy of the molecule is lowered. In this example, the hydrogen atom loses electronic charge to the chlorine atom and part of the charge originally distributed about the hydrogen atom is transferred permanently to the chlorine atom, so that the molecule has regions of positive and negative charge centred on the hydrogen and chlorine atoms respectively; the molecule is now said to possess a permanent *dipole*, the H—Cl bond being *polar*. Two such molecular orbitals are present in the water molecule, each giving rise to a polar bond (fig. 17).

A new (*hybridized*) orbital may be formed from the atomic orbitals of a single atom, thus enhancing the directional property. Hybridized orbitals are formed hypothetically by mixing together *s*, *p* etc. atomic orbitals in definite proportions so as to obtain maximum overlap with atomic orbitals of other atoms, leading to minimum

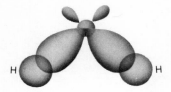

Figure 17.   Orbital representation of the formation of the H_2O molecule.

free energy of the compound formed. The process of mixing is called *hybridization*. The best-known examples of hybridization involve the carbon atom, the electronic structure of which is $1s^2\, 2s^2\, 2p_x\, 2p_y$ in the ground state; this would lead us to suppose that the atom is divalent and forms two bonds in a similar way to oxygen in water. However, the evidence obtained from studying carbon compounds (particularly their optical isomerism) demonstrates that carbon is tetravalent, with four bonds symmetrically directed in space towards the corners of a regular tetrahedron described around the carbon atom (fig. 18). To form these bonds, the two $2s$ and two $2p$ electrons

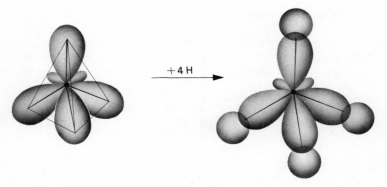

$+4\,H$

Figure 18.   Orbital representation of the formation of the CH_4 molecule.

are arranged to occupy four equivalent sp^3 hybridized orbitals which are highly directional, can each contain a pair of electrons with opposed spins, and have the required directional property, i.e. they point towards the corners of a regular tetrahedron. In methane, for example, the $1s$ orbitals of four hydrogen atoms overlap the four sp^3 orbitals of a carbon atom (fig. 18). The sp^3 orbitals can also overlap with similar orbitals on other carbon atoms to form carbon–carbon bonds as in propane (C_3H_8) (fig. 19). Another example of a structure where the carbon atoms form sp^3 bonds is diamond (fig. 20) in which the sp^3 bonds are responsible for the cohesion of the crystal (a 'giant' covalent molecule).

In the hydrocarbons ethylene, acetylene, and benzene, the tetravalency of carbon is maintained only by introducing 'double' or 'triple' bonds into the molecule, according to the classical formulae shown in fig. 21a. A single structure for benzene,

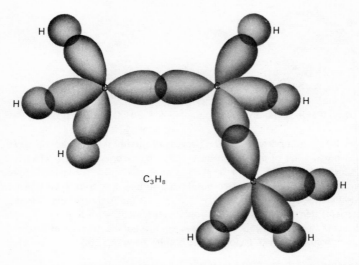

Figure 19.   Orbital representation of the formation of the C_3H_8 molecule.

either (i) or (ii), is misleading, since it suggests a distinction between those pairs of carbon atoms which are singly bonded and the remainder which are doubly bonded; such a distinction cannot be inferred from the chemical reactions of benzene. Again,

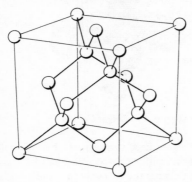

Figure 20.   The crystal structure of diamond.

although benzene can form addition compounds with hydrogen or with chlorine, these are formed much less readily than the corresponding compounds of ethylene. In attempting to explain these properties of benzene, the 'alternating double bond' formulation was adopted (fig. 21b) but it is now understood that carbon atoms can exist in states of different hybridization.

In ethylene, each carbon atom forms three hybridized orbitals by combining the $2s$ with two of the $2p$ orbitals, the resulting sp^2 orbitals having trigonal symmetry

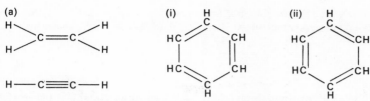

Figure 21 (a).   Classical formulae of ethylene, acetylene and benzene.

Figure 21 (b).   Alternating double bond formula of benzene.

(fig. 22): the three valencies are co-planar and directed towards the corners of an equilateral triangle, whilst the third $2p$ orbital retains an electron. The ethylene molecule is formed by the overlap of one sp^2 orbital from each carbon atom, four hydrogen atoms being bonded to the remaining four sp^2 orbitals. To complete the tetravalency

sp^2

Figure 22. sp^2 hybridized orbitals.

of carbon, the unchanged p orbitals overlap and exchange electrons (fig. 23). The double bond is thus a combination of sp^2 orbital overlap (the σ bond) and p orbital

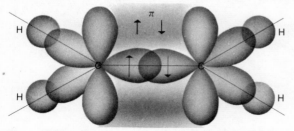

Figure 23.   Orbital representation of the C_2H_4 molecule.

35   Chemical structure and valency

overlap (the π bond). The complete $(\sigma + \pi)$ bond is stronger than an sp^3 carbon–carbon bond but weaker than two sp^3 bonds, as the reduction of ethylene by hydrogen demonstrates:

$$C_2H_4 + H_2 \rightarrow C_2H_6, \qquad \Delta H = -32\cdot7 \text{ kcal. mole}^{-1}.$$

In acetylene, the 'triple' bond between the carbon atoms is formed by the overlap of sp orbitals (formed from $2s$ and $2p$ orbitals by hybridization) and the two unchanged $2p$ orbitals. In the above examples ethylene (C_2H_4) and acetylene (C_2H_2), the unchanged p orbitals are mutually perpendicular and perpendicular also to the direction of the σ bonds. The carbon–carbon bond in acetylene is thus $(\sigma + 2\pi)$, which is stronger than the $(\sigma + \pi)$ 'double' bond in ethylene but weaker than three of the sp^3 bonds in methane. The C–C bond energies and distances associated with σ, $(\sigma + \pi)$ and $(\sigma + 2\pi)$ bonds are listed in table 4.

Table 4 Properties of C–C Bonds

Bond type	Example	Energy (kcal. mole^{-1})	d (Å)
σ	C_2H_6	-79	1·54
$(\sigma + \pi)$	C_2H_4	-141	1·33
$(\sigma + 2\pi)$	C_2H_2	-197	1·20
$(\sigma + 6\pi)$	C_6H_6	-116	1·40

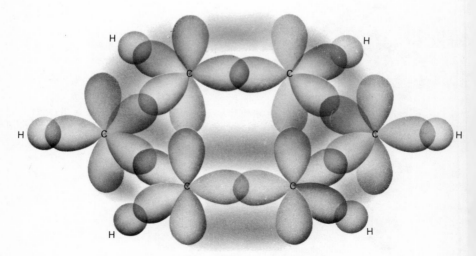

Figure 24. Orbital representation of the C_6H_6 molecule.

The carbon–carbon bond in benzene is listed in this table as $(\sigma + 6\pi)$. The carbon atoms form sp^2 hybridized orbitals as in ethylene; overlap of the p orbitals above and below the plane of the ring of six carbon atoms allows the π electrons (the six electrons within the overlapping $2p$ orbitals) to migrate around the ring (fig. 24).

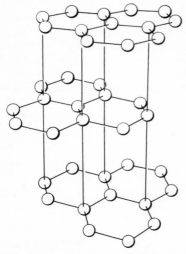

Figure 25.   The crystal structure of graphite.

A similar hybridized state occurs in graphite (fig. 25). The carbon atoms within a layer are rigidly held together by $(\sigma + n\pi)$ bonds where n is the number of carbon atoms in a layer. The layers are linked together by the much weaker van der Waals forces which results in their ability to glide over one another and accounts for the lubricant properties of graphite. In comparison, diamond (fig. 20) is the hardest naturally occurring substance and its abrasive properties are well known.

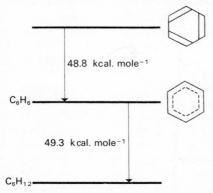

Figure 26.   The resonance energy of benzene.

We noted that the hydrogenation of ethylene is exothermic ($\Delta H = -32.7$ kcal. mole^{-1}), ethane thus having a lower energy than ethylene. We might expect that the heat of hydrogenation of benzene would be about -98 kcal. mole^{-1}, since there are three double bonds to be reduced ($C_6H_6 + 3H_2 \rightarrow C_6H_{12}$) but in fact $\Delta H = -49.3$ kcal. mole^{-1}. Hence benzene must be about 49 kcal. mole^{-1} lower in energy than either of the Kekulé structures for benzene (fig. 26). This extra stability of benzene arises from the free mobility of the π electrons – those which occupy the overlapping p orbitals of the six carbon atoms – and from the relief of σ-bond strain by a change in the hybridization of carbon. It is called the *resonance energy* of benzene; no single structural formula for benzene is adequate, and the molecule is to be considered as a resonance hybrid of (principally) the Kekulé structures and (partially) the three Dewar structures (fig. 27).

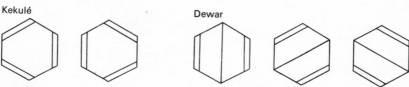

Kekulé   Dewar

Figure 27.   Kekulé and Dewar structures for benzene.

If a number of structures *a, b* etc. which can be pictorially represented (as, for example, the Kekulé and Dewar structures of the benzene molecule) contribute to produce a more correct structure *s* which cannot be so represented, then *s* is said to be a *resonance hybrid* of *a, b* etc. or to *resonate* between these structures.

It must be emphasized that we do not imply an equilibrium, as in the case of tautomerism; *a, b* etc. do not exist except as pictorial aids in trying to envisage *s*. The actual structure *s* is more stable (as shown by experiment) than would be any mechanical mixture of *a, b* etc. and the difference in energy is called the *resonance energy*.

So far we have considered electrovalent and covalent compounds separately, as though chemical compounds always belonged to one or other of these two classes. In fact this is never the case, and even in *homonuclear* molecules (those in which the component atoms are identical, such as H_2 or S_8) there are some ionic contributions from species such as H^+ and H^- in H_2 to the bonding energy – a factor that becomes more important in *heteronuclear* molecules such as HCl or H_2O. Again, in the ionic crystal NaF a small fraction of the electron charge is shared between a pair of adjacent ions, their contribution becoming more important as the interionic attraction increases. More precisely, if the distortion of the atomic orbital of the anion becomes large, a predominantly covalent bond is formed. Such distortion will increase with increasing radius of the anion and we can describe this effect by saying that a large anion is more *polarizable*, or has a greater *polarizability*, than a small anion. The distortion will also increase with reduction in the radius of the cation because charge density is greater at the surface of the smaller cation, so we say that a small cation has greater *polarizing power* than a large cation. Thus HCl is predominantly covalent and KCl is predominantly electrovalent, but LiCl has a greater covalent component of bonding than has KCl, although it is still mainly electrovalent; this covalent component is greater in iodides than in chlorides of the same cation. The two conditions for increased polarization, and hence for increase in covalency, were originally suggested by Fajans. Since the observed state is that in which both covalency and electrovalency are present, this must be the state of minimum energy.

We can now explain, in terms of their electronic structures, the formation of simple compounds such as KCl, $CaBr_2$, MgO and FeS which are mainly electrovalent, but in a large number of chemical compounds both types of valency are involved in maintaining the electronic structure. Consider, for example, the formation of crystalline ammonium chloride from ammonia and hydrogen chloride. Ammonia and hydrogen chloride are both predominantly covalent molecules. In ammonia, sp^3 hybridization occurs as in carbon, three of the sp^3 orbitals overlapping with the $1s$ orbitals of three hydrogen atoms whilst the remaining sp^3 orbital of the nitrogen atom contains a pair of electrons (the so-called 'lone pair'). As usual the sp^3 bonds point towards the corners of a tetrahedron (not a *regular* tetrahedron, because one of the orbitals is nonbonding as fig. 28 illustrates). If ammonia and hydrogen chloride are mixed, the concentration of negative charge associated with the lone pair increases the polarization of the H–Cl bond until eventually the hydrogen atom separates as a proton and becomes bonded to the 'lone-pair' orbital of the nitrogen atom. Since it is a proton which is transferred, an ammonium ion is formed, the chlorine atom retaining the electron from hydrogen and becoming a chloride ion.

Both electrovalency and covalency contributions are therefore present in solid ammonium chloride. The crystal lattice consists of ammonium ions and chloride ions, held together by electrovalency, the atoms within the ammonium ion owing

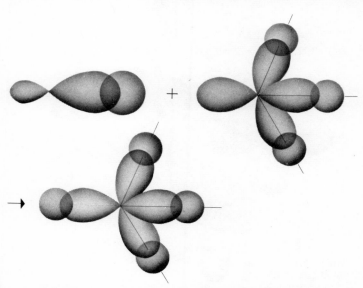

Figure 28.   Orbital representation of the formation of the NH_4^+ ion.

their cohesion to electron sharing or covalency (fig. 28). No new type of bond is introduced here since each of the four hydrogen atoms in NH_4^+ is bonded to the nitrogen atom by a pair of electrons and it is immaterial whether these originated one on each atom or both on the same atom. Once formed, the four N–H bonds are absolutely identical, and it seems unnecessary to give this type of valency another name (i.e. co-ordinate, co-ionic, or dative) as was originally the practice.

We can now consider the electronic structure of some more complex ions, envisaging these as being formed from their component atoms. In the perchlorate ion, ClO_4^-, the chloride ion forms four sp^3 hybridized orbitals:

$$Cl([Ne]3s^2\,3p^5) + 1\text{ electron} \rightarrow Cl^-[Ne]3s^2\,3p^6) \rightarrow Cl^-(4 \times sp^3).$$

The oxygen atom rearranges its electrons in order to leave one of the $2p$ orbitals vacant, for example

$$O([He]2s^2\,2p_x^2\,2p_y\,2p_z) \rightarrow O([He]2s^2\,2p_x^2\,2p_y^2)$$

and the $2p_z$ orbitals of four oxygen atoms overlap with the sp^3 orbitals of the chloride ion, leading to the regular tetrahedral structure shown in fig. 29.

A stable structure also results from the overlap of the p orbitals from three oxygen atoms with the sp^3 orbitals of the chloride ion; this represents the chlorate ion, in which the tetrahedral symmetry of ClO_4^- is degraded to the pyramidal symmetry of the ClO_3^- ion, with the lone pair now present at the apex of the pyramid.

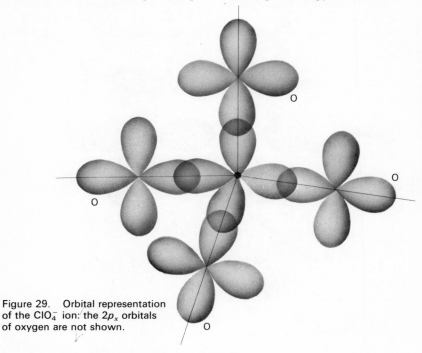

Figure 29. Orbital representation of the ClO_4^- ion: the $2p_x$ orbitals of oxygen are not shown.

In the nitrate ion, the nitrogen atom can be considered to acquire an electron and form three trigonal sp^2 orbitals:

$$N([He]2s^2\,2p^3)+1\text{ electron} \rightarrow N^-([He]3 \times sp^2).$$

The vacant p_z orbitals of three oxygen atoms (formed as above) overlap the sp^2 orbitals of nitrogen, forming the trigonal planar nitrate ion. Because of the greater electronegativity of oxygen compared with nitrogen, electron charge-transfer occurs leading to a final structure of $N^{\delta+}(O)_3^{\delta-}$. The nitric acid molecule is covalent: the hydrogen atom is bonded to one of the oxygen atoms of the nitrate group. On reaction with water or any solvent which can accept a proton, the hydrogen atom splits off as a proton, which has great polarizing power owing to its vanishingly small size and forms a covalent bond with the solvent molecule, e.g. H_3O^+ in water, $C_2H_5OH_2^+$ in ethanol, NH_4^+ in liquid ammonia. The nitrate group retains an electron and becomes the nitrate ion, NO_3^-.

Molecules or ions containing lone pairs may convert a simple ion into a complex ion by forming covalent bonds with it. Thus silver chloride is predominantly electrovalent and the ions have the configurations $Ag^+[Ar]3d^{10}$ and $Cl^-[Ar]$ respectively, this compound being sparingly soluble in water (by no means an uncommon property of electrovalent compounds). If we add ammonia or potassium cyanide, the lone pairs of the nitrogen atoms in NH_3 or CN^- enter the vacant $4s$ and $4p$ orbitals of the Ag^+ ion, forming a complex cation $\{Ag(NH_3)_2\}^+$ or a complex anion $\{Ag(CN)_2\}^-$ respectively. Both of these ions possess a linear configuration since sp hybridized orbitals are involved. The tetrammine-Cu(II) and tetracyano-Cu(I) ions are formed similarly and make use of sp^3 orbitals on the central atom, so that their configurations are tetrahedral; the two different oxidation states of copper in these ions should be noted.

What happens when d electrons or d orbitals are involved in the bonding? Consider the formation of the ferrocyanide ion by the following process:

$$Fe^{2+} +6CN^- \rightarrow \{Fe(CN)_6\}^{4-}$$

The electron structure of Fe^{2+} is $[Ar]3d^6$, the $4s$ electrons being removed from the iron atom in the formation of the Fe^{2+} ion. The d orbitals can contain a maximum of ten electrons, so that there are vacancies for four electrons in the Fe^{2+} ion, whilst the $4s$ and $4p$ orbitals are unoccupied and can contain a further eight electrons. Thus six electron pairs, from six CN^- ions, can be added to the Fe^{2+} ion:

However, the process does not occur in this way or there would be three different modes of attachment of CN^- ions, namely two to $3d$ orbitals, one to $4s$ orbitals, and three to $4p$ orbitals. In fact, the vacant orbitals in Fe^{2+}* (the asterisk indicates that the Fe^{2+} is in a 'paired' state, of higher energy than the normal ground state represented by Fe^{2+}) are hybridized, forming six equivalent d^2sp^3 orbitals:

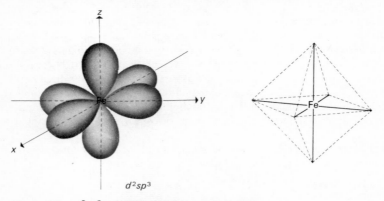

The ferricyanide ion is formed by the analogous process

$$Fe^{3+} + 6CN^- \rightarrow \{Fe(CN)_6\}^{3-}$$

and contains one less electron in the $3d$ orbital. The unpaired electron in this ion

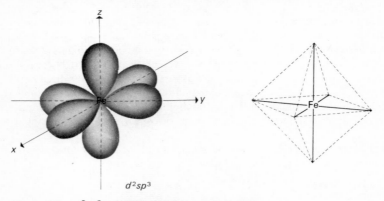

d^2sp^3

Figure 30. d^2sp^3 hybridized orbitals, as in Fe(III).

gives it a magnetic moment, and the ion is said to be *paramagnetic* in contrast to the ferrocyanide ion, which is *diamagnetic*.

The six d^2sp^3 orbitals are symmetrically distributed in space towards the corners of a regular octahedron (fig. 30). This arrangement of bonds, like the tetrahedral arrangement in carbon compounds, can give rise to isomerism, the compounds (a) and (b) in fig. 31 being identical whereas in (c) the Cl^- groups are adjacent.

The cations in fig. 31 belong to a series of complex ions based upon the Co^{3+} ion and may be considered to have been formed by the successive replacement of NH_3 groups in hexammino-Co(III) by Cl^- ions:

$$\{Co(NH_3)_6\}^{3+} + 2Cl^- \rightarrow \{CoCl_2(NH_3)_4\}^+ + 2NH_3, \quad etc$$

The series extends from $\{Co(NH_3)_6\}^{3+}$ to $\{CoCl_6\}^{3-}$, all the members using d^2sp^3 orbitals of the Co^{3+} ion. This is not the only hybridized orbital which results from

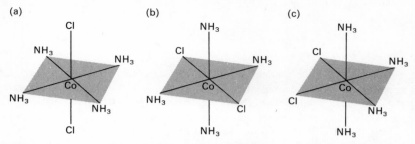

Figure 31. *Cis–trans* isomerism in $\{CoCl_2(NH_3)_4\}^{3+}$; (a) and (b) *trans*, (c) *cis*.

the use of d orbitals. In the anion tetracyano-Ni(II), the arrangement of the CN^- ions around the Ni^{2+} is planar, i.e. the four bonds are directed towards the corners of a square with Ni^{2+} at its centre. The hybridized orbitals of the Ni^{2+} are designated dsp^2 and are formed by combining one $3d$ orbital with the vacant $4s$ orbital and two vacant $4p$ orbitals of Ni^{2+}.

2·5·2 *The metallic bond*

The energy of cohesion in metals is derived from another form of ion–electron interaction. A metal in the elemental state consists of positively charged ions bound mainly by the valence electrons, which are moving at random throughout the structure and are responsible for the electrical and thermal conduction in metals. If we consider that the lattice energy of a metal crystal is represented by the energy change of the process

$$n\,M^+\,(gas) + n\,electrons \rightarrow metal\,(crystal)$$

then the magnitude of this change is equal to the sum of the ionization energy and the sublimation energy of the metal. Thus for sodium, $I_{Na} = 118$ kcal. g-atom^{-1} and $S_{Na} = 26$ kcal. g-atom^{-1}, so that its lattice energy is -144 kcal. g-atom^{-1}. The metallic bond is non-directional, and the structures of most metals are very simple from the geometrical point of view.

The tendency to exhibit a given type of valency can be considered qualitatively. If two atoms differ greatly in electronegativity, e.g. sodium and fluorine, then transfer of electrons leads to predominant electrovalency, but if the atoms are similar in their electronegativities (chlorine and oxygen for example) or if the atoms are identical and possess nearly-completed valence electron shells, then orbital overlap leads to predominant covalency.

When the atoms are identical or closely similar (e.g. copper and gold) and have few valence electrons, they combine by forming a molecular orbital to which all the free electrons contribute leading to the production of the metallic bond. In a metal the valence electrons are therefore almost completely de-localized, i.e. they are not associated with any particular metal atom. In crystalline sodium each sodium atom retains ten electrons in the configuration: Na^+ ($1s^2\ 2s^2\ 2p^6$), the remaining $3s$ electron from each atom forming a molecular orbital enclosing all the sodium atoms.

2·5·3   *Van der Waals forces*

From the study of the covalent bond, we can now picture the molecule of an organic compound such as acetamide, CH_3CONH_2, (m.p. 82°C.) in terms of the overlap of the appropriate orbitals. The orbitals used by the carbon atom in the CH_3 group are sp^3, whilst those of the remaining carbon atom are the planar sp^2; π electrons exist in both the sp^2 carbon atom and the nitrogen atom (which is also using sp^2 bonds). The distribution of electron charge is hence unbalanced throughout the molecule, which is said to be *polar* or to possess a permanent dipolar charge. If the molecules can be aligned so that the positive end of one dipole is adjacent to the negative end of a dipole in another molecule, then a form of attraction (dipole–dipole interaction) can be envisaged and a cohesive energy may be expected, albeit of smaller magnitude than that associated with electrovalent or covalent bonds. The melting points of organic crystals are low compared with those of electrovalent crystals or covalent crystals as a direct consequence of the smaller cohesive energy in the crystalline state of organic compounds. It must be noted that when the crystal of acetamide melts it is the dipole–dipole interactions which are overcome by the thermal energy imparted to the crystal, the *intermolecular* linkages (those between the molecules) being broken whilst the *intramolecular* bonds (those within the molecule) remain intact.

If we consider a molecule which, from its symmetry, cannot have a permanent dipole, for example methane, we must explain the nature of the cohesive energy in its crystalline state. Normally methane is in the gaseous state, the boiling point and melting point of this substance being $-161·5$°C. and $-182·5$°C. respectively. Clearly, little thermal energy is required to produce changes in state since the cohesive energies are of much lower magnitude than in the case of acetamide.

Modern valence theory shows that the intermolecular attraction energy between any two molecules is proportional to their polarizabilities (page 38) and inversely proportional to the sixth power of their distance apart. If the electronic charge distribution in methane is changing with time, the charge arising from the valence electrons at any instant may not be symmetrical with respect to the C–H bonds and an instantaneous dipole is set up in the molecule. This induces in turn a dipole in a neighbouring molecule the direction of which will lead to attraction between the molecules. The time-average of these instantaneous dipoles, and hence the resultant dipole of the molecule, is zero, but their continuous formation and synchronous interaction hold the molecules together in solid methane and in similar crystals. In fact, this form of interaction contributes to the binding energy in all crystals, but its contribution in (for example) acetamide is much less than that of the dipole–dipole interaction.

The forces which arise from the interactions of permanent and of induced dipoles are referred to collectively as van der Waals forces.

Certain compounds exhibit anomalies in their physical and chemical behaviour. For example: the melting point of *o*-nitrophenol is 45°C., whereas the melting points of the *m*- and *p*- isomers are 97°C. and 114°C. respectively; acetic acid exists largely in the form of dimers $(CH_3CO_2H)_2$; water is a liquid at room temperature whilst hydrogen sulphide (of higher molecular weight) is a gas. These anomalies suggest that in such systems a further type of bond is operative, associated with bonding between a hydrogen atom and a strongly electronegative atom in the same molecule or in neighbouring molecules, leading to intramolecular hydrogen bonding and intermolecular hydrogen bonding respectively. A single hydrogen atom in these compounds behaves as though bonded to two other atoms, resulting in increased attractive energy within a molecule (fig. 32a), between molecules (fig. 32b) or even between two individual atoms (fig. 32c).

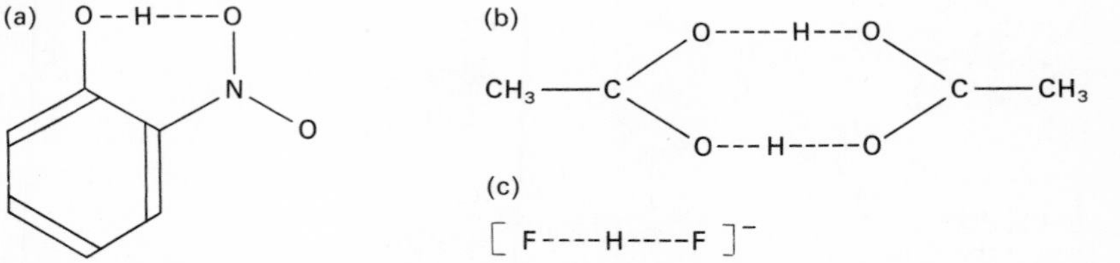

Figure 32.   Hydrogen-bonded species: (a) *o*-nitrophenol (b) acetic acid dimer (c) HF_2^- ion.

The energy of the hydrogen bond varies with the species involved, being about 5 kcal. mole^{-1} in the case of water and about 30 kcal. g -ion^{-1} in the HF_2^- ion. It is of most importance between atoms of high electronegativity, e.g. $F\cdots H\cdots O$, $Cl\cdots H\cdots N$, but some evidence suggests that hydrogen bonds may be operative between bromine and oxygen, for example intermolecular $C\cdots H\cdots O$ in crystalline ethylene carbonate,

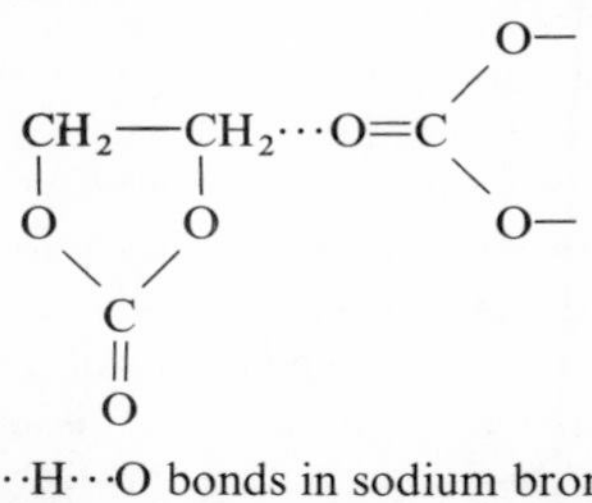

and $Br\cdots H\cdots O$ bonds in sodium bromide dihydrate, $NaBr2H_2O$.

It should be recognized that in no given example does the interaction correspond solely to one of the bond types so far discussed. For example, even in the hydrogen molecule there is some contribution from the ionic species H^+ and H^-, and part of the lattice energy of silver chloride is due to covalent Ag–Cl bonding. However, in many substances a single type of bond is of most importance, e.g. the ionic 'bond' in sodium chloride or the covalent bond in diamond, so we can associate certain structural and physical properties with each of the principal bond types (electro-valent, covalent, van der Waals and metallic). We omit the hydrogen bond from the list of principal types, regarding it as modifying the properties of a structure already formed, or capable of being formed, by other types of valency, as in the examples of NH_4F and H_2O.

2·6 Physical and structural characteristics of the principal bond types

In table 5 some physical and structural characteristics associated with each of the principal types of chemical bonds are summarized.

2·6·1 *Mechanical properties*

The hardness of materials is often expressed by Moh's scale of scratch hardness which ranges from 1 to 10, each material being capable of scratching those of lower hardness number:

1	talc	6	orthoclase
2	gypsum	7	quartz
3	calcite	8	topaz
4	fluorspar	9	corundum
5	apatite	10	diamond

Both electrovalent compounds, e.g. topaz $(Al_2SiO_4)(F, OH)_2$ and fluorspar CaF_2 and covalent compounds, e.g. quartz $(SiO_2)_n$ and corundum $(Al_2O_3)_m$, are represented within this scale, showing that hardness is not a distinguishing feature between these two types of valency. Van der Waals interactions are of low energy and do not give rise to mechanically strong crystals, thus explaining the friability of organic crystals which are held together by forces of the van der Waals type.

In metallic crystals, deformation of the crystal takes place by *gliding*, a process that occurs most easily along the planes of most closely packed atoms in the metal crystal (see chapter 3). The characteristic malleability of copper and the brittleness of tungsten are associated with the degree of close packing.

Another mechanical property of crystals (intimately connected with the type of bond present) is *cleavage*, the property of breaking cleanly in certain directions; it is not observed in metals, since these deform in the manner already described. The cleavage planes represent surfaces across which the binding forces are relatively weak, e.g. mica, calcite (cleavage occurring parallel to the faces of a rhombohedron), and fluorspar (cleaves along planes parallel to the faces of an octahedron). Quartz lacks cleavage, because there is an even distribution of bonds in all directions.

2·6·2 *Thermal properties*

Electrovalent and covalent compounds generally have high melting points, e.g. NaCl (801°C.), MgO (2800°C.), SiC (2700°C.), diamond ($>$ 3500°C.). Organic crystals

Table 5 Some Properties of Bond Types

Property	Bond type			
	Electrovalent	Covalent	Van der Waals	Metallic
Mechanical	Strong and hard crystals	Strong and hard crystals	Weak and soft crystals	Variable strength; glide deformation
Thermal	High m.p.; low coefficient of thermal expansion; ions in the melt	High m.p.; low coefficient of thermal expansion; molecules in the melt	Low m.p.; high coefficient of thermal expansion	Variable m.p.; long liquid interval
Electrical	Insulators; conduction in the melt by ion-transport	Insulators in the solid and in the melt	Insulators	Conduction by electron-transport
Optical	Absorption and related properties are those of component ions (similar in solution)	Absorption different in solution (and in the gaseous state) from that of the solid	Absorption properties are those of the individual molecules and are similar in solution and in the gaseous state	Opaque; properties similar in the liquid state; transparent to high-energy radiation, e.g. x-rays
Structural	Non-directional coordination number (C.N.) variable	Strongly directional; C.N. variable	Non-directional	Non-directional; C.N. high (8 or 12)

are not covalent since the covalent molecules in the crystal are bound to one another only by van der Waals forces. They have relatively low melting points in contrast to the very high values for purely covalent compounds such as SiC and diamond. The melting points of electrovalent compounds increase with rising ionic charge, but for constant ionic charge the melting points decrease with increasing interionic distance r (table 6).

Table 6   Melting points of electrovalent compounds

	NaF	NaCl	NaBr	NaI	MgO
r (Å.)	2·31	2·82	2·98	3·24	2·11
m.p. (°C.)	988	801	755	651	2,800

The melting points of metals vary considerably, e.g. mercury -38°C., osmium 2700°C. All metals have a long *liquid interval* (the temperature range between melting point and boiling point), e.g. gallium 1953 degC., copper 1512 degC., but electrovalent and covalent compounds have a liquid interval only one-tenth that of metals.

2.6.3   *Electrical properties*

Electrovalent compounds conduct electricity in the molten state and in solution in a polar solvent by ion transport, a characteristic that may be regarded as a criterion of the electrovalent bond. Covalent compounds and van der Waals compounds are insulators in the solid state and in the melt, whereas metals conduct readily due to the presence of electrons which are free to move about the crystal as a whole. The small conductivity of semi-conductors is due to resonance between metallic and covalent bond types, the metallic contribution at normal temperatures being extremely small.

2·6·4   *Optical properties*

The light absorption of ionic crystals is mainly in the ultra-violet region of the spectrum, so that they appear colourless. The optical properties of the crystal are the sum of the properties of the component ions since the electrons are localized in orbitals, but ions which contain transition metals (those having incompletely filled d orbitals) are usually coloured because optical absorption occurs in the visible region of the spectrum.

In covalent compounds the electron orbitals overlap and hence the optical properties of these compounds are quite different from those of their constituent elements. It is noticeable that colour sometimes develops with an increasing percentage of covalent character, as in the silver halides, which also display an increased *departure from additivity*, δ, of the ionic radii (i.e. the difference between the interionic separation and the sum of the radii of the ions), this departure becoming larger with rising polarizability of the anion (table 7).

Table 7 Departure from additivity of silver halides

	AgF (colourless)	AgCl (colourless)	AgBr (pale yellow)	AgI (yellow)
r Å.	2·47	2·78	2·88	2·80
$(r^+ + r^-)$ Å.	2·59	3·07	3·22	3·46
δ Å.	0·12	0·29	0·34	0·66

In van der Waals compounds the optical properties are those of the component molecules, which means that they are similar in solution and in the gaseous state. Visible light is scattered by electrons so that metals appear opaque because their electrons are distributed over the entire crystal and therefore scatter all the light, but to radiation of higher energy, e.g. X-rays, metals are transparent.

2·6·5 *Structural properties*

Only the covalent bond exhibits directional character. For example, a chloride ion experiences the same force of attraction in whichever direction it approaches a sodium ion during the formation of a sodium chloride crystal, whereas in methane a hydrogen atom must approach a carbon atom along the direction of one of the sp^3 orbitals for bond formation to occur.

The number of nearest neighbours around any given atom or ion is called the *co-ordination number*. In covalent and electrovalent structures the coordination numbers are similar, but in metals the figure is usually eight or twelve. In van der Waals compounds the molecules pack together to obtain a minimum energy state and the separation of nearest-neighbour atoms of different molecules is about 3·7 Å. In certain crystals this may be reduced to as low a value as 2·5 Å. Another attractive force which is the result of intermolecular hydrogen bonding is operative in these cases, the determination of such small distances being a frequent means of recognizing hydrogen bonds.

Problems

1. The ionization energies I_M of lithium and caesium are 5·39 eV. and 3·89 eV. respectively and the corresponding heats of sublimation S_M are Li, 38·4; Cs, 18·7 kcal. g-atom^{-1}. Account for the following values of the lattice energies of the chlorides: LiCl, -199; CsCl, -152 kcal. mole^{-1}.

2. From the data of question 1, together with the following additional information, calculate the electron affinity of chlorine (1 eV per molecule = 23·06 kcal mole^{-1}):

> heats of formation, ΔH_f^0: LiCl, $-97·7$; CsCl, $-106·3$ kcal. mole^{-1}
> heat of dissociation of Cl_2: 57·1 kcal. mole^{-1}.

3. Discuss the bonding in the predominantly covalent molecules $CHCl_3$, $CHCl$: $CHCl$, N_2O_4, H_2SO_4.

4. Show that the ion $\{CoCl_2(NH_3)_4\}^+$ may exhibit geometrical (cis–trans) isomerism and that the ion $\{CoBrCl(H_2O)(NH_3)_3\}^+$ may exhibit optical (*dl*) isomerism.

5. Criticize the following statements:

(a) Covalent compounds melt and boil at much lower temperatures than do electrovalent compounds.

(b) Electrovalent and covalent compounds are generally soluble in water and in organic solvents respectively.

(c) Metals and hydrogen are evolved at the cathode in electrolysis.

Chapter 3
Thermochemistry and thermodynamics

Thermochemistry is concerned with the heat changes that accompany chemical reactions and is based upon the energy conservation law, which states in essence: 'energy can be converted from one form to another but cannot be created or destroyed'. The expenditure of energy of one kind in any process involves the production of an equivalent amount of energy of other kinds, i.e. heat, light and work are interconvertible. The celebrated cannon-boring by Rumford in 1798 first introduced the idea of equivalence between work and heat, the quantitative significance of this relationship being deduced by Joule in 1840 (the equalities 1 calorie = 4·184 joules = 4·184 × 10^7 erg remind us of his achievement).

Thermodynamics is a much wider subject than thermochemistry, and is concerned with the energy changes accompanying chemical processes of all types. These energy changes can be used to determine the equilibrium position of a reacting system, and also to show whether a given reaction is possible. Thermodynamics is quite independent of atomic and molecular models and thus of changes in these models as new scientific ideas are introduced. Modern chemistry is, however, much concerned with models of systems and an ability to relate thermodynamic quantities to molecular processes is useful in the study of chemistry, although not necessary for the study of thermodynamics itself.

The equations of thermodynamics do not give information about rates of reactions. For example: a gas mixture composed of one mole of chlorine and one mole of hydrogen is thermodynamically unstable with respect to one mole of hydrogen chloride, the free energy decrease accompanying this spontaneous reaction being approximately −22·8 kcal. mole^{-1} of hydrogen chloride formed. However, thermodynamics tells us neither that the mixture of chlorine and hydrogen can be kept in a dark place indefinitely, nor that in the presence of ultra-violet light the reaction takes place with explosive violence as a study of chemical kinetics will reveal.

The law of conservation of energy is based upon practical experience: perpetual motion, for example, has never been demonstrated, otherwise energy could be created by such a process. A direct outcome of the law of conservation of energy is the first law of thermodynamics, which states that *the total energy of a system and its surroundings is constant* (the term *system* refers to a specific quantity of matter). A system and its surroundings which cannot exchange energy with any other system and its surroundings is called an *isolated* system. An example of the first law of thermodynamics (fig. 33) would be a gas in a given state (defined by pressure P_1 and volume V_1) changing to another state P_2, V_2 by path I and then returning to the original state by another route (path II). The first law of thermodynamics requires that the energy in state 1 shall be the same at the end of the whole cyclic process as it was at the beginning, otherwise (if the cycle involved a net increase of energy) the repetition of cycles $1 \to 2 \to 1$ would result in the creation of energy contrary to the first law of thermodynamics.

The energy change in moving from state 1 to state 2 is given by equation (3.1). The notation used is common in thermodynamics. The change in any property X of the

$$\Delta U = U_2 - U_1 \tag{3.1}$$

system is represented by ΔX, where ΔX is the value of X after the change minus the value of X before the change; U is the internal (intrinsic) energy of the system, but as we shall see later the intrinsic energy of a substance is not numerically equal to its heat of formation.

3·1 Energy and work

In general, the system illustrated by fig. 33 may either lose or gain energy in going from state 1 to state 2. This change in energy may appear as work (w) or heat (q). By convention, w is considered positive when it represents work done by the system, whilst q is positive when it represents heat absorbed by the system from the surroundings (as in an endothermic reaction). A positive q leads to an increase of the internal energy U of the system; a positive w leads to a decrease of U.

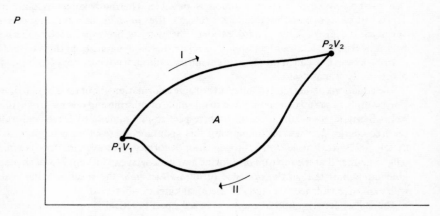

Figure 33.   The forward and return paths of a gas between two states.

If ΔU, equation (3.1), represents the increase in internal energy of the system when the work done by the system is w and the heat absorbed by the system is q, then equation (3.2) may be formulated. Equations (3.1) and (3.2) are the mathematical

$$\Delta U = q - w \tag{3.2}$$

representation of the first law of thermodynamics. The individual values of q and w depend upon the path followed, but their difference is independent of the path, and depends only upon the initial and final states of the system.

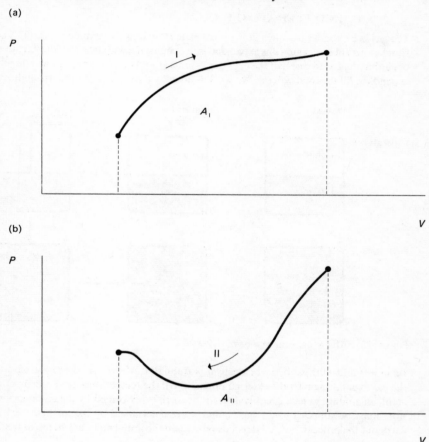

(a)

(b)

Figure 34.   The two stages in the cycle of figure 33.

In chapter 4 we shall show that the work done by the expansion of an ideal gas against a constant pressure P is $P \Delta V$, where ΔV is the change in volume of the gas. Fig. 33 may be redrawn for the two stages of the cycle as in figs. 34a and 34b. The work done is different for the two routes I and II and is measured by the areas under the curves A_I and A_{II}; the net work performed during the cycle is given by $A_I - A_{II}$, which is equal to the area A enclosed by the two curves (fig. 33). If q is the heat absorbed during the cycle, then from (**3.2**) $q = w$, since $\Delta U = 0$.

53   Thermochemistry and thermodynamics

3·1·1 Reversible and irreversible processes

In thermodynamics the term *reversible* has a further meaning beyond that associated with equilibria such as equation (3.3). In figs. 35 and 36 two processes are illustrated.

$$C_2H_5CO_2Et + H_2O \rightleftharpoons C_2H_5CO_2H + EtOH \tag{3.3}$$

The gas in a cylinder is shown in its initial state (1) and in its expanded state (2). The simplest way of envisaging this expansion is to imagine the withdrawal of the partition confining the gas to one half the cylinder volume (3 → 4) so that the gas immediately expands to fill the total volume. No work is done by the system on the surroundings,

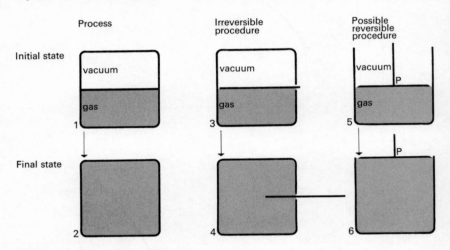

Figure 35.   The expansion of a gas.

i.e. $w = 0$, and if the gas behaves ideally $q = 0$ and thus $\Delta U = 0$. In the process 5 → 6, the gas expands against the external pressure p. If the temperature is to remain constant, an amount of heat q, equivalent to the work w performed by the gas in expansion, must be supplied to the gas; q and w are determined by the method used to carry out the process, but ΔU depends only upon the initial and final states, as noted previously.

Fig. 36 illustrates the formation of zinc sulphate in aqueous solution. In the process 3 → 4, the zinc dust is added to the copper sulphate solution and copper is precipitated. In this process, w is sensibly zero and q is negative since heat is evolved by the system from the free energy change of the chemical reaction. In the process 5 → 6, the same reaction is carried out in a galvanic (Daniell) cell by means of which the electron flow can be made to do electrical work; in this case q is negligibly small but w is positive, whilst the free energy change now produces the electrical work w.

The derivation of the work done by the expansion of a gas, $w = P\,\Delta V$, assumed a state of balance in the system: the gas expanded through a succession of equilibrium stages, for each of which the piston was moved back by the infinitesimal length dl.

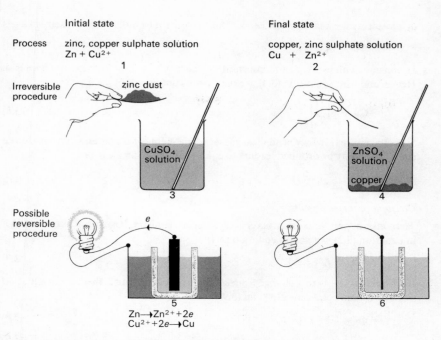

	Initial state	Final state
Process	zinc, copper sulphate solution Zn + Cu²⁺ 1	copper, zinc sulphate solution Cu + Zn²⁺ 2

Process: zinc, copper sulphate solution $Zn + Cu^{2+}$ — copper, zinc sulphate solution $Cu + Zn^{2+}$

Irreversible procedure: zinc dust — CuSO₄ solution — ZnSO₄ solution, copper

Possible reversible procedure

$$Zn \longrightarrow Zn^{2+} + 2e$$
$$Cu^{2+} + 2e \longrightarrow Cu$$

Figure 36. The formation of zinc sulphate solution.

This is a thermodynamically reversible process because an infinitesimal increase in the external pressure would cause the piston to compress the gas and the work performed by the gas in a reversible expansion could be stored. This work represents the maximum work that could be obtained from the process, although more work could be obtained for the same change in volume ΔV if the external pressure were increased; an increase of external applied pressure leads to compression, however, since the process is reversible.

In practice, if a gas is expanded against a piston the pressure of the gas is greater than the external pressure. This represents an irreversible process and less work than $P \Delta V$ is done by the gas so that the system is no longer in temperature and pressure equilibrium with the surroundings. Spontaneous processes occur because of a lack of balance in real systems, hence all real processes are irreversible. The closest approach to reversibility is attained, in practice, in measuring the e.m.f. of a galvanic cell by a potentiometer (page 225).

3·1·2   *Constant volume processes*

If a process takes place at constant volume, the work of expansion is zero. If w relates only to this form of work, then from equation (3.2) we derive equation (3.4), where

q_V represents the heat absorbed at constant volume. The molar heat capacity of a gas

$$\Delta U = q_V \tag{3.4}$$

at constant volume, C_V, and constant pressure, C_P, will be defined in chapter 4. Hence, and using equation (3.4), we may write equation (3.5).

$$C_V = \left(\frac{\partial U}{\partial T}\right)_V \tag{3.5}$$

Since the internal energy of an ideal gas is independent of volume and of pressure, the subscript V may be dropped leading to equation (3.6) for an ideal gas.

$$C_V = \frac{dU}{dT} \tag{3.6}$$

3·1·3 Constant pressure processes

The constant pressure system is very common in chemistry. If we substitute $w = P\,\Delta V$ in equation (3.2), we obtain equation (3.7):

$$\Delta U = q_P + P\,\Delta V. \tag{3.7}$$

If ΔU and ΔV apply to a change from state 1 to another state 2, then, using equation (3.1), we obtain equations (3.8) and (3.9):

$$q_P = U_2 - U_1 + P(V_2 - V_1) \tag{3.8}$$

$$= (U_2 + PV_2) - (U_1 + PV_1). \tag{3.9}$$

Since P, V and U are properties of the state of the system, $(U + PV)$ is also determined by the state of the system. The quantity $(U + PV)$ is denoted by H, the *heat content* or *enthalpy* of the system. Hence, from equations (3.7) and (3.9) we deduce equations (3.10) and (3.11).

$$q_P = H_2 - H_1 = \Delta H \tag{3.10}$$

$$\Delta H = \Delta U + P\,\Delta V \tag{3.11}$$

In equation (3.11), ΔH refers to constant pressure conditions and ΔU refers to constant volume conditions. The molar heat capacity of a gas at constant pressure may be defined by equation (3.12) in a manner analogous to that in equation (3.6).

$$C_P = \frac{dH}{dT} \tag{3.12}$$

From equations (3.6) and (3.12) we may deduce the following relationships for an ideal gas:

$$C_P - C_V = \frac{dH}{dT} - \frac{dU}{dT} \tag{3.13}$$

$$= \frac{dU}{dT} - \frac{d(PV)}{dT} - \frac{dU}{dT} \tag{3.14}$$

$$= \frac{d(RT)}{dT} \tag{3.15}$$

$$= R. \tag{3.16}$$

To increase the temperature of a gas at constant volume, its internal energy must be increased. To increase the temperature of a gas at constant pressure, heat must be supplied to the gas both to increase the internal energy of the gas and to produce the work of expansion, w. For one mole of an ideal gas, heated from $(T-1)°$ to $T°$, the work done is given by equation (3.17).

$$w = \int_{T-1}^{T} P\,\Delta V = \int_{T-1}^{T} R\,\Delta T = R \tag{3.17}$$

The gas constant thus represents the work done by one mole of an ideal gas in expanding against a constant external pressure, while the temperature is increased by one degree.

From equations (3.10) and (3.11), we note that the heat gained or lost by a system is identified with ΔH, the change in the enthalpy of the system. Thus if ΔH is positive, the system has absorbed heat from its surroundings (endothermic reaction), whilst if ΔH is negative the enthalpy of the system has decreased and heat has been given out (exothermic reaction).

Before beginning a study of thermochemistry in terms of the enthalpy changes of reacting systems we must consider in what way the law of conservation of energy is more fundamental than the law of conservation of mass.

The relationship between mass and energy was deduced by Einstein and is given by equation (3.18).

$$\Delta U = \Delta m\, c^2 \tag{3.18}$$

In an ordinary chemical reaction the value of ΔU would be less than about 100 kcal. mole^{-1}, or 4.184×10^{12} erg mole^{-1}. If the velocity of light, c, is taken as 2.998×10^{10} cm. sec.$^{-1}$, Δm is approximately 4.6×10^{-9} g., which would not be detected by ordinary chemical means and confirms that for chemical processes the law of conservation of mass is sufficient. We can contrast this change with a nuclear reaction such as equation (3.19):

$$^4N + {}^2H \rightarrow {}^{12}C + {}^4He. \tag{3.19}$$

In this reaction, the loss in mass is 0.0145 a.m.u., equivalent to 2.16×10^{-5} erg, or 3.11×10^8 kcal. mole^{-1}. (1 a.m.u. $= 1.648 \times 10^{-24}$ g.)

3·2 Thermochemistry

Consider any reaction such as equation (3.20).

$$A + B \rightarrow C + D. \tag{3.20}$$

In general, the sum of the heat contents of the products is not equal to the sum of the heat contents of the reactants and the system has an associated enthalpy change, given by equation (**3.21**).

$$\Delta H = \Sigma H \text{ (products)} - \Sigma H \text{ (reactants)} \qquad (\mathbf{3.21})$$

ΔH can be positive (endothermic reaction) or negative (exothermic reaction). The temptation to associate the positive ΔH with the exothermic reaction can be avoided by remembering that ΔH refers to the *system* and not to the surroundings. The quantity ΔH, expressed by equation (**3.21**), is the enthalpy (heat) change of reaction and this equation forms the basis of thermochemistry.

We must now consider the meaning and determination of ΣH (products) and ΣH (reactants). Their meaning is simply explained by equations (**3.22**) and (**3.23**).

$$\Sigma H \text{ (products)} = H(\text{C}) + H(\text{D}) \qquad (\mathbf{3.22})$$

$$\Sigma H \text{ (reactants)} = H(\text{A}) + H(\text{B}) \qquad (\mathbf{3.23})$$

Their determination requires more explanation and we shall consider a specific example, represented by equation (**3.24**).

$$\text{Na (cryst.)} + \tfrac{1}{2}\text{Cl}_2 \text{ (gas)} \rightarrow \text{NaCl (cryst.)} \qquad (\mathbf{3.24})$$

From previous arguments, the enthalpy change of this reaction is given by equation (**3.25**)

$$\Delta H(\text{NaCl}) = H(\text{NaCl}) - [H(\text{Na}) + \tfrac{1}{2}H(\text{Cl}_2)] \qquad (\mathbf{3.25})$$

While we can measure $\Delta H(\text{NaCl})$, we cannot measure the individual enthalpies and the use of a *standard state* is therefore invoked. This is defined as the lowest enthalpy (and free energy) state of a substance at 25°C., and at a pressure of one atmosphere. The heat contents of all elements in their standard states are chosen to be zero, so from equation (**3.25**) we may write $H^0(\text{NaCl}) = \Delta H^0(\text{NaCl})$ in which the latter symbol represents the standard heat of formation of one mole of sodium chloride and the standard state is symbolized by the superscript 0. In view of the importance of the heat of formation, it is accorded the particular symbol ΔH_f, so we may write $\Delta H_f^0(\text{NaCl})$ to represent the heat of formation of sodium chloride from the elements in their standard state ($-98\cdot2$ kcal. mole^{-1}). It is noteworthy that the heat of formation is a special case of the heat of reaction described by equation (**3.21**).

We shall consider next the oxidation of carbon (graphite), for which three thermochemical equations, (**3.26**) to (**3.28**), can be written:

$$\text{C (graphite)} + \text{O}_2 \text{ (gas)} \rightarrow \text{CO}_2 \text{ (gas)} \quad \Delta H_f^0 = -94\cdot1 \text{ kcal. mole}^{-1} \quad (\mathbf{3.26})$$

$$\text{C (graphite)} + \tfrac{1}{2}\text{O}_2 \text{ (gas)} \rightarrow \text{CO (gas)} \quad \Delta H_f^0 = -26\cdot4 \text{ kcal. mole}^{-1} \quad (\mathbf{3.27})$$

$$\text{CO (gas)} + \tfrac{1}{2}\text{O}_2 \text{ (gas)} \rightarrow \text{CO}_2 \text{ (gas)} \quad \Delta H^0 = -67\cdot7 \text{ kcal. mole}^{-1}. \quad (\mathbf{3.28})$$

The total effect of equations (**3.27**) and (**3.28**) in terms of both chemical species and enthalpy change is expressed by equation (**3.26**). This introduces the concept known as Hess's law of constant heat summation: *if a reaction is carried out in stages, the algebraic sum of the enthalpy changes of the separate stages is equal to the enthalpy* *change of the complete reaction as carried out in one stage.* In other words, ΔH depends only upon the initial and final stages of the process, as already discussed. This is a consequence of the first law of thermodynamics. The equations (**3.26**) to (**3.28**) can be represented graphically by fig. 37, illustrating an alternative statement of Hess's law; *the sum of the enthalpies taken in order in a cyclic process is zero*; in this example, it means that $\Delta H_{\mathrm{I}} + \Delta H_{\mathrm{II}} - \Delta H = 0$.

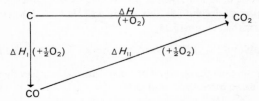

Figure 37.   Thermodynamic cycle for the formation of the oxides of carbon.

It is rarely possible to determine a heat of formation from direct calorimetric measurements. The reaction $C + \frac{1}{2}O_2 \rightarrow CO$, for example, cannot be used to measure the heat of formation of carbon monoxide because in practice an unknown quantity of carbon dioxide is also formed. The widest applications of Hess's law are to processes such as the formation of carbon monoxide, sodium sulphate, or ethane.

For a second example of thermochemical cycles, consider the evaluation of the heat of formation for a compound such as ethanol, which cannot be formed directly from its elements. The heat of formation is still defined with respect to the elements in their standard states, as equations (**3.29**) to (**3.32**) demonstrate.

$$2C \text{ (graphite)} + 3H_2 \text{ (gas)} + \tfrac{1}{2}O_2 \text{ (gas)} \rightarrow C_2H_5OH \text{ (liq.)} \tag{3.29}$$

$$C \text{ (graphite)} + O_2 \text{ (gas)} \rightarrow CO_2 \text{ (gas)} \qquad \Delta H_f^0(CO_2) = -94\cdot1 \tag{3.30}$$

$$H_2 \text{ (gas)} + \tfrac{1}{2}O_2 \text{ (gas)} \rightarrow H_2O \text{ (liq.)} \qquad \Delta H_f^0(H_2O) = -68\cdot3 \tag{3.31}$$

$$C_2H_5OH \text{ (liq.)} + 3O_2 \text{ (gas)} \rightarrow 2CO_2 \text{ (gas)} + 3H_2O \text{ (liq.)} \qquad \Delta H^\circ = -327\cdot0. \tag{3.32}$$

If equation (**3.30**) is multiplied by 2, equation (**3.31**) multiplied by 3 and equation (**3.32**) subtracted from their sum, re-arrangement leads to equation (**3.29**); this equation represents the heat of formation of ethanol. The corresponding enthalpy changes are shown by equation (**3.33**)

$$(-94\cdot1 \times 2) + (-68\cdot4 \times 3) - (-327\cdot0) = -66\cdot4 \tag{3.33}$$

and the algebraic sum, $-66\cdot4$ kcal. mole^{-1}, is $\Delta H_f^0(C_2H_5OH)$.

The reaction in equation (**3.32**) is an example of the complete combustion of an organic compound, the associated ΔH (sometimes called the heat of combustion) being a special case of the heat of reaction. An enthalpy of hydrogenation can be defined similarly.

The formation of liquid water from its elements is represented by equation (3.31). If the product of this reaction had been steam, the corresponding enthalpy of formation would have been $-57 \cdot 8$ kcal. mole^{-1}. Steam is higher in enthalpy than water by $10 \cdot 6$ kcal. mole^{-1}, which represents the latent heat of vaporization of water and further exemplifies the need for the exact specification of the physical states in thermochemical equations. In some of the above equations, carbon has been specified in the form of graphite, the standard state of carbon; the use of diamond (which is thermodynamically unstable with respect to graphite) is very costly and leads to different numerical results in accordance with equation (3.34).

$$C \text{ (diamond)} \rightarrow C \text{ (graphite)} \qquad \Delta H° = -0 \cdot 5 \text{ kcal. mole}^{-1} \qquad \textbf{(3.34)}$$

Returning to a study of water, we note that it could be formed by reacting together solutions of acids and bases, as in equations (3.35) and (3.36).

$$Na^+OH^-\text{(aq.)} + H^+Cl^-\text{(aq.)} \rightarrow Na^+Cl^-\text{(aq.)} + H_2O \qquad \Delta H° \qquad \textbf{(3.35)}$$

$$H^+\text{(aq.)} + OH^-\text{(aq.)} \rightarrow H_2O \qquad \Delta H° \qquad \textbf{(3.36)}$$

The standard enthalpy of formation of sodium hydroxide is $-102 \cdot 0$ kcal. mole^{-1}, but when sodium hydroxide dissolves in water an enthalpy change takes place which equation (3.37) shows to be dependent upon the concentration of the final solution.

$$NaOH \text{ (cryst.)} + xH_2O \text{ (liq.)} \rightarrow Na^+ \text{ (aq.)} + OH^- \text{ (aq.)} \qquad \Delta H_s \qquad \textbf{(3.37)}$$

We use the term enthalpy of solution (ΔH_s) to describe the heat change of this process, the state of infinite dilution being chosen as the standard state for solutions.

Let one mole of sodium hydroxide be dissolved in a small quantity of water, producing an enthalpy change ΔH_1. This solution, if diluted, undergoes a further enthalpy change, ΔH_2, and so on for $\Delta H_3, \Delta H_4, \ldots \Delta H_i$, the heat of solution at infinite dilution being defined by equation (3.38).

$$\Delta H_s^0 = \sum_i \Delta H_i \qquad \textbf{(3.38)}$$

In other words, ΔH_s^0 is the enthalpy change per mole accompanying dissolution in such a quantity of water that, upon further dilution, there is no measurable heat change.

We can try to understand these heat changes in terms of a model for the process. A solid dissolves because it interacts with the solvent. In the case of NaOH in water an exothermic change is observed, the Na^+ and OH^- ions which are present in the crystal becoming hydrated by molecules of water (i.e. they are loosely bound to the water molecules by ion–dipole interactions). In a small quantity of water the ions may not be as fully hydrated as possible because there is not enough water for all the ions present. A sodium ion can, on average, be hydrated by six water molecules. We may think of this as a spherical region in the solution consisting of the central ion surrounded by six water molecules forming the hydration sphere. The processes of initial solution and subsequent dilution involve electrical interactions, and heat energy is exchanged between the solution and its surroundings. At infinite dilution (represented by aq.) we may assume complete hydration with no interactions (since the hydrated ions are widely separated) and consequently no further exchange of energy upon further dilution.

The relevant data for the species involved in equation (**3.35**) are as follows:

	$-\Delta H_f^0$	$-\Delta H_s^0$
NaOH	102·0	10·1
HCl	22·1	17·6
NaCl	98·2	−1·3
H_2O	68·3	—

The enthalpy changes for equations (**3.35**) and (**3.36**) are given by (**3.39**).

$$[\Delta H_f^0(H_2O, \text{liq.}) + \Delta H_f^0(\text{NaCl, cryst.}) + \Delta H_s^0(\text{NaCl})]$$

$$-[\Delta H_f^0(\text{NaOH, cryst}) + \Delta H_s^0(\text{NaOH}) + \Delta H_f^0(\text{HCl, gas}) + \Delta H_s^0(\text{HCl})] \quad (\textbf{3.39})$$

This is evaluated as -13.4 kcal. mole^{-1} and is very different from the enthalpy change for the reaction in equation (**3.31**) in which water is formed by another process. The two values can be considered in the light of fig. 38, this cyclic process being similar to the Born–Haber cycle described in chapter 2. The value of -13.4 kcal. mole^{-1} is sometimes called the *heat of neutralization* and represents the heat of reaction between one gram-equivalent of a strong acid and one gram-equivalent of a strong base both at infinite dilution. The value is the same whichever strong acid and strong base are used (it is not the same if weak acids or weak bases are involved).

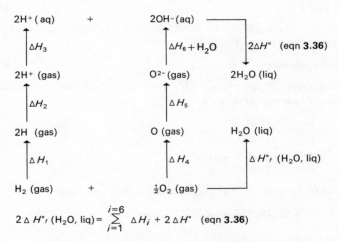

$$2 \Delta H^{\circ}_f(H_2O, \text{liq}) = \sum_{i=1}^{i=6} \Delta H_i + 2 \Delta H^{\circ} \quad (\text{eqn } \textbf{3.36})$$

Figure 38.   Cyclic processes representing the formation of water by two routes.

A strong acid is fully dissociated in aqueous solution and the heat of reaction with a strong base is represented by equation (**3.36**). In reacting the same strong acid with a weak base, work has to be done to ionize the weak base, since this is not a spontaneous reaction, e.g. $K_b(NH_3) = 1\cdot8 \times 10^{-5}$. Thus the enthalpy changes occurring in reactions with weak acids and bases do not relate solely to the process of equation (**3.36**) and are consequently different from $-13\cdot4$ kcal. $mole^{-1}$. The differences are related to the values of K_a or K_b but not in a simple way so that the dissociation constants cannot be evaluated from the enthalpy changes with any accuracy.

3·2·1   *Temperature effects*

The enthalpies of reaction vary with temperature. Differentiating equation (**3.21**) with respect to temperature leads to equations (**3.40**) and (**3.41**).

$$\left(\frac{\partial H}{\partial T}\right)_P = \left(\frac{\partial H_{\text{products}}}{\partial T}\right)_P - \left(\frac{\partial H_{\text{reactants}}}{\partial T}\right)_P \tag{3.40}$$

$$= \Delta C_P \tag{3.41}$$

Integration over the temperature range T_1 to T_2 may be expressed by equation (**3.42**).

$$\Delta H_{T_1} - \Delta H_{T_2} = \int_{T_1}^{T_2} \Delta C_P \, dT \tag{3.42}$$

In general, C_P varies with temperature in the manner shown in equation (**3.43**) and (over small temperature ranges) equation (**3.44**).

$$C_P = a + bT + cT^2 + dT^3 + \ldots \tag{3.43}$$

$$C_P = a + bT \tag{3.44}$$

These equations were developed first by Kirchoff and we shall demonstrate their application by the reaction in equation (**3.45**).

$$N_2 \text{ (gas)} + 3H_2 \text{ (gas)} \rightleftharpoons 2NH_3 \text{ (gas)} \tag{3.45}$$

The data up to the term in T^2 apply between 0°C. and 1200°C.; we shall assume that terms higher than cT^2 are negligible in C_P.

	a	$10^3 b$	$10^7 c$
N_2	6·52	1·25	−0·01
H_2	6·95	−0·20	4·81
NH_3	6·19	7·89	−7·28

$\Delta H_f^0(NH_3)$ is $-11\cdot0$ kcal. $mole^{-1}$; the value at 598°K. will be evaluated:

$$\Delta C_P = 2C_P(NH_3) - C_P(N_2) - 3C_P(H_2)$$

$$= -14\cdot99 + (15\cdot13 \times 10^{-3} T) + (29\cdot00 \times 10^{-7} T^2)$$

$$\int_{T_1}^{T_2} \Delta C_P \, dT = -14\cdot99(T_2 - T_1) + 7\cdot565 \times 10^{-3}(T_2 - T_1)^2$$

$$- 14\cdot50 \times 10^{-7}(T_2 - T_1)^3.$$

Since T_1, to which the value $\Delta H_f^0(\text{NH}_3)$ applies, is 298°K., the integral is -3.86 kcal.; from equation **(3.45)** this refers to the formation of two moles of ammonia, so $\Delta H_f(\text{NH}_3)$ at 598°K. is -12.9 kcal. mole^{-1}.

3·2·2 *Calorimetry*

Equation **(3.32)** represents the reaction of ethanol in oxygen and implies its complete combustion. The measurement of the associated enthalpy change is one of the easier calorimetric experiments which can be performed in the laboratory, using a 'bomb' calorimeter (fig. 39).

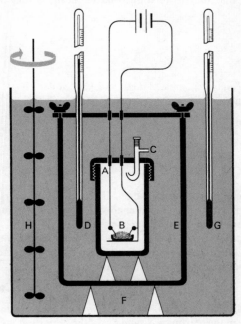

Figure 39. A bomb calorimeter.

A weighed sample B is placed in the crucible of the steel bomb, which is then filled with oxygen at a pressure between 15 and 25 atmospheres. An electric current is passed through a wire spiral resting in the sample to start the combustion reaction, heat is evolved, and the associated temperature rise in the water filling the calorimeter E is measured with the Beckmann thermometer D. The calorimeter is contained in a large vessel of water F agitated by the stirrer H, any temperature change in F being recorded by another Beckmann thermometer G.

The experimental arrangement insulates the calorimeter thermally from its surroundings (hence the name adiabatic calorimeter) and the apparatus is calibrated by means of a substance possessing an accurately known heat of combustion. Results with errors of less than 0·01 per cent are obtainable. A good primary standard for calibration is benzoic acid, $C_6H_5CO_2H$, the heat of combustion of which is $-771·13 \pm 0·08$ kcal. mole^{-1} at 25°C.

The combustion being studied takes place at constant volume – the volume of the bomb – so no $P\,\Delta V$ work is performed by the system and from equation (**3.4**) the change in heat content corresponds to ΔU. In order to calculate ΔH (the heat of combustion) from the data, we make use of equation (**3.11**); if the number of moles of gaseous products is n_2, and if the number of moles of oxygen consumed during the combustion is n_1, there is an increase in volume of $(n_2-n_1)V$ litre, where V is the molar volume (22·4 litre). The work done by the system is then $P(n_2-n_1)V$, where P is the pressure in the bomb, assuming that the gas mixture behaves ideally. From the equation

$$P\,\Delta V = \Delta n\,.\,RT$$

equation (**3.11**) becomes

$$\Delta H = \Delta U - (n_2 - n_1)RT$$

where R is expressed in the same units (cal. mole^{-1} deg.$^{-1}$ or kcal. mole^{-1} deg.$^{-1}$) as ΔU. In the combustion of ethanol, $n_2 - n_1 = 5 - 3 = 2$.

$$\Delta U^\circ = -328·2 \text{ kcal. mole}^{-1}$$

$$\Delta U^\circ = -327·0 \text{ kcal. mole}^{-1}$$

3·3 Thermodynamics

Under constant pressure conditions, the enthalpy change ΔH represents the energy change for a reaction when no work is done and the free energy change ΔG represents the maximum amount of energy which can be obtained as useful work.

The difference, $\Delta H - \Delta G$, is that part of the energy change which cannot be converted into useful work and depends upon both the temperature and a factor characteristic of the particular system considered (represented by ΔS) so that

$$\Delta H - \Delta G = T\Delta S. \qquad (3.46)$$

ΔS is called the *entropy change* of the reaction. ΔS is a *state function* like ΔH and depends upon the difference between the entropies, S_1 and S_2, of the initial and final states but not upon the path followed between these two states: $\Delta S = S_2 - S_1$.

Since ΔH and ΔG in equation (**3.46**) both have the units of energy $\div$ mass (usually kcal. mole^{-1} or cal. mole^{-1}) S must have the units of energy $\div$ (mass $\times$ temperature) (usually cal. mole^{-1} deg.$^{-1}$). Under certain isothermal conditions, ΔS is represented by the enthalpy change of the process divided by the temperature at which it occurs. For example, the latent heat of fusion of ice is 1440 cal. mole^{-1}:

$$H_2O(\text{cryst.}) \rightarrow H_2O(\text{liq.}), \qquad \Delta H = +1440 \text{ cal.}$$

At 273°C.,

$$\Delta S = \frac{\Delta H}{T} = \frac{1440}{273} = +5·27 \text{ cal. mole}^{-1} \text{ deg.}^{-1}$$

An increase in entropy always corresponds to a more random arrangement of the atoms, molecules, etc. in the system, which is generally typical of spontaneous processes, although in a few cases a decrease in entropy is more than compensated by a large decrease in enthalpy (for example in spontaneous crystallization from a supersaturated solution).

On raising the temperature of a mass of gas at constant volume heat is absorbed, so that an increase in entropy occurs with greater randomization of the molecular velocities (fig. 40).

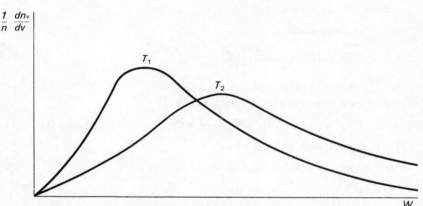

Figure 40. The distribution of velocity of gas molecules (Boltzmann): $T_1 < T_2$.

As we have stated, the driving force of chemical reactions is the tendency for the free energy, G, to decrease, so that $\Delta G = \Sigma G_{\text{products}} - \Sigma G_{\text{reactants}}$, is negative. From equation (3.46), ΔH and $T \Delta S$ may be positive or negative for a spontaneous change, provided that ΔG itself is negative. For example, when iodine monochloride is formed from its elements at 25°C.:

$$\tfrac{1}{2}I_2(\text{gas}) + \tfrac{1}{2}Cl_2(\text{gas}) \rightarrow ICl(\text{gas}) \tag{3.48}$$

$$\Delta H^0 = +4.2 \text{ kcal. mole}^{-1}, \qquad \Delta S = +18.5 \text{ cal. mole}^{-1} \text{ deg.}^{-1}$$

$$\Delta G^0 = +4.2 - \frac{(298.16 \times 18.5)}{1,000}$$

$$= -1.3 \text{ kcal. mole}^{-1}.$$

When water is formed:

$$H_2(\text{gas}) + \tfrac{1}{2}O_2(\text{gas}) \rightarrow H_2O(\text{liq.}) \tag{3.47}$$

$$\Delta H^0 = -57.8 \text{ kcal. mole}^{-1} \qquad \Delta S = -10.6 \text{ cal. mole}^{-1} \text{ deg.}^{-1}$$

$$\Delta G^0 = -57.8 - \frac{(-10.6 \times 298.16)}{1,000}$$

$$= -54.6 \text{ kcal. mole}^{-1}.$$

When ammonium nitrate dissolves in water, a considerable reduction of temperature is observed:

$$NH_4NO_3^- + H_2O \rightarrow NH_4^+(\text{hyd.}) + NO_3^-(\text{hyd.}). \tag{3.49}$$

The process is endothermic to the extent of $+6\cdot2$ kcal. mole^{-1}.* The entropy change ΔS is $+25\cdot9$ cal. mole^{-1} deg.$^{-1}$ and $\Delta G = +6\cdot2 - 7\cdot7 = -1\cdot5$ kcal. mole^{-1}.

Thermodynamic data can be obtained from a study of the e.m.f.s of cells and it is possible to show that, if the e.m.f. of a cell when balanced on the potentiometer is E, then for the reaction occurring

$$\Delta G = -nFE \tag{3.50}$$

$$\Delta S = \left(\frac{\partial \Delta G}{\partial T}\right)_P = nF\left(\frac{\partial E}{\partial T}\right)_P \tag{3.51}$$

the symbols having the meanings given on page 64.

As examples, we will consider the cell:

$$\text{Hg} | \text{Hg}_2\text{O(satd)}, \text{KOH}(a_\pm = 1) | \text{KCl}(a_\pm = 1), \text{Hg}_2\text{Cl}_2\text{(satd)} | \text{Hg} \tag{3.52}$$

in which the reaction is

$$\text{Hg}_2\text{Cl}_2 + 2\text{KOH} \rightarrow 2\text{KCl} + \text{H}_2\text{O} + \text{Hg}_2\text{O} \tag{3.53}$$

and the cell:

$$\text{Cd} | \text{CdCl}_2 2\tfrac{1}{2}\text{H}_2\text{O(satd)}, \text{AgCl(satd)} | \text{Ag} \tag{3.54}$$

with the reaction:

$$\text{Cd} + 2\text{AgCl} \rightarrow \text{CdCl}_2 + 2\text{Ag}. \tag{3.55}$$

The relevant data, the resultant ΔG and ΔS, and ΔH derived from equation (3.46) are given in table 8.

Table 8 Thermodynamic Data from the E.M.F.s of Cells

Cell	E (25°C.) (volt)	$\left(\dfrac{dE}{dT}\right)_P$ (volt deg.$^{-1}$)	ΔG (kcal. mole^{-1})	ΔS (cal. mole^{-1} deg.$^{-1}$)	ΔH Reaction (kcal. mole^{-1})	
(3.52)	0·154	·000831	−7·10	38·3	4·32	(3.53)
(3.54)	0·675	−·000648	−31·18	−29·9	−40·1	(3.55)

Problems

1. State Hess's law and outline how it may be verified experimentally.
2. Explain why the heat of reaction is a fundamental concept in thermochemistry

---

* Moles H_2O per mole NH_4NO_3:   3   10   1000 ∞

   $\Delta H_s(NH_4NO_3)$ kcal. mole^{-1}:   4·0   5·8   6·1   6·2

and show that all other thermochemical definitions follow from it. Hence, define the terms *heat of formation* and *heat of solution* with reference to thermochemistry.

3. Explain fully the statements 'the standard heat of formation of sulphur dioxide is -70.8 kcal. mole^{-1}', and 'an endothermic reaction is accompanied by an absorption of heat by the system from its surroundings, so that ΔH is positive'.

4. Define Hess's law of thermochemistry. The heats of combustion of ethanol, graphite and hydrogen are 327 kcal. mole^{-1}, 94.1 kcal. g-atom^{-1} and 68.3 kcal. mole^{-1} respectively, at 25°C. and 1 atmosphere pressure. Calculate the heat of formation of ethanol at 25°C.

5. When 1 g-atom of diamond is oxidized, 94.6 kcal. of heat are liberated and when 1 mole of hydrogen is oxidized, 68.3 kcal. of heat are liberated. If the heat of combustion of ethane is -370 kcal. mole^{-1} and if the heat change accompanying the conversion of diamond to graphite is -0.5 kcal. g-atom^{-1}, all processes being referred to 25°C., calculate the heat of formation of ethane.

6. Define (i) heat of solution and (ii) heat of neutralization. Explain the constancy of the heat of neutralization of a dilute solution of a strong acid by a dilute solution of a strong base. Why is it necessary to specify dilute solutions?

The following heats of solution per gram have been recorded:

$$NH_3 \text{ (gas)} \qquad \Delta H = -0.494 \text{ kcal.}$$
$$HI \text{ (gas)} \qquad \Delta H = -0.150 \text{ kcal.}$$
$$NH_4I \text{ (cryst.)} \qquad \Delta H = +0.024 \text{ kcal.}$$

For the reaction NH_3 (gas) + HI (gas) → NH_4I (cryst.), the heat change in forming crystalline ammonium iodide is -0.300 k cal. g.$^{-1}$ Calculate the heat of neutralization of hydriodic acid by aqueous ammonia in dilute solution, and comment on the value obtained. If all the above data refer to a temperature of 25°C., explain why the heat change in forming NH_4I (cryst.) is different from the standard heat of formation of this substance (-48.3 kcal. mole^{-1}). Supplementary data may be found in Appendix E.

7. Explain how the heat of solution at infinite dilution for rubidium hydroxide is obtained experimentally. The following reaction and data refer to 25°C. and 1 atmosphere pressure. Deduce the heat of formation of rubidium sulphate.

$$H^+ \text{ (aq.)} + OH^- \text{ (aq.)} \rightarrow H_2O \text{ (liq.)} \qquad\qquad \Delta H° = -13.4 \text{ kcal.}$$
$$RbOH \text{ (cryst.)} \rightarrow Rb^+ \text{ (aq.)} + OH^- \text{ (aq.)} \qquad\qquad \Delta H° = -15.0 \text{ kcal.}$$
$$Rb_2SO_4 \text{ (cryst.)} \rightarrow 2Rb^+ \text{ (aq.)} + SO_4^{2-} \text{ (aq.)} \qquad\qquad \Delta H° = +5.8 \text{ kcal.}$$
$$Rb \text{ (cryst.)} + \tfrac{1}{2}O_2 \text{ (gas)} + \tfrac{1}{2}H_2 \text{ (gas)} \rightarrow RbOH \text{ (cryst.)} \quad \Delta H° = -98.9 \text{ kcal.}$$
$$H_2 \text{ (gas)} + S \text{ (cryst.)} + 2O_2 \text{ (gas)} \rightarrow H_2SO_4 \text{ (aq.)} \qquad \Delta H° = -216.9 \text{ kcal.}$$
$$H_2 \text{ (gas)} + \tfrac{1}{2}O_2 \text{ (gas)} \rightarrow H_2O \text{ (l.)} \qquad\qquad \Delta H° = -68.3 \text{ kcal.}$$

Chapter 4
The states of matter

Matter exists in three main states: gaseous, liquid and solid. It will be convenient to discuss the properties of matter under these classes, although certain types of substances, such as vitreous materials and 'liquid crystals', do not fall clearly into one or other of them.

Gases are characterized by the large volume changes consequent upon variations in their temperature or pressure, and by their ability to completely fill all the available space. Gases are miscible in all proportions and differ markedly from liquids and solids in that many of their properties are independent of their chemical nature and may be described by general gas laws.

Solids have definite volumes (which do not change appreciably with variations in pressure or temperature) and specific shapes. A study of the solid state is essentially a study of the crystalline state since almost all solids are crystalline. Many of those which are described as amorphous (e.g. charcoal or powdered boron) are, in fact, crystalline although the crystals are of very small dimensions and the material does not appear crystalline to the naked eye. The term amorphous (Gk *amorphos*, shapeless) is best restricted to those solids in which the regularity of the structure extends locally over a range of only a few molecular dimensions (for example glass) or in which the crystal size has been reduced to these small dimensions by some physical or chemical process, as in the case of colloidal sulphur.

A liquid, like a gas, has no definite form and takes up the shape of any containing vessel into which it is placed, but occupies a definite volume. It has a boundary surface which restricts its extent and which is responsible for many of the properties associated with the liquid state. The cohesive forces between the molecules of a liquid are, in general, much stronger than those between the molecules of a gas but substantially weaker than those responsible for cohesion in solids. Thus under normal conditions of temperature and pressure gases behave as an assemblage of freely moving atoms or molecules whereas solids under these conditions form rigid structures. The intermediate nature of the forces operative in liquids has made the study of this state of matter very difficult and at the present time no completely satisfactory theory of the liquid state exists.

The so-called colloidal state is not a state of matter but rather a system composed of very small solid or liquid particles (ranging from approximately 0·01 micron to 0·1 micron) known as the *disperse phase*, and a suspensory phase (the *dispersion medium*) which may itself be in either the liquid or the gaseous state.

4·1 **The gaseous state**

The relationships between pressure, volume and temperature can be expressed for most gases in terms of the gas laws and a combination of them (the *equation of state*). The laws of Boyle and Charles are the result of experimental studies on gases. Boyle's law states that *at constant temperature, the volume of a fixed mass of gas varies inversely as its pressure.* Hence if two conditions of a gas are represented by $P_1 V_1$ and $P_2 V_2$, then

$$P_1 V_1 = P_2 V_2 \tag{4.1}$$

$$\text{or } (PV)_T = \text{constant}, \tag{4.2}$$

the subscript T indicating that the temperature is constant. Charles's law, sometimes referred to as Gay-Lussac's law, states that *at constant pressure, the volume of a fixed mass of gas expands by the same fraction of its volume at 0°C. for every 1 deg. C. rise in temperature.* Thus if V_0 is the volume of a given mass of gas at 0°C., and V_t is the corresponding volume at t°C., both at the same pressure, then from Charles's law

$$V_t = V_0 + t\alpha V_0 \tag{4.3}$$

where α is the coefficient of cubical expansion of the gas. The limiting value of α measured at low pressure and high temperature (under these conditions the gas laws are most closely obeyed) is approximately 0·0036609, or $\dfrac{1}{273·16}$, for all gases. Thus

$$V_t = V_0 \left(1 + \frac{t}{273·16}\right). \tag{4.4}$$

It follows from equation (**4.4**) that the volume of any gas would decrease to nothing at an absolute zero temperature of $-273·16$°C. if it remained gaseous; the absolute temperature $T°$ corresponding to t°C. is thus given by $(t+273·16)$ and from (**4.4**)

$$V_T = \frac{V_0 T}{T_0} \tag{4.5}$$

$$\text{or } \left(\frac{V_T}{T}\right)_P = \left(\frac{V_0}{T_0}\right)_P \tag{4.6}$$

the subscript now indicating constant pressure. Hence at constant pressure, the volume of a fixed mass of gas varies directly as its absolute temperature, an alternative statement of Charles's law that is the basis of the ideal gas scale of temperature.

4·1·1 *The gas constant*

Consider a fixed mass of gas under the conditions P_1, V_1, T_1, being changed in two stages, the first an *isothermal* change (at constant temperature) to P_2, V, T_1, and the

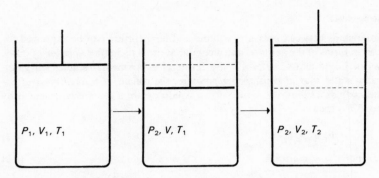

Figure 41. The change of conditions for a gas: $P_2 > P_1$; $T_2 > T_1$.

second an *isopiestic* change (at constant pressure) to P_2, V_2, T_2; it can be imagined that the gas is enclosed in a cylinder by a piston (fig. 41), From equation (**4.1**)

$$(P_1 V_1)_{T_1} = (P_2 V)_{T_1}. \tag{4.7}$$

From equation (**4.6**)

$$\left(\frac{V}{T_1}\right)_{P_2} = \left(\frac{V_2}{T_2}\right)_{P_2}. \tag{4.8}$$

Hence, eliminating V between equations (**4.7**) and (**4.8**)

$$\frac{P_1 V_1}{T_1} = \frac{P_2 V_2}{T_2} \tag{4.9}$$

$$\text{or } \frac{PV}{T} = \text{constant.} \tag{4.10}$$

This constant is, per mole of gas, the gas constant R. Hence

$$PV = RT. \tag{4.11}$$

The value of R may be calculated from equation (**4.11**). Consider one mole of gas at s.t.p.: then $P = 1$ atm. and $T = 273 \cdot 16°$K. Since under the stated conditions V is very nearly $22 \cdot 41$ l. for all gases,

$$R = \frac{22 \cdot 41}{273 \cdot 16} = 0 \cdot 0821 \text{ litre atm. mole}^{-1} \text{ deg.}^{-1}$$

In other units $R = 8 \cdot 314 \times 10^7$ erg mole^{-1} deg.$^{-1} = 1 \cdot 987$ cal. mole^{-1} deg.$^{-1}$ These three units of R are those most frequently required in chemical calculations. Equation (**4.11**) is the equation of state for an imaginary ideal gas which obeys exactly the laws of Boyle and Charles; all real gases depart from the equation under most conditions but at low pressures and high temperatures they approximate very closely to the ideal gas and the equation of state (**4.11**) is a useful concept with which to describe their behaviour (the range is specific to the gas considered).

Example. Three grammes of nitrogen gas are confined at a pressure of 708 mm. mercury and a temperature of 357°C. Assuming that the gas behaves ideally, what volume does it occupy? Let $R = 0.082$ litre atm. mole^{-1} deg.$^{-1}$; the atomic weight of nitrogen is 14·01.

$$P \text{ in atm.} = \frac{708}{760}$$

$$T \text{ in } °K. \text{ (absolute)} = 357 + 273.16 = 630.16.$$

The volume occupied by one mole of nitrogen under the given conditions of T and P is $0.082 \times 630.16 \times \frac{760}{708} = 55.468$ l. The volume occupied by 3 g. of nitrogen $55.468 \times \frac{3}{28.02} = 5.939$ l. R is very nearly the same for all gases as a consequence of Avogadro's law, which states that *equal volumes of all gases under the same conditions of temperature and pressure contain equal numbers of molecules.*

A further experimentally derived gas law is Dalton's law of partial pressures. This may be stated: *if two or more gases (which do not react with one another) are mixed at constant temperature, then each gas exerts the same pressure as it would if it alone occupied the whole of the given containing volume.* This pressure is its *partial pressure*, the total pressure exerted by the mixture of gases being equal to the sum of the partial pressures of its component gases:

$$P = p_1 + p_2 + \ldots + p_i \tag{4.12}$$

or concisely

$$P = \sum_i p_i \tag{4.13}$$

where the subscript i indicates that the sum is taken over the number of different gases in the mixture.

Example

(i) Let 250 ml. of oxygen at 760 mm. mercury expand to fill 2 l. at a constant temperature of 0°C. The new pressure of the oxygen gas is given by Boyle's law:

$$p(O_2) \times 2000 = 760 \times 250$$

$$p(O_2) = 95 \text{ mm.}$$

(ii) Let 500 ml. of hydrogen expand under the same conditions as in (i). Then

$$p(H_2) = \frac{760 \times 500}{2,000} = 190 \text{ mm.}$$

(iii) Let 250 ml. of oxygen and 500 ml. of hydrogen, each at 1 atm. pressure and 0°C., be mixed and allowed to expand under the same conditions as in (i). From Dalton's law, equation (**4.13**)

$$P = p(O_2) + p(H_2) = 285 \text{ mm.}$$

Extending equation (**4.11**) to n moles of a gas:

$$PV = nRT. \tag{4.14}$$

Thus for a mixture of gases:

$$PV = (n_1 + n_2 + \ldots + n_i)RT. \tag{4.15}$$

P and V are the total pressure and total volume respectively and $n_1, n_2, \ldots n_i$ are the numbers of moles of the various species present in the gas mixture.

4·1·2 Deviations from the gas laws

An ideal gas is one which exactly obeys the gas laws, but to what extent do real gases depart from the gas laws and to what causes can we ascribe such non-ideality?

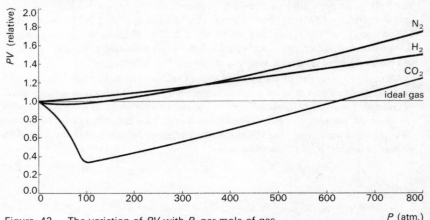

Figure 42.   The variation of PV with P, per mole of gas.

Boyle's law, equation (4.2), suggests that the PV product is a constant, at any temperature. In fig. 42 the value of PV relative to its value at 1 atm. pressure is plotted against the pressure for hydrogen and nitrogen at 0°C. and for carbon dioxide at 40°C. (Carbon dioxide liquefies at or below 31°C. under a pressure of 75 atm. or more.) The graph shows that deviation from Boyle's law is considerable at high pressure. For P lying in the range 1 to 10 atm. the deviation is less than 5 per cent except for the easily liquefiable carbon dioxide. Thus real gases do not obey Boyle's law at all pressures or temperatures but conform to it most closely at *low* pressures and *high* temperatures.

Table 9   Mean Coefficient of Expansion,
0° to 100°C

P(atm.)	$10^5\alpha(H_2)$	$10^5\alpha(N_2)$	$10^5\alpha(CO_2)$
1	366	368	372
50	358	400	811
200	314	433	1115
500	278	315	349
1,000	218	200	206

In table 9, the values of the coefficient of cubical expansion (α), equation (**4.3**), are listed for hydrogen, nitrogen and carbon dioxide at pressures between 1 atm. and 1000 atm. Thus α is not a constant (0·0036609) at all pressures but tends to this value at low pressures, whilst the most easily liquefied gas shows the most marked deviation.

The accuracy with which Avogadro's law applies can be judged by measuring experimentally the volume occupied by 1 mole of gas at s.t.p. (table 10).

Table 10   The Molar Volumes of Various Gases

Gas	Molecular weight	Molar volume (l. at s.t.p.)	Critical temperature (°K.)
H_2	2·016	22·425	33
N_2	28·016	22·402	126
O_2	32·000	22·394	154
CO_2	44·010	22·264	304
NH_3	17·032	22·084	406
CH_3Cl	55·491	21·879	—

It will again be seen that the deviations from 22·41 l. are related to the ease with which the gases liquefy.

4·1·3   *The kinetic theory of gases*

The properties of an ideal gas and the departure of real gases from ideal behaviour can be described by the kinetic theory of gases. The following postulates concerning the hypothetical ideal gas are made:

(i) Gases are composed of molecules which, at normal temperatures and pressures, are separated from one another by distances which are large relative to the size of the molecules (the volume of the molecules is negligible relative to the total volume of the gas).

(ii) The molecules exert no attraction upon one another.

(iii) The gas molecules are in a state of constant rapid motion, and elastic impacts of the molecules with the walls of the containing vessel produce the pressure of the gas.

(iv) The gas molecules are elastic spheres, which possess only kinetic energy due to their translational motion. This energy is dependent upon the temperature of the gas, the total energy of the gas being unaltered by intermolecular collisions.

We next develop the properties of the ideal gas in terms of these postulates. The molecules of gas are in constant motion but they do not all have the same speed and their directions of movement are furthermore completely random. The velocity $\mathbf{v}$ of a molecule can be represented by a vector having components $\mathbf{v}_x$, $\mathbf{v}_y$ and $\mathbf{v}_z$ parallel to three mutually perpendicular axes x, y and z (fig. 43). Thus

$$\mathbf{v} = \mathbf{v}_x + \mathbf{v}_y + \mathbf{v}_z \tag{4.16}$$

73   The states of matter

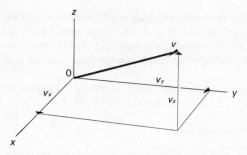

Figure 43. The resolution of a velocity vector **v**.

$$\text{or } v^2 = v_x^2 + v_y^2 + v_z^2. \tag{4.17}$$

Since no direction of movement is preferred, the mean value of any component is zero, i.e. values of $+v_x$ and $-v_x$ etc. are equally probable. However, the mean square velocities $\bar{v}_x^2$ etc. are not zero and it follows that

$$\bar{v}_x^2 = \bar{v}_y^2 = \bar{v}_z^2 = \tfrac{1}{3}\bar{v}^2. \tag{4.18}$$

Let there be N molecules of gas confined in a vessel of volume V cm.[3] Let n_a molecules per cm.[3] have speed v_a in any direction. Of these, n_1 per cm.[3] are assumed to have a component $\pm c_1$ in a given direction: for example along the x-axis, n_2 have a component $\pm c_2$ in the same direction, and so on. In a small interval of time Δt, a fraction of the n_1 molecules strike 1 cm.[2] of wall with a velocity $+c_1$, i.e. the fraction contained within the typical volume element $(c_1 \Delta t)$ cm.[3] The number of molecules in this volume element moving towards the wall is $\tfrac{1}{2}n_1 c_1 \Delta t$, and they impact with the wall of the vessel at the rate of $\tfrac{1}{2}n_1 c_1$ per second. Since the collisions are assumed to be perfectly elastic, no energy is lost in the collision process and the speed before and after impact is the same. The momentum of each of the n_1 molecules, of mass m, is mc_1 so the change of momentum per second is $2mc_1$ perpendicular to the wall for each impact and for $\tfrac{1}{2}n_1 c_1$ impacts per second the change of momentum is $mn_1 c_1^2$ per second. For all positive components of velocity along the x axis, the total change of momentum Δp_x per second is given by:

$$\Delta p_x = m[n_1 c_1^2 + n_2 c_2^2 + \ldots]. \tag{4.19}$$

The mean square velocity along the x-axis, $\bar{v}_x^2$, is given by

$$\bar{v}_x^2 = \frac{n_1 c_1^2 + n_2 c_2^2 + \ldots}{n_1 + n_2 + \ldots} = \frac{\sum\limits_i n_i c_i^2}{\sum\limits_i n_i}. \tag{4.20}$$

Since $\sum\limits_i n_i = n_a$ for all molecules of speed v_a, and using equations (**4.20**) and (**4.18**),

$$\Delta p_x = mn_a \bar{v}_x^2 = \tfrac{1}{3}mn_a \bar{v}_a^2. \tag{4.21}$$

For all possible velocities v_a, v_b, v_c etc., the total change in momentum Δp is given by

$$\Delta p = \tfrac{1}{3}mn_a\bar{v}_a^2 + \tfrac{1}{3}mn_b\bar{v}_b^2 + \ldots \tag{4.22}$$

If $\bar{v}^2$ is the mean square velocity of the molecules, defined by:

$$\bar{v}^2 = \frac{n_a\bar{v}_a^2 + n_b\bar{v}_b^2 + \ldots}{n_a + n_b + \ldots} \tag{4.23}$$

and n is the total number of molecules per cm.[3] given by:

$$n = n_a + n_b + \ldots = \frac{N}{V} \tag{4.24}$$

$$\text{then } \Delta p = \tfrac{1}{3}mn\bar{v}^2 \tag{4.25}$$

$$\text{and hence } \Delta p = \frac{1}{3}\frac{mN\bar{v}^2}{V}. \tag{4.26}$$

From Newton's second law the force acting on a body is equal to the rate of change of momentum, and pressure is the force per unit area exerted on the walls of the vessel by the molecules so

$$P = \frac{1}{3}\frac{mN\bar{v}^2}{V} \tag{4.27}$$

since Δp, from equation (4.26), represents the total change of momentum per second resulting from impacts on 1 cm.[2] of wall. Thus

$$PV = \tfrac{1}{3}mN\bar{v}^2. \tag{4.28}$$

This is the fundamental equation of the kinetic theory, from which the gas laws may be derived as follows.

4·1·4 *Boyle's law*

In an ideal gas the energy of the molecules is due entirely to their translational motion and the kinetic energy, E_K, of all N molecules in a mole of gas is $\tfrac{1}{2}mN\bar{v}^2$. At constant temperature, the kinetic energy remains constant and from equation (4.28):

$$(PV)_T = \tfrac{2}{3}(\tfrac{1}{2}mN\bar{v}^2) = \tfrac{2}{3}(E_K) = \text{constant} \tag{4.29}$$

which is Boyle's law. From equations (4.11) and (4.28):

$$\tfrac{1}{3}mN\bar{v}^2 = \tfrac{2}{3}E_K = RT. \tag{4.30}$$

It follows that the internal energy per mole is independent of the volume and this is therefore a thermodynamic definition of an ideal gas.

4·1·5 *Charles's law*

We may deduce from equation (4.30) that molecules have zero kinetic energy at the absolute zero of temperature whilst kinetic energy increases in direct proportion to the absolute temperature. Hence, at constant pressure

$$V \propto E_K \propto T \tag{4.31}$$

which is Charles's law.

4·1·6 *Avogadro's law*

If equal volumes of two gases are confined at the same pressure and temperature

$$P_1 V_1 = P_2 V_2 \tag{4.32}$$

i.e. $\tfrac{1}{3} N_1 m_1 \bar{v}_1^2 = \tfrac{1}{3} N_2 m_2 \bar{v}_2^2 \tag{4.33}$

since $T_1 = T_2 \qquad E_{K_1} = E_{K_2} \tag{4.34}$

i.e. $\tfrac{1}{2} m_1 \bar{v}_1^2 = \tfrac{1}{2} m_2 \bar{v}_1^2. \tag{4.35}$

Hence from (**4.33**),

$$N_1 = N_2 \tag{4.36}$$

which is Avogadro's law.

From equation (**4.28**), the root mean square velocity is given by

$$\sqrt{\bar{v}^2} = \sqrt{\frac{3PV}{mN}}. \tag{4.37}$$

If V is the molar volume then mN is the molecular weight, M, of the gas, and from (**4.11**)

$$\sqrt{\bar{v}^2} = \sqrt{\frac{3RT}{M}}. \tag{4.38}$$

Note that the root mean square (r.m.s.) velocity $\sqrt{\bar{v}^2}$ is not equal to the mean speed $\bar{c}$.
Example. For nitrogen gas at 0°C. the value of the r.m.s. velocity may be evaluated :

$$\sqrt{\bar{v}^2} = \sqrt{\left(3 \times 8 \cdot 31 \times 10^7 \times \frac{273 \cdot 16}{28 \cdot 016} \right)}$$

$$= 4 \cdot 93 \times 10^4 \text{ cm. sec.}^{-1}$$

The mean speed $\bar{c}$ is actually $\sqrt{\tfrac{8}{3}\pi}\sqrt{\bar{v}^2}$,* which is equal to $4 \cdot 54 \times 10^4$ cm. sec.$^{-1}$ for nitrogen gas. The r.m.s. velocity of an ideal gas increases with temperature but not with pressure: equation (**4.37**) shows that $\sqrt{\bar{v}^2}$ is proportional to $\sqrt{PV}$ which, for an ideal gas, is independent of P (fig. 42).

* See for example Moelwyn-Hughes, E. A., *Physical chemistry*, 2nd rev. edn, Pergamon. 1961, eq. (41), p. 39.

Gaseous diffusion

The density of a gas is given by

$$d = \frac{M}{V}.$$ (4.39)

Hence from equations (4.37) and (4.38)

$$\sqrt{\bar{v}^2} = \sqrt{\frac{3P}{d}}$$ (4.40)

and at constant pressure the r.m.s. velocity of the molecules in a gas is inversely proportional to the square root of the density. This provides a theoretical basis for Graham's law of gaseous diffusion which assumes that the rate of diffusion of a gas is proportional to the r.m.s. velocity of its molecules.

4·1·8 *Brownian movement and the Avogadro constant*

In 1827 the botanist Brown observed that microscopic pollen grains suspended in water exhibited continuous random motion. This erratic movement is now called Brownian motion and supports the kinetic theory very strikingly. It has been observed with all kinds of small particles and suspensory media and is due to the fact that water molecules are in constant motion in every direction with different speeds so that a solid particle is bombarded on all sides by these moving water molecules. In any given instant the forces on the particle do not balance and a net impulse in a given direction ensues, but at the next moment the same particle may receive a net impulse in a different direction and with a different magnitude so that its motion is changing continuously. Smaller particles move more rapidly than larger particles because the larger the particle, the more water molecules bombard it, and the more likely it is that the net impulse will be zero.

Perrin studied Brownian movement with suspensions of gamboge and mastic in water and it is from his results that the *Avogadro constant* was evaluated. This is usually given the symbol N and represents the number of molecules in a g-molecule, the number of atoms in a g-atom or the number of ions in a g-ion:

1 mole of H_2O is 18·016 g.
1 g-atom of Cu is 63·540 g.
1 g-ion of Na^+ is 22·991 g.

Perrin obtained values for N in different experiments between $6·5 \times 10^{23}$ and $7·2 \times 10^{23}$, the currently accepted value being $6·023 \times 10^{23}$. The weight, m_C, of a carbon atom, for example, may be obtained by dividing the atomic weight by N, i.e. $m_C = 1·992 \times 10^{-23}$ g. Atomic weights are now expressed in terms of $^{12}C = 12·0000$ so that the atomic weight of oxygen becomes 15·999. The gas constant per molecule is the Boltzmann constant, k:

$$k = \frac{R}{N} = 1·380 \times 10^{-16} \text{ erg deg.}^{-1} \text{ mole}^{-1}.$$

We have noted that not all gas molecules have the same velocity and the distribution of these varying velocities was deduced by Maxwell in 1860. If $\dfrac{dn_v}{n}$ represents the fraction of the total number, n, of molecules in a gas of molecular weight M, having velocities between v and $(v+dv)$, then (without proof here)

$$\frac{dn_v}{n} = 4\pi \left(\frac{M}{2\pi RT}\right)^{\frac{3}{2}} \exp\left(\frac{-Mv^2}{2RT}\right) . v^2 \, dv. \tag{4.41}$$

In fig. 40 the significance of equation (4.41) is illustrated. The area under each curve is equal to the total number of molecules and the height of an ordinate corresponds to the fraction of molecules possessing the corresponding velocity, v; the maximum ordinate indicates the most probable velocity.

If the temperature of the gas is increased, the distribution of velocities becomes wider and the most probable velocity becomes larger, whilst the number of molecules with high velocities is at the same time increased considerably.

If E is the kinetic energy per mole of molecules of velocity v:

$$E = \tfrac{1}{2}Mv^2. \tag{4.42}$$

Hence, in equation (4.41)

$$M^{\frac{3}{2}}v^2 \, dv = \sqrt{(2E)}dE. \tag{4.43}$$

From equations (4.41) and (4.43)

$$\frac{dn_E}{n} = \frac{2\pi}{(\pi RT)^{\frac{3}{2}}} \exp\left(-\frac{E}{RT}\right) . \sqrt{(E)}dE \tag{4.44}$$

where n_E is the number of molecules in a total of n, which possess kinetic energy within the range from E to $E + dE$. This is the Maxwell–Boltzmann law of distribution of kinetic energy.

In studying reaction and diffusion rates, etc., we are concerned with the proportion of molecules having energy in excess of a given value, say E_0. This may be deduced by integration of the distribution equation (4.44), a simplified treatment of which leads to the result:

$$n_E = n \exp\left(-\frac{E_0}{RT}\right) \tag{4.45}$$

where n_E is the number of molecules, in the total number n, which possess energy in excess of the value E_0 per mole.

For example: if

$$E_0 = 10 \text{ kcal. mole}^{-1} \text{ at } 25°C.,$$

$$n_E = n \exp(-16 \cdot 7)$$

$$\frac{n_E}{n} \approx 6 \times 10^{-8}.$$

The kinetic theory and real gases

Two assumptions made in the treatment of the ideal gas require revision when considering real gases; these are:

(i) Molecules exert no force of attraction upon one another.

(ii) The volume of the molecules is negligible in comparison with the total volume of gas.

It is evident that particles of solids and liquids attract one another and from the fact that all gases liquefy under suitable conditions it is evident also that a similar attraction, albeit of smaller magnitude, exists between the molecules of a real gas.

Figure 44. The Joule–Thomson experiment ($T_1 > T_2$, in general).

The existence of such attractive forces was proved by the porous plug experiment of Joule and Thomson (fig. 44). A gas passed through a porous plug of silk, asbestos or unglazed earthenware was generally found to become cooler (the Joule–Thomson effect) due to the *internal* work of expansion of the gas (a similar effect is observed if the gas expands into a vacuum); hydrogen and helium were found to become warmer in this experiment, an anomaly that will be discussed later (page 83).

It can be shown that the temperature change per mole of gas streamed ΔT is given by

$$\Delta T = \left[\frac{T\left(\frac{\partial V}{\partial T}\right)_P - V}{C_P} \right] \Delta P \tag{4.46}$$

where T is the absolute temperature, V is the molar volume of the gas, ΔP is the pressure difference across the porous plug, C_P is the molar heat at constant pressure and $\left(\frac{\partial V}{\partial T}\right)_P$ is the rate of change of V with T at constant pressure. For an ideal gas, $PV = RT$ and so

$$\left(\frac{\partial V}{\partial T}\right)_P = \frac{R}{P} = \frac{V}{T}. \tag{4.47}$$

Hence $\quad T\left(\frac{\partial V}{\partial T}\right)_P - V = 0 \tag{4.48}$

and, from equation (**4.46**), $\Delta T = 0$, so there is no Joule–Thomson effect for an ideal gas. In the case of a real gas the cooling must therefore be attributed to the effect of intermolecular attractive forces which are overcome in streaming the gas through the porous plug.

Volume of molecules. When two molecules approach each other, the attraction between them at a given small distance of separation is small compared with the repulsion due to the proximity of their electron systems, which is very large at very small distances. Even if a molecule was negligibly small compared with the volume occupied by the gas, it would have an effective *collision diameter*, ξ. This may be taken as the distance of closest approach of two molecules in a gas. Molecules must therefore have a finite volume. If the diameter of a molecule is taken to be equal to the collision diameter, then the volume v_m of a molecule is given by

$$v_m = \frac{4\pi}{3}\left(\frac{\xi}{2}\right)^3 = \frac{1}{6}\pi\xi^3. \tag{4.49}$$

The collision diameter of a gas molecule is on average about 4 Å., hence

$$v_m = \frac{\pi}{6}(4^3 \times 10^{-24}) \simeq 3 \times 10^{-23} \text{ cm.}^3 \tag{4.50}$$

The number of molecules per ml. at s.t.p., the Loschmidt number, is about $2 \cdot 7 \times 10^{19}$, so the average volume of space occupied per molecule is $\frac{1}{2 \cdot 7} \times 10^{-19}$ ml. $= 3 \cdot 7 \times 10^{-20}$ ml. At normal pressures the volume of the molecules is about $0 \cdot 1$ per cent of the total gas volume, but at a pressure between 100 atm. and 200 atm. the volume of the molecules is about 10 per cent of the total volume and no longer negligible.

By subjecting it to cooling and compression, a gas can be first liquefied and then

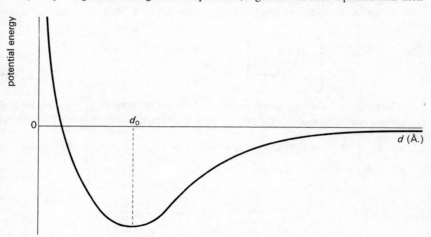

Figure 45. A Morse curve.

solidified. The compressibility of a solid is small, showing that molecules have a limiting volume which means that in a gas the space available for movement is less than the occupied volume. Since molecules can approach one another only to the limit of the collision diameter, repulsion forces must operate strongly at small distances of molecule separation. Fig. 45 illustrates a Morse curve representing the change in potential energy of a system comprising two molecules as a function of their separation distance, d. At large values of d, the interactional energy tends to zero (i.e. the forces of attraction are negligible), but as d decreases the system becomes more stable and its potential energy falls. There is a minimum in the potential energy curve at $d = d_0$, evidently d_0 is approximately the collision diameter ξ, but as d becomes much smaller than ξ the potential energy of the system increases rapidly (approximately as d^{-8}) leading to an unstable, or improbable, system.

1·10   The van der Waals equation

A modification of the ideal gas equation of state (**4.11**), was proposed by van der Waals in 1873. As a molecule is about to strike the wall of its containing vessel, the forces on it are unbalanced and a net attraction towards the bulk of the gas exists. The effect of this is to decrease the impact of the molecule on the wall and so reduce the pressure of the gas. The force exerted on such a molecule is proportional to the density (the number of molecules present), so the number of molecules striking the wall at any instant is also proportional to the density and the total attractive force is proportional to (density)^2 or to $\dfrac{1}{V^2}$. Thus the corrected pressure is $\left(P + \dfrac{a}{V^2}\right)$ where a is a constant, and $\dfrac{a}{V^2}$ is the *internal cohesive pressure*.

The finite size of the molecules reduces the effective volume, so the corrected volume may be represented as $(V-b)$ in which b is the co-volume and may be shown to equal $4v_m$. Hence

$$\left(P + \frac{a}{V^2}\right) . (V-b) = RT \tag{4.51}$$

which is the van der Waals equation of state for a real gas; table 11 lists the values of a and b for several gases.

Table 11   The van der Waals Constants a and b

Gas	a (l.^{2} atm. mole^{-1})	$10^2 . b$ (l. mole^{-1})
He	0·03	2·4
H_2	0·25	2·7
O_2	1·3	3·1
N_2	1·4	3·9
CO_2	3·6	4·3
NH_3	4·0	3·6

At low pressures V is large, $\dfrac{a}{V^2}$ is therefore small, and b is small with respect to V; hence equation (**4.51**) approximates to

$$PV = RT$$

so the real gas is behaving ideally, cf. equation (**4.11**). At slightly higher pressures b is still small with respect to V, hence

$$PV \simeq RT - \frac{a}{V}. \tag{4.52}$$

Under these conditions PV is consequently less than RT and decreases with increase in P, which explains the 'dip' in the curves for N_2 and CO_2 (fig. 41) caused by the internal cohesive pressure, $\dfrac{a}{V^2}$.

At fairly high pressure b is significant with respect to V, but $\dfrac{a}{V^2}$ is still small compared to P if a is small. Hence

$$P(V-b) \simeq RT \tag{4.53}$$

or

$$PV = RT + Pb. \tag{4.54}$$

PV is now greater than RT and rises with increase in P. Hydrogen has a small value of a and so equation (**4.53**) predominates at ordinary temperatures (fig. 41).

4·1·11   *Calculation of the Joule–Thomson effect*

The van der Waals equation may be used to predict the sign and magnitude of the Joule–Thomson effect, Expanding equation (**4.51**)

$$PV \simeq RT + Pb - \frac{a}{V} + \frac{ab}{V^2}. \tag{4.55}$$

$\dfrac{ab}{V^2}$ is of small magnitude, and V in the small term $\dfrac{a}{V}$ may be replaced by $\dfrac{RT}{P}$. Hence

$$PV = RT - \frac{aP}{RT} + Pb \tag{4.56}$$

or

$$V = \frac{RT}{P} - \frac{a}{RT} + b. \tag{4.57}$$

Differentiating equation (**4.57**) with respect to T, at constant pressure:

$$\left(\frac{\partial V}{\partial T}\right)_P = \frac{R}{P} + \frac{a}{RT^2}. \tag{4.58}$$

From equation (**4.56**),

$$RT = P(V-b) + \frac{aP}{RT}. \tag{4.59}$$

Therefore $\quad \dfrac{R}{P} = \dfrac{(V-b)}{T} + \dfrac{a}{RT^2}$
$$\tag{4.60}$$

and substituting in equation (**4.58**)

$$\left(\dfrac{\partial V}{\partial T}\right)_P = \dfrac{V}{T} + \dfrac{2a}{RT^2} - \dfrac{b}{T} \tag{4.61}$$

or $\quad T\left(\dfrac{\partial V}{\partial T}\right)_P - V = \dfrac{2a}{RT} - b.$
$$\tag{4.62}$$

Substituting in equation (**4.46**)

$$\Delta T = \left(\dfrac{2a}{RT} - b\right) . \Delta P. \tag{4.63}$$

Table 12 illustrates the applicability of equation (**4.63**) to the calculation of the Joule–Thomson coefficient $\dfrac{\Delta T}{\Delta P}$ for the gases hydrogen, nitrogen and carbon dioxide at 0°C.

Table 12 Calculation of Joule–Thomson Coefficients

Gas	a	b	C_P	$\dfrac{\Delta T}{\Delta P}$	
	($l.^2$ atm. $mole^{-1}$)	(l. $mole^{-1}$)		(deg. $atm.^{-1}$ $mole^{-1}$) calculated	observed
H_2	0·25	0·027	0·29	−0·02	−0·03
N_2	1·4	0·039	0·30	+0·30	+0·32
CO_2	3·6	0·043	0·38	+0·73	+1·3

The negative value of $\dfrac{\Delta T}{\Delta P}$ for hydrogen indicates that at 0°C. this gas is warmer after passing through a porous plug from a pressure P to a slightly lower pressure $(P - \Delta P)$. Evidently the attractive forces in hydrogen are very small at 0°C. and table 11 shows that a has a very low value whereas b is about the same as for other gases. Thus the term $\dfrac{2a}{RT} - b$ in equation (**4.63**) is negative for hydrogen.

The Joule–Thomson *inversion temperature*, T_i, may be defined by putting $\Delta T = 0$ in equation (**4.63**):

$$T_i = \dfrac{2a}{bR}. \tag{4.64}$$

Evidently for $T < T_i$, $\dfrac{T}{\Delta P}$ is positive, and for $T > T_i$, $\dfrac{\Delta T}{\Delta P}$ is negative. Calculated values of T_i for the gases listed in table 12 are

	H_2	N_2	CO_2
T_i(°K.)	226	876	2 042

The experimental values of T_i are not always in good agreement with the calculated values, for example $T_i(H_2) = 190°K.$, but equation (4.64) reveals the different orders of magnitude involved.

4·1·12   *The molar heat capacity of a gas*

The molar heat capacity of a gas is the number of calories required to raise the temperature of one mole of the gas through 1 deg. C. Since $PV = RT$, a rise in temperature will be accompanied by an increase in P or V, or in both; if V increases, work is done against the external pressure and the energy required for this work must be supplied as heat, less heat being needed if the volume of the gas is kept constant. The gas must obviously be below its inversion temperature before decrease in pressure leads to cooling, as is the case at room temperature for oxygen and nitrogen (but not for hydrogen and helium). Two molar heats are recognized: molar heat capacity at constant volume, and molar heat capacity at constant pressure.

Molar heat capacity at constant volume, C_V. The temperature of one mole of gas is raised by 1 deg. C. at constant volume when no external work is done, the heat supplied to the gas manifesting itself as an increase in the energies of the molecules. From the kinetic theory postulates, gas molecules possess energy only on account of their translatory motion, equal to $\frac{3}{2}RT$ per mole, hence

$$C_V = \frac{3R}{2}, \quad \text{or 3 cal. deg.}^{-1} \text{ approximately.}$$

This argument applies only to monatomic gases; if the gas is diatomic, e.g. oxygen, then the molecules undergo rotational and vibrational motions which are dependent upon temperature. In general the molar heat at constant volume is given by

$$C_V = \frac{3R}{2} + n. \tag{4.65}$$

For monatomic gases $n = 0$, but at room temperature $n = 2$ cal. deg.$^{-1}$ for diatomic gases and 4–5 cal. deg.$^{-1}$ for polyatomic gases.

Molar heat capacity at constant pressure. If one mole of gas is heated at constant pressure through 1 deg., the heat absorbed is manifested as an increase in the kinetic energy of translation, and (for diatomic and polyatomic molecules) an increase in the energies of rotation and vibration, in addition to which it provides energy for the work of expansion against the constant external pressure.

Consider the gas at a volume V_1 enclosed by a piston in a cylinder and under an external pressure P (fig. 46). The gas is heated through 1 deg. and expands to a new

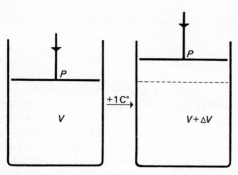

Figure 46. The work of expansion of a gas against a constant external pressure.

volume $(V+\Delta V)$. Since P is a force per unit area, the work done in raising the piston by an infinitesimal length dl is given by $P\pi r^2\,dl = P\,dV$, where r is the radius of the piston face. The total work done (w) in expanding the gas from volume V to $(V+\Delta V)$ is given by:

$$w = \int_{V}^{(V+\Delta V)} P\,dV = P\,\Delta V. \tag{4.66}$$

Thus C_P is given by:

$$C_P = \frac{3R}{2}+n+w. \tag{4.67}$$

From the gas laws, $P\,\Delta V = R\,\Delta T$, but since $\Delta T = 1$, $P\,\Delta V = w = R$. Hence

$$C_P = \frac{5R}{2}+n. \tag{4.68}$$

The ratio of $\dfrac{C_P}{C_V}$ (which is also the ratio of their specific heats) varies with the atomicity of the gas (table 13).

Table 13 The Ratio $\dfrac{C_P}{C_V}$ for Different Types of Gases

Atomicity	$\gamma = \left(\dfrac{C_P}{C_V}\right)$	Example	γ
1	1·67	Argon	1·67
2	1·40	Nitrogen	1·41
3	1·29	Carbon dioxide	1·31

Since γ may be determined by measuring the velocity of sound in a gas, the atomicity can be found experimentally. The values in column four of table 13 illustrate the results of this method.

4·2 The solid state

Most well-defined solid substances are crystalline. The word crystal comes from the Greek *krustallos* meaning ice and was first applied to rock crystal or quartz (thought to be water permanently congealed by intense cold). The term *crystal* is now used to cover a multitude of solid substances, including minerals, rocks, soil, sand, snow, diamonds, rubies and other precious stones, salt, sugar, penicillin, the vitamins and nearly all other solid chemical substances. Still crystalline, although not so completely, are hair, silk, cotton, nylon and stretched rubber, but a number of solids such as glass and certain synthetic plastics are not crystalline. We shall see that this term implies a high degree of regularity in most solids, whereas in gases and liquids disorder is the rule. The very shape of crystals seems unnatural, since curved or rounded outlines are more common in nature and the edges and plane faces associated with crystals occur only infrequently.

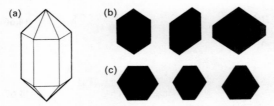

Figure 47. Steno's figures. (a) An idealized crystal of quartz; (b) Selected vertical sections of actual crystals of quartz; (c) Selected transverse sections of actual crystals of quartz.

An early observation by Stensen (1669) revealed a fundamental property of crystals. Stensen, often called by the Latin form Steno, cut transverse and longitudinal sections of natural crystals such as quartz and traced their outlines on paper (fig. 47). He noted that whatever the shape or size of the section, the angles between corresponding edges (or faces) in crystals of the same substance always had a constant value. This finding led to the law of constant interfacial angles which has subsequently been extended and fully explained in terms of the structure of crystals.

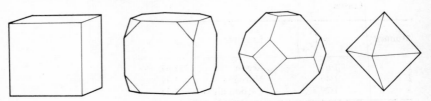

Figure 48. Variation in the habit of NaCl.

In crystals direction is more important than size and shape. For example, sodium chloride crystallizes from water in cubes, but when it is crystallized from a 5 per cent to 10 per cent solution of urea, other faces (octahedral) are also present (fig. 48) and the sodium chloride is said to have changed its *habit*. Increasing the percentage of urea increases the development of the octahedral faces until finally the shape of the sodium chloride crystal is an octahedron. Fig. 49 shows two habits of potassium sulphate; it may be shown that the angles between corresponding faces, such as *ab*, *ac* and *ad*, have constant values in each crystal and are characteristic of the substance.

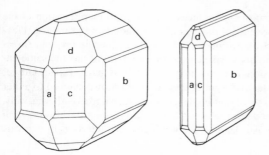

Figure 49.   Two habits of potassium sulphate.

Figs. 48 and 49 suggest symmetrical arrangements of various sets of faces. Crystal symmetry is an important subject but we cannot discuss it in detail in this book. The drawings in figs. 50 and 51 illustrate the symmetry of a simple cube. Rotation of a crystal about an *n*-fold axis of symmetry brings the crystal into a congruent aspect *n* times during a rotation of 360°. Planes of symmetry (or mirror planes) divide a crystal into two halves related to each other as an object is to its mirror image. In all there are 23 symmetry elements associated with a cube but there are no symmetry planes normal to the three-fold rotation axes. Only shapes based on the rotation symmetries of degree (*n*) 1, 2, 3, 4, 6, or combinations of these, are found in crystals because only with regular figures of such symmetry can space be filled (fig. 52).

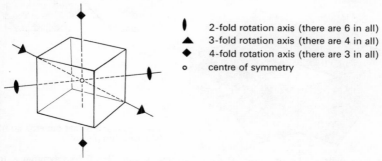

2-fold rotation axis (there are 6 in all)
3-fold rotation axis (there are 4 in all)
4-fold rotation axis (there are 3 in all)
o   centre of symmetry

Figure 50.   Symmetry axes in a cube.

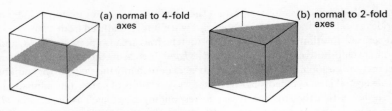

Figure 51. Symmetry planes in a cube.

The well-defined arrangement of crystal faces is an external manifestation of the internal structure of the components of the crystal. The underlying geometrical feature of a crystal is its lattice (or *space lattice*) which may be defined as a regular three-dimensional arrangement of points in space such that each point has the same environment in the same orientation. Fig. 53 illustrates the most general space lattice; one unit cell is shown alone at (a) and eight of these cells are shown stacked together at (b). The unit cell is defined by three non-coplanar vectors **a, b** and **c** or alternatively, by the three scalars a, b and c and the angles α, β and γ. Special relationships between these axial lengths and angles can lead to the unit cells characterized by Bravais in 1848 (fig. 54).

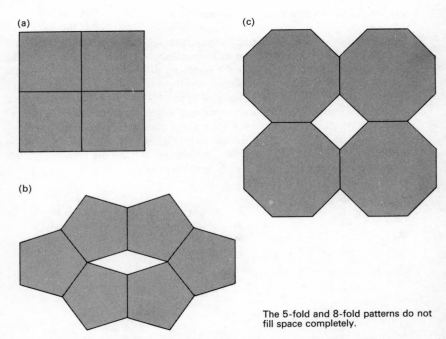

The 5-fold and 8-fold patterns do not fill space completely.

Figure 52. Patterns based upon (a) 4-fold symmetry units, (b) 5-fold symmetry, (c) 8-fold symmetry units.

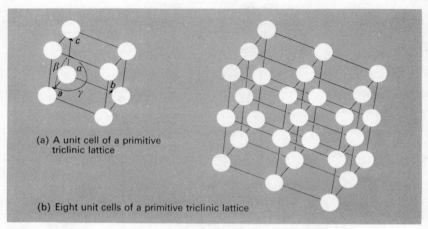

(a) A unit cell of a primitive triclinic lattice

(b) Eight unit cells of a primitive triclinic lattice

Figure 53.   The unit cell in a triclinic lattice.

Table 14   Characteristics of the Seven Crystal Systems

System	Axial relationships	Examples
Triclinic	$a \neq b \neq c$	$CuSO_4 . 5H_2O$
	$\alpha \neq \beta \neq \gamma \neq 90°, 120°$	$K_2Cr_2O_7$
Monoclinic	$a \neq b \neq c$	$CaSO_4 . 2H_2O$
	$\alpha = \gamma = 90° ; \beta \neq 90°, 120°$	$C_{12}H_{22}O_{11}$
Orthorhombic	$a \neq b \neq c$	$BaSO_4$
	$\alpha = \beta = \gamma = 90°$	KNO_3
Tetragonal	$a = b \neq c$	KH_2PO_4
	$\alpha = \beta = \gamma = 90°$	SnO_2
Cubic	$a = b = c$	$NaCl$
	$\alpha = \beta = \gamma = 90°$	C (diamond)
Hexagonal	$a = b \neq c$	C (graphite)
	$\alpha = \beta = 90° ; \gamma = 120°$	H_2O (ice)
Trigonal	$a = b = c$	$CaCO_3$
	$\alpha = \beta = \gamma \neq 90°, <120°$	$NaNO_3$

4·2·1   *Miller indices*

A convenient notation evolved by Miller (1839), permits a simple description of any crystal face or plane. Let a, b and c represent the periodicities (repeat distances) along the crystallographic axes x, y and z respectively (fig. 55), and let the plane ABC be drawn to intercept these axes at a, b and c. This plane is defined as the *parametral* plane and is designated by the Miller indices (111).

If any other plane LMN makes intercepts a/h, b/k, c/l along the axes x, y and z respectively, then its Miller indices are expressed by the ratio of the intercepts of the

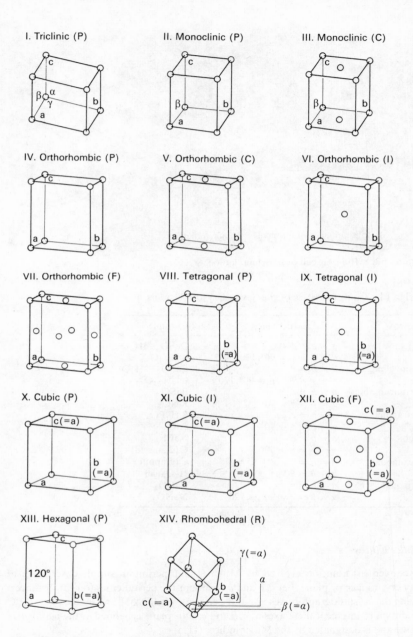

Figure 54. The Bravais lattices; the interaxial angles are 90° unless indicated by a general symbol or numerical value.

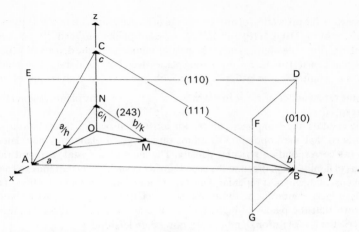

Figure 55. The Miller indices of crystal planes.

parametral plane to those of the plane under consideration, LMN. Thus this plane is described as the plane (hkl) where h, k and l are integers. In the example shown,

$$\frac{a}{h} = \frac{a}{2}, \quad \frac{b}{k} = \frac{b}{4} \quad \text{and} \quad \frac{c}{l} = \frac{c}{3};$$

hence LMN is the plane (243). If the plane had intercepted the y-axis at $-b/4$, the other intercepts remaining the same, then the Miller indices would have been written ($2\bar{4}3$).

A plane such as ABDE is parallel to the z-axis and we may say that it intercepts this axis at infinity, its Miller indices being (110) since it intercepts the x- and the y-axes at a and b respectively. Again, the plane BDGF intercepts the y-axis at b and is parallel to both the x- and the z-axes, so that its indices are (010). We therefore have a geometric description of any crystal plane in terms of the parametral plane (111).

Experience has shown that the Miller indices of the actual faces of a crystal are small numbers and rarely does such an index exceed 4 (the law of rational indices).

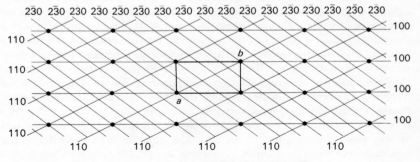

Figure 56. Families of parallel planes: (100), (110) and ($2\bar{3}0$).

Fig. 56 represents the projection of an assemblage of lattice points on to the xy plane, with the traces of the (100), (110) and ($2\bar{3}0$) families of planes outlined. We see immediately that as the Miller indices increase in value numerically, the density of lattice points (reticular density) on the corresponding planes decreases, i.e. if the lattice under discussion is a primitive cubic lattice (a lattice with one point at each corner of the unit cube), the reticular densities are in the ratio $1 : \dfrac{1}{\sqrt{2}} : \dfrac{1}{\sqrt{13}}$ for the planes (100), (110) and ($2\bar{3}0$) respectively.

In simple crystals, the component atoms (or ions) often occupy the positions of lattice points so that the population of atoms on any given plane may be related directly to the corresponding reticular density. The faces of a crystal represent the terminations of families of planes and the crystal grows in such a way that the external faces are planes of the highest reticular density – a more stable system than that of a crystal with surfaces exhibiting, on the atomic scale, relatively large holes. As we have already shown that the planes of highest reticular density are also those of lower Miller indices, the law of rational indices can now be understood.

We can consider the concept of families of planes (hkl) in relation to fig. 56. The Miller indices of any given family of planes can always be determined by examining the intercepts of the plane closest to, but not passing through, the origin of the lattice. For example, if we select the family ($2\bar{3}0$), then if the origin of the lattice is taken as the intersection of the vectors **a** and **b**, the nearest plane to the origin intercepts the x-axis at $\dfrac{a}{2}$ and the y-axis at $-\dfrac{b}{3}$. The intercept along the z-axis is in this case $\dfrac{c}{\infty}$ so the Miller indices are in fact ($2\bar{3}0$), but we might have chosen another plane of this family (the same distance from the origin) and discovered that it intercepts the x-axis at $-\dfrac{a}{2}$ and the y-axis at $\dfrac{b}{3}$ so that the Miller indices are ($\bar{2}30$). It is a consequence of the symmetry of this projected lattice array that the two Miller symbols ($2\bar{3}0$) and ($\bar{2}30$) identify the same family of planes. The different planes (hkl) which are related by the symmetry of the lattice constitute a crystal *form*, written $\{hkl\}$; in this example, the form $\{230\}$ comprises the planes (230), ($\bar{2}30$), ($2\bar{3}0$) and ($\bar{2}\bar{3}0$), the last two of which are contained in fig. 56.

The physical properties of crystals are described by relationships between measurable quantities such as density, which is defined by mass and volume – two quantities that are measurable without reference to direction. However, a property such as thermal expansion is defined by the relationship between extension and change in temperature. Extension has direction and its magnitude generally varies in different directions. Such directional effects in connexion with physical properties are given the general name of *anisotropy*. This is a most important feature of crystals and may be regarded as a criterion of the crystalline state, but certain reservations are needed because crystals of high symmetry may have the same value for a given property in more than one direction. For example, cubic crystals transmit light with the same velocity in all directions in the crystal (i.e. the refractive index is constant for all directions) and they are consequently described as optically *isotropic*. Cubic crystals are isotropic for many but not all properties; they are, as an example, anisotropic for elasticity and photoelasticity. Cubic crystals and indeed all crystals must be regarded as potentially anisotropic but their symmetry may lead to special relationships for certain physical properties.

4·2·2 *Isomorphism, polymorphism and allotropy*

During a study of the crystalline phosphates and arsenates of the alkali metals, Mitscherlich (1819) noted that salts of similar chemical composition exhibited the same crystalline form, e.g. $Na_2HPO_4 . H_2O$ and $Na_2HAsO_4 . H_2O$. The word *isomorphous* was introduced to describe the replaceable element, the term being later extended to include the relationship between compounds. Many examples are known, such as K_2SO_4 and K_2SeO_4, $CuSO_4 . 5H_2O$ and $CuSeO_4 . 5H_2O$, and $K_2SO_4 . Cr_2(SO_4)_3 . 24H_2O$ and $K_2SO_4 . Al_2(SO_4)_3 . 24H_2O$.

Subsequent investigations into the structure of solids showed that an even wider definition of isomorphism is desirable. Consider the following pairs of substances:

$$NaNO_3 \quad CaCO_3$$
$$BaSO_4 \quad KBF_4$$
$$KIO_4 \quad CaWO_4$$

These pairs of compounds exhibit similar crystal structures despite their chemical dissimilarity. The important conditions for structural isomorphism in its wider sense are firstly that the components of each pair of substances must be similar in size and shape, and secondly that an electrical charge balance must be maintained; for example, in the first pair, the radii of the 'spherical' ions Na^+ and Ca^{2+} are 0·95 Å. and 0·99 Å. respectively, whilst the planar ions NO_3^- and CO_3^{2-} also have similar size and shape:

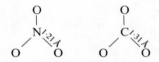

On the other hand, $NaNO_3$ and KNO_3, although chemically similar are not isomorphous ($r_{K^+} = 1·33$ Å.). The radius of the Ba^{2+} ion is 1·35 Å. and the ions SO_4^{2-} and BF_4^- both form tetrahedral groupings in which the bond distances S–O and B–F are 1·44 Å. and 1·40 Å. respectively; consequently barium sulphate and potassium tetrafluoroborate are isomorphous.

Numerous solids exist in more than one crystalline modification (*polymorphism*). A particular crystal structure depends for its formation upon its environment during the growth process. Physical factors such as temperature, pressure and concentration as well as the presence of foreign substances all help to modify the crystal habit. Interconversion of polymorphs takes place at a given transition temperature for a specified pressure, but not all transitions are reversible:

zinc blende (ZnS) $\xrightarrow{1024°C.}$ wurtzite (ZnS)

quartz (SiO_2) $\xrightarrow{870°C.}$ tridymite (SiO_2) $\underset{}{\overset{1470°C.}{\rightleftharpoons}}$ cristobalite (SiO_2)

Polymorphism in elements is often called *allotropy*, the different elemental modifications being *allotropes*. Only one of the modifications is stable under given conditions, but it does not follow that the other forms revert spontaneously to the stable phase. The term stable is meaningful only in reference to a given set of conditions; the reference state or *standard state* for elements refers to a temperature of 25°C. and a simultaneous pressure of 1 atm., the phrase 'normal conditions' often meaning conditions of temperature and pressure closely similar to the standard conditions. The standard state of elemental carbon is graphite. Diamond, however, shows no tendency to transform to graphite except at very high temperatures (in an inert atmosphere). Considerable energy is required to disrupt the diamond structure and rearrange it to that of graphite under normal conditions, even though the less stable form is in a higher (more positive) energy state.

Allotropy can be subdivided into two classes, monotropy and enantiotropy.

4·2·3   *Monotropy*

This term describes the condition where one crystal modification is stable over the whole range of its existence, the other form (or forms) invariably being metastable. Since the vapour pressure curve for the β-phase in fig. 57 lies everywhere above that for the α-phase, the β-phase tends to revert to the α-phase. In no circumstances can the solid α-form be converted directly to the β-form and to obtain the metastable form the α-phase must be melted or vaporized and cooled rapidly.

The graphite–diamond system exhibits monotropy, the m.p. of graphite being 3670°C. and its b.p. 4200°C. so that the difficulty of performing the economically

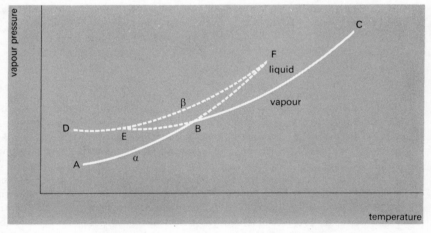

Figure 57. α- and β-phases exhibiting a monotropic relationship. AB, vapour pressure–temperature curve of the α-phase; BC, liquid–vapour phase boundary; DF, vapour pressure–temperature curve of the β-phase; B, triple point at which the α-phase, the liquid and the vapour are in equilibrium (m.p. of α-phase); E, m.p. of the β-phase under its own vapour pressure; F, transition temperature of α- and β-phases (hypothetical, since it lies above both m.p.s).

favourable transformation of graphite into diamond can be appreciated. Other examples of monotropic systems are white P – red P, O_2 – O_3, and various compounds such as calcite ($CaCO_3$) – aragonite ($CaCO_3$).

4·2·4   Enantiotropy

Two modifications are enantiotropic if each has a definite range of stability and changes into the other at a definite temperature (the transition temperature) in either direction (fig. 58). If the α-phase is heated rapidly, transformation may be suspended

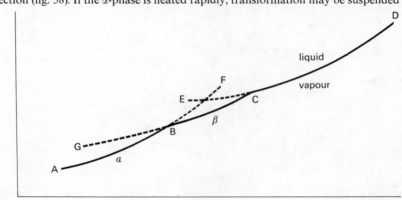

temperature

Figure 58.   α- and β-phases exhibiting an enantiotropic relationship. AB, vapour pressure–temperature curve for the α-phase; BC, vapour pressure–temperature curve for the β-phase; CD, liquid–vapour phase boundary; B, triple point at which the α-phase, the β-phase, and the vapour are in equilibrium; C, triple point at which the β-phase, the liquid, and the vapour are in equilibrium (m.p. of the β-phase).

and so BF represents a range in which the α-phase is metastable; similarly, CG and BG represent the supercooling curves of the liquid and β-phases respectively. The diagram shows how an enantiotropic substance can melt at different temperatures according to the rate of heating. Sulphur is a well-known example of an enantiotropic substance (fig. 59). Since the m.p. of the monoclinic phase of sulphur increases with rising pressure, the specific volume of the solid must be less than that of the liquid with which it is in equilibrium, in contrast to the ice–water system (le Chatelier–Braun principle, page 137). Other examples of enantiotropic systems are those of elemental tin, ammonium chloride, and ammonium nitrate.

Some substances show both monotropic and enantiotropic transitions for example, silica (SiO_2):

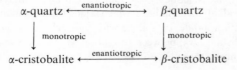

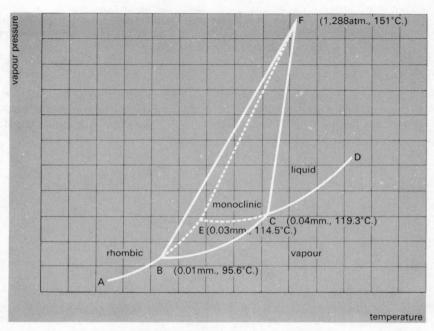

Figure 59. A portion of the phase diagram for sulphur (not to scale): an example of enantiotropy. AB, vapour pressure–temperature curve for rhombic sulphur; B, triple point (transition point at 96·5°C) at which rhombic, monoclinic, and vapour phases are in equilibrium. BC, vapour pressure–temperature curve for monoclinic sulphur; E, m.p. of rhombic sulphur under its own vapour pressure (rapid heating); C, m.p. of monoclinic sulphur (114·5°C); BF, CF, the effect of external pressure on the rhombic–monoclinic and monoclinic–liquid transitions respectively; EF, the effect of external pressure on the solidification of the supercooled liquid to form rhombic sulphur.

4·3   Crystal chemistry

In chapter 2 we discussed the nature and characteristics of interatomic forces and noted that chemical structures could be classified according to the predominant interatomic force. We conclude our study of the solid state of matter by amplifying this classification and by describing the structures of some compounds.

Crystal chemistry relates the physical and chemical properties of a substance to its internal structure, endeavouring both to interpret properties in terms of known structural features and to associate certain structural characteristics with measured properties. The subject originated about 1920, following Bragg's analyses of the structures of the crystalline alkali metal halides, which (apart from caesium chloride, caesium bromide and caesium iodide) crystallize with the rock salt structure type (fig. 11). The equilibrium distance, r_0, between the cation M^+ and the anion X^- is one-half of the repeat distance in the cubic unit cell, the r_0 values for the alkali metal halides with the NaCl structure being listed in table 15. We can trace the progressive increase in r_0 in, for example, moving vertically from NaF to NaI or in moving horizontally from LiBr to RbBr, the increase is regular, the difference Δ' between r_0 for two halides of a given cation being almost independent of the cation, whilst the difference Δ between r_0 for two alkali halides with a given anion is almost independent of the anion. This suggests that each ion possesses its own characteristic radius:

$$r_0(\text{NaCl}) = r(\text{Na}^+) + r(\text{Cl}^-)$$

$$r_0(\text{KCl}) = r(\text{K}^+) + r(\text{Cl}^-)$$

whence

$$r_0(\text{KCl}) - r_0(\text{NaCl}) = r(\text{K}^+) - r(\text{Na}^+) \qquad \textbf{(4.69)}$$

which is the same for all pairs of Na^+/K^+ halides.

Table 15 Interatomic Distances in the Alkali Metal Halides (Å.)

	Li^+	Δ	Na^+	Δ	K^+	Δ	Rb^+	Δ	Cs^+
F^-	2·01	0·30	2·31	0·36	2·67	0·15	2·82	0·19	3·01
Δ'	0·56		0·50		0·47		0·47		
Cl^-	2·57	0·24	2·81	0·33	3·14	0·15	3·29		
Δ'	0·18		0·16		0·15		0·14		
Br^-	2·75	0·22	2·97	0·32	3·29	0·14	3·43		
Δ'	0·25		0·26		0·24		0·23		
I^-	3·00		3·23		3·53		3·66		

It must be remembered that the radius of a given ion depends upon its environment. For example, $r(\text{Na}^+)$ in NaCl is 0·95 Å., but in sodium metal, $r(\text{Na}) = 1·86$ Å. Evidently the radius of any given species is strongly dependent upon the nature of the interatomic forces acting upon it.

4·3·1   *The structure of elements*

The metals of the groups IA, IB and IIA of the periodic table and the 'transition' metals form relatively simple structures: the cubic close-packed arrangement (A1), the body-centred cubic arrangement (A2), and the hexagonal close-packed arrangement (A3). A1 and A3 represent two ways of close packing to the same degree spheres of equal size (fig. 60). Any three close-packed layers have two of these layers in an identical array whilst the third layer can be superposed upon the first two layers in one of two ways. Thus we obtain the succession

        A1: 1 2 3 1 2 3 1 2 ...
        A3: 1 2 1 2 1 2 1 2 ...

In the structure types A1 and A3 each sphere is in contact with twelve other spheres, so the coordination number is twelve. The radius of the metal atom can be taken as one-half the distance of closest approach of any two spheres.

(a) Cubic close-packed (A1)   (b) Hexagonal close-packed (A3)

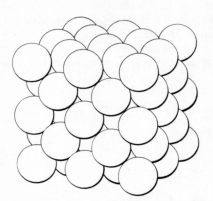

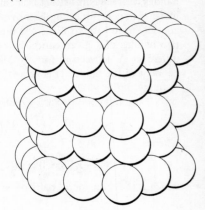

Figure 60.   Close-packing of equal spheres.

If the spheres have radius r, we now show that the volume of space occupied per sphere is $5.66r^3$ (the volume of each sphere is $4.19r^3$). In fig. 60a eight face-centred unit cells are represented. Let the side length of one cubic unit cell be m. Then the volume of the cube is m^3, but $m\sqrt{2}$ (a face diagonal) is equal to $4r$ (since the spheres are close-packed); thus the volume of the cube may be written as $\left[\dfrac{4r}{\sqrt{2}}\right]^3$. Since four atoms are associated with a face-centred unit cell, the volume occupied per sphere is

$$\frac{1}{4}\left[\frac{4r}{\sqrt{2}}\right]^3 = 5.66r^3.$$

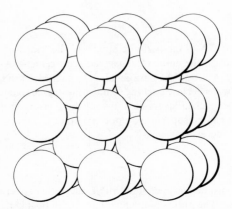

Figure 61.   The body-centred cubic arrangement of equal spheres (A2).

A similar calculation for the A3 structure shows the same degree of close-packing.

The body-centred cubic structure, A2, represents a slightly less close-packed array of equal spheres (fig. 61); the volume occupied per sphere is $6 \cdot 16r^3$ in this arrangement, and the coordination number is eight.

The high coordination numbers 8 and 12 are characteristic of the metallic bond. Important mechanical properties of metals arise through deformation of the structure by gliding along close-packed planes, there being four close-packed planes in A1 parallel to (111), whereas in A3 there is only one (normal to the vertical c-axis of the hexagonal unit cell) and in the 8-coordinated A2 structure there are no close-packed planes. We find that the malleable metals such as copper, silver, nickel and γ-iron have the cubic close-packed structure whereas the harder and more brittle metals such as chromium, tungsten and α-iron have the A3 or A2 structures. The metallurgical importance of iron is related to its ability to crystallize with either the A1 or A2 structure according to heat treatment.

A study of elements in the B-groups of the periodic table enables us to trace a continuous transition of bond type from the true metals of group IB, which we have discussed already, to the molecular compounds formed by the halogen molecules.

Iodine (fig. 62) and the other halogens form diatomic molecules of the type X_2. The bond between the atoms is mainly covalent but cohesion in the crystal is not

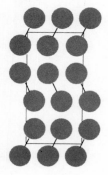

Figure 62.   The structure of iodine projected on to the XZ plane.

due to covalent bonds. The much weaker van der Waals forces are responsible for holding the molecules together in the solid. The heats of sublimation and the melting points of the crystalline halogens are low:

	F_2	Cl_2	Br_2	I_2
m.p.°C.	-223	-103	-7	114
$r(X-X)$ (Å.)	$1\cdot42$	$1\cdot99$	$2\cdot29$	$2\cdot66$

The distance between molecules in the crystal varies from about 2·5 Å in F_2 to about 3·5 Å in I_2.

Selenium forms infinite helical chains parallel to the c-axis of a hexagonal unit cell (fig. 63). The atoms in each chain are linked by covalent bonds and the chains are

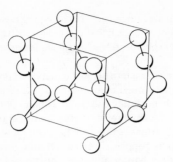

Figure 63. The structure of β-selenium.

linked by van der Waals forces. The angle Sé—$\widehat{Se}$—Se is about 104°, which is indicative of directional or covalent character. In the case of sulphur (in the same periodic group) a molecule S_8 is formed (fig. 64) with a S—$\widehat{S}$—S bond angle of 105°.

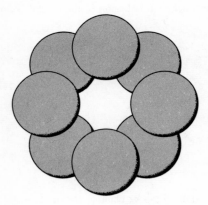

Figure 64. Orthorhombic sulphur: the molecule S_8.

The structures of arsenic (fig. 65) and of bismuth, in group VB, may be considered as superposed sheets of atoms with bond angles of about 100°, leading to non-planarity of the sheets. Each atom is coordinated by six other atoms, but three of these neighbours are appreciably closer than the other three. The high melting points and high electrical conductivity of antimony and bismuth indicate a degree of metallic character.

The structures of germanium and tin resemble that of diamond (fig. 20), but both (and especially tin) exhibit metallic character which is completely absent in diamond. This effect is well established in zinc and cadmium (group IIB). These elements have hexagonal structures that are very nearly close-packed, the axial ratio, c/a, in zinc

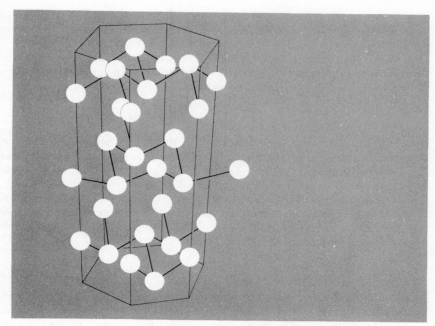

Figure 65. The structure of arsenic showing the arrangement of the atoms in layers.

being about 1·9 whilst for the hexagonal close-packed structure (fig. 60b) this ratio is 1·63. Of the twelve neighbours of any zinc atom, six are closer than the others.

Thallium and lead are B-group elements, but they have close-packed structures possibly due to stable electron configurations representing atoms which are not fully ionized:

$$Tl^+ \quad [Kr]\, 4d^{10}\, 4f^{14}\, 5s^2\, 5p^6\, 5d^{10}\, 6s^2$$
$$Pb^{2+} \quad [Kr]\, 4d^{10}\, 4f^{14}\, 5s^2\, 5p^6\, 5d^{10}\, 6s^2$$

The states of ionization expected from the position of these elements in the periodic table are Tl^{3+} and Pb^{4+}. These ions are known but they are unstable in aqueous solution with respect to the species Tl^+ and Pb^{2+}, this feature of the elements thallium and lead being called the 'inert pair' (in this case $6s^2$) effect.

The continuous change in bond type exemplified by the elements in groups IIB to VIIB is reflected in their properties. Brittleness increases along the periodic group and 'open' or low coordination structures are formed which produce a volume contraction on melting to a relatively close-packed liquid structure:

$$\text{Volume contraction cm.}^3\,\text{g.}^{-1}$$

Zn	$-0{\cdot}0108$
Bi	$+0{\cdot}0034$
cf. H_2O	$+0{\cdot}083$

The $(8 - n)$ 'rule' can be observed to apply in this series of elements and an element in periodic group nB will generally form $(8 - n)$ covalent bonds, as with zinc to bromine and with cadmium to iodine for example, but there are exceptions.

The inert gases crystallize with cubic close-packed structures. The interatomic forces are very weak van der Waals forces and the melting points of the crystals are very low:

He $-272°C.$
Rn $-71°C.$

Certain diatomic molecules such as CO, N_2, HCl and O_2 also have cubic close-packed structures because they are in free rotation in the solid state, a phenomenon noticed by Hendricks in 1930 during a study of long-chain alkyl ammonium halides and discussed theoretically by Pauling in the same year.

The combination of two elements produces a range of widely differing binary compounds including ionic structures such as potassium fluoride and magnesium oxide, metallic alloys such as the copper–gold mixtures, and molecular compounds such as mercuric chloride and carbon dioxide.

4·3·2   Binary metal systems

The true metals copper and gold have the cubic close-packed structures already described (A1). They form a complete range of solid solutions (which are like liquid solutions, i.e. homogeneous within a given range). Initially the addition of copper to gold leads to a structure in which the atoms are distributed in a completely random manner on the same sites that are occupied in the pure metals, the unit cell dimension decreasing in proportion to the concentration of copper added (the atomic radii are $r(Cu) = 1·28$ Å. and $r(Au) = 1·44$ Å.). At a composition corresponding to CuAu a similar random replacement occurs if the molten alloy is quenched rapidly, but if the same alloy is carefully annealed, the copper and gold atoms separate into layers; because of their different atomic sizes the ratio c/a is equal to 0·93 and the structure is tetragonal (fig. 66a). Another 'ordered' phase exists at the composition Cu_3Au, in this case a cubic structure in which the lattice sites are occupied in a regular

(a) CuAu   (b) Cu₃Au

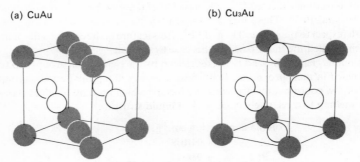

Figure 66.   Ordered structures in the Cu–Au system.

manner (fig. 66b); these ordered structures are termed superlattice structures. The rearrangement of the atoms into an ordered phase evidently lowers the free energy of the system with respect to the random solid solution, although the entropy is decreased in the same process. Silver and gold also form a complete range of solid solutions but no superlattice structures are obtained because the radii of the silver and gold atoms are approximately equal (due to the 'lanthanide contraction', see page 110) and under these conditions there is no free energy lowering for a super-lattice structure. It may be noted that both of the ordered phases have primitive (P) Bravais lattices.

The electrical conductivity of quenched Cu–Au alloys shows a smooth variation with composition, but with the annealed specimens maxima occur at the compositions CuAu and Cu_3Au. In general it is not possible to characterize an alloy by a chemical formula, and in this particular system the chemical composition is also insufficient to define its properties.

The silver–cadmium binary system (fig. 67) is more complex than the one just discussed. The α-phase is pure silver and can form solid solutions with up to about 40 per cent cadmium whilst a β-phase which has a structure type similar to CsCl

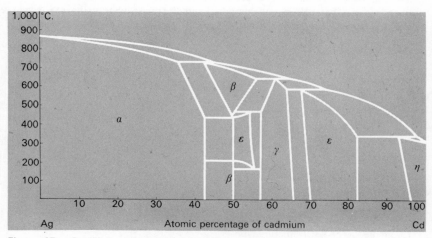

Figure 67.   Equilibrium diagram for the silver–cadmium alloys.

appears at 50 per cent cadmium. A comparison of fig. 68 (showing the structure of some of the phases present in the Ag–Cd system) and fig. 69 (representing the 'CsCl' structure type), reveals that the β-AgCd is statistically body-centred whereas CsCl is a primitive lattice. The γ-phase is a complex cubic unit cell containing 52 atoms which is mechanically very hard and brittle. The ε-phase represents an approximately hexagonal close-packed structure, the lattice sites being occupied by both Ag and Cd atoms in a completely random manner. Pure cadmium is represented by the η-phase which is also nearly a hexagonal close-packed structure, but it may be noted

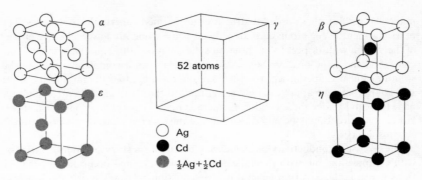

Figure 68. The structures of some phases present in the Ag–Cd system.

from the phase diagram that cadmium takes up only about 4 per cent of silver into solid solution. Fig. 70 shows X-ray powder photographs of various mixtures of silver and cadmium. The diffraction lines characteristic of each phase can be readily traced and this data may be used to derive phase diagrams. The regions in which two phases co-exist can be seen and compared with the phase diagram (fig. 68). No super-lattice structures are formed in this system.

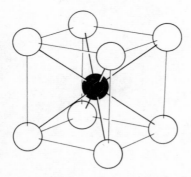

Figure 69. The CsCl structure type.

Fig. 71 shows the structure of sodium thallide, NaTl. Each atom is coordinated by eight atoms (four of each type) and the radius of the sodium atom is 1·62 Å. This value lies between the value found in sodium metal (1·86 Å.) and that found in sodium chloride (0·95 Å.), which indicates that the bonding in NaTl is mainly metallic but with some degree of ionic character (as its electrical conductivity and the relatively high coordination of the structure suggest).

The ideal covalent compound is diamond (fig. 20) in which the three-dimensional 'giant' molecule is formed by tetrahedral sp^3 bonds of length 1·545 Å. The hardness of this substance is well known, and its melting point is greater than 3500°C., but it is worth emphasizing that these are properties of covalent compounds; the low melting

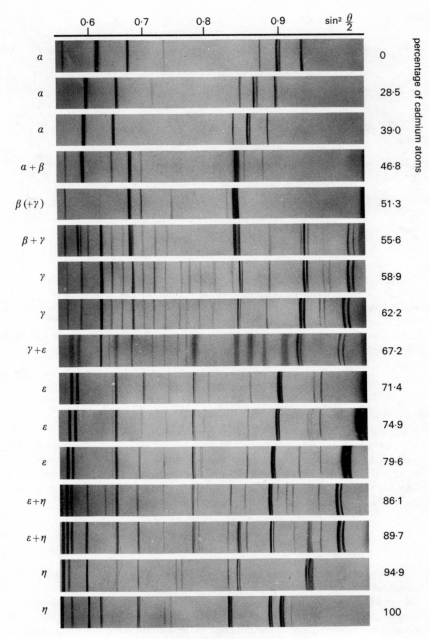

Figure 70.   X-ray powder photographs of silver–cadmium alloys.

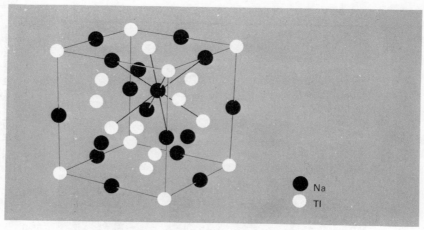

Figure 71. The structure of NaTl.

points and 'softness' of organic compounds, often attributed incorrectly to covalent bonding, are due to the fact that covalent molecules are linked in the solid state by van der Waals forces and it is these weaker forces that are broken when the crystal is melted or mechanically ruptured.

The closely related structures (fig. 72) of zinc blende and wurtzite, both ZnS, are very common:

Zinc blende structure				Wurtzite structure				
BeS	ZnS	CdS	HgS	AlAs		GaAs		
BeSe	ZnSe	CdSe	HgSe	AlSb		GaSb	InSb	
BeTe	ZnTe	CdTe	HgTe		MgTe		ZnS	CdS CdSe

If these structures were mainly ionic, the ions would be represented as Zn^{2+} and X^{2-}. Covalency requires overlap of the atomic orbitals, but the true state is intermediate between these extremes and so the charges on the ions are numerically smaller than those representing the ionic state. Several of these compounds with wurtzite structure are *semi-conductors*, their specific resistances, ρ, being between those of a typical conductor (copper) and a typical insulator (diamond):

	Cu		GaAs	GaSb	InSb	C (diamond)
ρ, ohm cm. (at 25°C.)	1.73×10^{-6}		40	100	0.01	10^{12}

We have emphasized the absence of pure bond type in the structures of compounds and it must be accepted that a given compound will contain some degree of each of the principal types of interatomic forces. Often one of these will predominate: for example, we think of sodium chloride as an ionic compound, but accurate calculations of the lattice energy of sodium chloride reveal that there is a small contribution to the energy from covalent and van der Waals forces. We cannot describe this

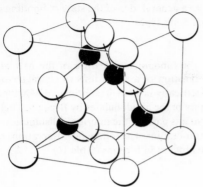

(b) The zinc blende structure

(c) The wurtzite structure

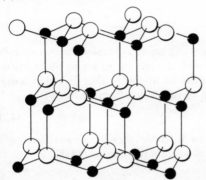

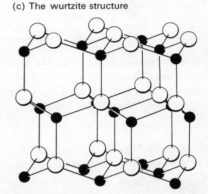

Figure 72.   The ZnS structure types: zinc blends and wurtzite.

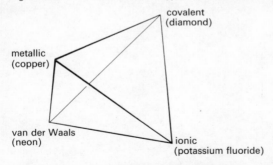

Figure 73.   Bond type: the substances in parentheses represent close approaches to the pure bond types. Any given compound will have an actual bonding system represented by a point within the tetrahedron.

107   The states of matter

intermediate, or resonance, structure pictorially and its evaluation can be made only in terms of wave mechanics, but fig. 73 gives a general idea of the state of bonding in a given compound in terms of the principal bond types.

4·3·3   *Ionic compounds*

Since the ionic bond is non-directional, the fundamental feature of the MX and MX_2 structure types is the geometric disposition of a set of ions of characteristic radius in a manner which is as a whole electrically neutral. The principal MX types are 'CsCl', 'NaCl' and 'ZnS'. The early study of the alkali halides by Bragg has been mentioned and we noted that his measurements gave us the interionic distances and also the idea of ions of approximately constant radius. The following observations by Landé (1920) led to an assignment of individual radii for ions (table 16).

Table 16   'NaCl' Type Crystals

	r_0 (Å.)		r_0 (Å.)
MgO	2·104	MnO	2·218
MgS	2·595	MnS	2·605
MgSe	2·725	MnSe	2·725

It was considered that in the two sulphides and (more especially) the two selenides the anions were in a close-packed array with the cations occupying the interstices (fig. 74). The replacement of Mg by Mn does not appear to alter the anion contact appreciably, except in the two oxides, and we can deduce from the figure:

$$2r_0\sqrt{2} = 4r(X^{2-}) \qquad (4.70)$$

whence $r(Se^{2-}) = 1·93$ Å. and $r(S^{2-}) = 1·84$ Å. A table of ionic radii was drawn up in 1926 by Goldschmidt, a modern version of which is reproduced in table 17.

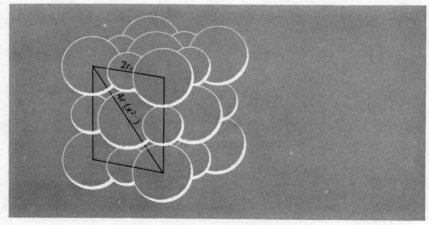

Figure 74.   The NaCl structure with the anions close-packed.

Table 17 Ionic Radii

Values are in Ångstrom units and correspond to 6-coordination

	I	II	III	IV	V	VI	VII	VIII
1							H^- 1·54	
2	Li^+ 0·60	Be^{2+} 0·31	B —	C —	N	O^{2-} 1·40	F^- 1·36	
3	Na^+ 0·95	Mg^{2+} 0·65	Al^{3+} 0·50	Si^{4+} 0·41	P	S^{2-} 1·84	Cl^- 1·81	
4	K^+ 1·33	Ca^{2+} 0·99	Sc^{3+} 0·81	Ti^{3+} 0·76 Ti^{4+} 0·68	V^{2+} 0·88 V^{3+} 0·74 V^{4+} 0·60	Cr^{2+} 0·84 Cr^{3+} 0·63 Cr^{4+} 0·56	Mn^{2+} 0·80 Mn^{3+} 0·66 Mn^{4+} 0·54	Fe^{2+} 0·80 Fe^{3+} 0·64 Co^{2+} 0·72 Co^{3+} 0·63 Ni^{2+} 0·69 Ni^{3+} 0·62
	Cu^+ 0·96	Zn^{2+} 0·74	Ga^{3+} 0·62	Ge^{4+} 0·62	As	Se^{2-} 1·98	Br^- 1·95	
5	Rb^+ 1·48	Sr^{2+} 1·13	Y^{3+} 0·93	Zr^{4+} 0·80	Nb	Mo —	Tc —	Ru^{4+} 0·63 Rh^{3+} 0·68 Pd^{2+} 0·80 Pd^{4+} 0·65
	Ag^+ 1·26	Cd^{2+} 0·97	In^{3+} 0·81	Sn^{4+} 0·71	Sb	Te^{2-} 2·21	I^- 2·16	
6	Cs^+ 1·69	Ba^{2+} 1·35	La^{3+} 1·15	Hf^{4+} 0·78	Ta	W^{4+} 0·66	Re^{4+} 0·72	Os^{4+} 0·65 Ir^{4+} 0·64 Pt^{4+} 0·65
	Au^+ 1·37	Hg^{2+} 1·10	Tl^+ 1·44 Tl^{3+} 0·95	Pb^{2+} 1·21 Pb^{4+} 0·84	Bi	Po —	At —	
7	Fr^+ 1·76	Ra^{2+} 1·43	Ac^{3+} 1·11					

Lanthanide elements

Ce^{3+} 1·02	Pr^{3+} 1·00	Nd^{3+} 0·99	Pm^{3+} 0·98	Sm^{3+} 0·97	Eu^{3+} 0·97	Gd^{3+} 0·97
Tb^{3+} 1·00	Dy^{3+} 0·99	Ho^{3+} 0·97	Er^{3+} 0·96	Tm^{3+} 0·95	Yb^{3+} 0·94	Lu^{3+} 0·93

Actinide elements

Th^{3+} 1·08	Pa^{3+} 1·06	U^{3+} 1·04	Np^{3+} 1·02	Pu^{3+} 1·01	Am^{3+} 1·00
Th^{4+} 0·95	Pa^{4+} 0·91	U^{4+} 0·89	Np^{4+} 0·88	Pu^{4+} 0·86	Am^{4+} 0·85

Other ions

NH_4^+ 1·48 OH^- 1·53

Large differences exist between the radii of a given element in different states of combination:

$$
\begin{array}{cccc}
 & S^{2-} & S & S\ (\text{in } SO_2) \\
r(\text{Å.}) & 1\cdot84 & 1\cdot12 & 0\cdot94
\end{array}
$$

In general, radii decrease with increasing positive charge since the electrons move in a progressively stronger field and are bound more strongly to the central portion of the atom. In the case of the lanthanons, where the occupancy of the inner $4f$ electron level is increased with a rise in atomic number, the effective nuclear charge is not exactly balanced by the added electron without a decrease in volume. Thus the ionic radius decreases from $1\cdot18$ Å. to $0\cdot99$ Å. along the series Ce^{3+} to Lu^{3+}, the atomic number increasing from 58 to 71 (lanthanide contraction). A series of isoelectronic positive ions shows the expected decrease in radius with increase in positive charge:

$$
\begin{array}{cccc}
 & Na^+ & Mg^{2+} & Al^{3+} \\
r(\text{Å.}) & 0\cdot95 & 0\cdot65 & 0\cdot50
\end{array}
$$

but a series of isoelectronic negative ions shows very little change in radius with change in ionic charge:

$$
\begin{array}{cccc}
 & P^{3-} & S^{2-} & Cl^- \\
r(\text{Å.}) & 2\cdot0 & 1\cdot84 & 1\cdot81
\end{array}
$$

The addition of electrons does not alter the principal quantum number of the occupied orbitals.

4·3·4   *MX structures*

The highest coordination exhibited in MX structures is that of $8:8$ in the 'CsCl' type. This is the structure of CsCl, CsBr, CsI, NH_4Cl, NH_4Br and NH_4I, to quote only a few. The structural arrangement has been illustrated in fig. 69. When anions of radius 1 Å. are in contact with each other, the radius of the 'hole' at the centre of any eight anions is $0\cdot732$ Å. This may be deduced as follows:

The length of the cube diagonal $= 2r_+ + 2r_-$.

The length of the cube edge $= 2r_-$.

But

$$2r_-\sqrt{3} = 2r_+ + 2r_-.$$

Whence

$$\frac{r_+}{r_-} = 0\cdot732.$$

The ratio r_+/r_- is called the *radius ratio* and gives some idea of the coordination to be expected for given ions, although its predictions are not always accurate.

If we consider reducing the value of r_+ while keeping r_- constant, it is clear that for r_+/r_- less than $0\cdot732$ no closer approach of the anions can be obtained. A reduction of the lattice energy with further decrease in r_+ can be produced, however, if the

'NaCl' structure with 6:6 coordination is adopted (fig. 11), but this also has a lower limit of the radius ratio at 0·414.

The lattice energy of an ionic crystal of type MX can be represented closely by the equation:

$$U(r_0) = \left(\frac{-NAe^2}{Jr_0}\right)\left(1 - \frac{\rho}{r_0}\right) \tag{4.71}$$

For the alkali halides, $\frac{\rho}{r_0}$ is approximately 0·1, and substituting the values of the constants in equation (4.71) we obtain

$$U(r_0) = \frac{-298\cdot7\,A}{r_0}\,\text{kcal. mole}^{-1} \tag{4.72}$$

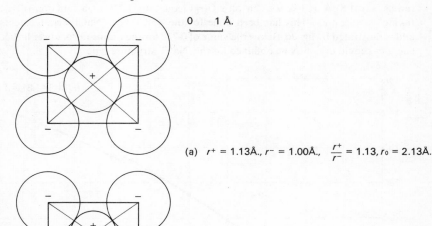

0   1 Å.

(a) r^+ = 1.13Å., r^- = 1.00Å., $\frac{r^+}{r^-}$ = 1.13, r_0 = 2.13Å.

(b) r^+ = 0.73Å., r^- = 1.00Å., $\frac{r^+}{r^-}$ = 0.73, r_0 = 1.73Å.

(c) r^+ = 0.52Å., r^- = 1.00Å., $\frac{r^+}{r^-}$ = 0.52, r_0 = 1.73Å.

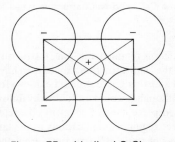

Figure 75.   Idealized CsCl structures.

with r_0 measured in Å. The Madelung constant A is a geometric factor, determined by the structural arrangement and charges of the ions present. It has the following values for MX structures:

MX	'CsCl'	'NaCl'	'ZnS'
A	1·763	1·748	1·639

It may be thought at first that the 'CsCl' structure type will always be more stable (more negative value of the lattice energy) than those of 'NaCl' and 'ZnS' whatever the value of r_0. However, we have remarked that in the 'CsCl' structure type the length of the cube diagonal is $2r_+ + 2r_-$ when the anions are in close contact. If r_+ is decreased such that $\frac{r^+}{r_-}$ is less than 0·732, no change in the effective value of r_0 occurs (fig. 75) and hence no change in the lattice energy. If we assume a constant anion radius, say 1·81 Å. (Cl$^-$), we can plot $U(r_0)$ (equation **4.72**), as a function of r_+, taking $r_0 = r_+ + r_-$. This has been done for the 'CsCl' and 'NaCl' arrangements and is illustrated by fig. 76. Below the value of 0·732 for the radius ratio, lower lattice energies should evidently be obtained for the 'NaCl' structure type.

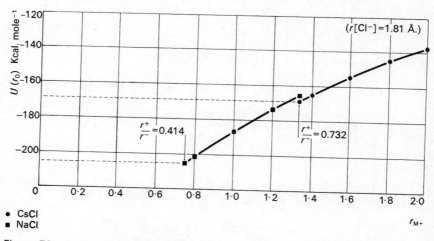

Figure 76.   Lattice energies curves for MCl in the CsCl and NaCl structure types as a function of r_{m+}.

Assuming that the same degree of ionic character is retained, the 'NaCl' structure has a lower limiting radius ratio of 0·414, so that the 'ZnS' structure should then have a lower lattice energy; it is doubtful, however, if a further curve should be drawn for the 'ZnS' structure using equation (**4.72**) since although it would undoubtedly follow the pattern of the curves in fig. 76, the increased percentage of covalent character present in the zinc blende and wurtzite structures requires modifications to the lattice energy equation. In table 18 the radius ratios of some MX structures are listed

Table 18 Radius Ratios for MX Compounds

'CsCl'		'NaCl'				'ZnS'			
CsCl	0·93	LiF	0·44	MgO	0·46	AgI	0·58	ZnS	0·40
CsBr	0·87	LiI	0·28	BaO	0·96	BeS	0·17	ZnSe	0·37
CsI	0·78	NaF	0·44	MgS	0·35	BeSe	0·16	ZnTe	0·33
NH_4Cl	0·82	KF	0·98	BaS	0·73	BeTe	0·14	CuF	0·71
NH_4Br	0·76	KI	0·62	MgSe	0·33	CuCl	0·53	CuI	0·44
NH_4I	0·69	RbF	1·09	BaSe	0·68				
TlCl	0·80	RbI	0·69	CaTe	0·45				
TlI	0·67	CsF	1·24	BaTe	0·61				
		AgF	0·93	AgCl	0·70				

in terms of the structure type actually observed at normal temperatures and pressures. The radius ratio 'rule' is evidently not strictly obeyed and the 'NaCl' structure type is often preferred outside its radius ratio limits, mainly because this concept treats the structures as purely ionic and this is not completely true even for the alkali metal and certainly not true for the zinc blende and wurtzite structures.

A more complete treatment requires a quantitative lattice theory. We shall discuss the effect qualitatively by using the idea of *polarization*, which can be envisaged as a distortion of the electron distribution of an ion by the presence of neighbouring ions. The polarizability of an ion measures the distortion which can be produced in this way and is associated with easily deformable electron clouds – a property usually associated with anions although large cations also have appreciable polarizabilities (table 19).

Table 19 Polarizabilities of Some Ions

Li^+	0·08	Be^{2+}	0·03	O^{2-}	3·1	F^-	0·99
Na^+	0·21	Mg^{2+}	0·12	S^{2-}	7·3	Cl^-	3·1
K^+	0·85	Ba^{2+}	2·1	Se^{2-}	6·4	Br^-	4·2
Cs^+	2·8			Te^{2-}	9·6	I^-	6·3

The effectiveness of an ion in deforming the electron distribution of its neighbours (its polarizing power) can be measured approximately by the strength of its electric field, ze/r^2 (table 20). This property and that of polarizability belong to both anions

Table 20 Polarizing Power of Some Ions

Li^+	1·6	Be^{2+}	17	O^{2-}	1·2	F^-	0·57
Na^+	1·0	Mg^{2+}	3·3	S^{2-}	0·66	Cl^-	0·30
K^+	0·57	Ba^{2+}	0·98	Se^{2-}	0·55	Br^-	0·26
Cs^+	0·37			Te^{2-}	0·45	I^-	0·21

and cations although to varying degrees. It is significant that the non-inert-gas type cations are anomalous in their ability to deform the electron clouds of anions to a much greater extent than is suggested by their size. For example, the ions Cu^+, Ag^+

and Hg^{2+} are comparable in size to Na^+, K^+ and Sr^{2+} respectively, although the physical and chemical properties of their halides are quite different.

If polarization may be regarded as a partial overlap of orbitals, it is reasonable to find that the interionic separations are less than the sum of the corresponding ionic radii (table 21).

Table 21 Interionic Distances (r_0) in the Potassium and Silver Halides, and Radii Sums (Σr_i)

Halide	Σr_i (Å.)	r_0 (Å.)
KF	2·69	2·67
KCl	3·14	3·15
KBr	3·28	3·30
KI	3·50	3·53
AgF	2·62	2·46
AgCl	3·07	2·78
AgBr	3·21	2·89
AgI	3·25*	2·80

* The ionic radii have been corrected to the 4:4 coordination found in AgI. The radii for 8 coordination and 4 coordination are 3 per cent greater and 5 per cent less respectively than the corresponding 6 coordination radii which are the standard values listed in table 17.

It will be noted that the variation between Σr_i and r_0 for the silver halides increases with increasing polarizability of the anion, whilst for the potassium halides $\Sigma r_i \simeq r_0$.

4·3·5   *MX_2 structures*

The MX_2 structures are very numerous and of a more diverse character than those of the type MX. The maximum coordination of 8:4 is observed in the 'CaF_2' or

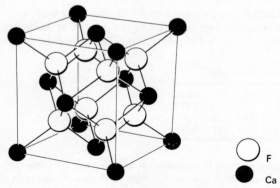

F

Ca

Figure 77.   The structure type CaF_2 (fluorite).

fluorite structure type (fig. 77). Each calcium ion is coordinated octahedrally (i.e. in directions normal to the faces of a regular octahedron) by eight fluoride ions and each fluoride ion is coordinated tetrahedrally by four calcium ions; the positions of anion and cation can be interchanged (in Na_2O for example), this arrangement being termed the antifluorite structure. As with the caesium chloride arrangement, the radius ratio for 'CaF_2' is >0.732.

The 6:3 coordination is typified by rutile, TiO_2 (fig. 78), in which each titanium atom is coordinated hexahedrally (i.e. in directions normal to the faces of a cube) by

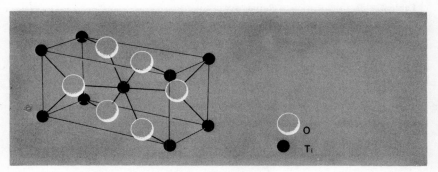

Figure 78.   The structure type TiO_2 (rutile).

six oxygen atoms and each oxygen atom is coordinated by three titanium atoms to form an isosceles triangle. The radius ratio limits for this structure type are 0.732 to 0.414.

The third simple MX_2 structure type which we shall describe is the 4:2 coordinated structure of cristobalite (fig. 79). This may be considered as derived from zinc

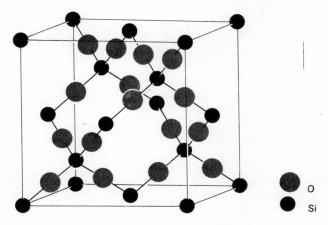

Figure 79.   The structure type SiO_2 (cristobalite).

115   The states of matter

blende (fig. 72a), because the 'SiO$_2$' structure is obtained if silicon atoms are placed on both the Zn and S sites with oxygen atoms mid-way between them. Hence each silicon atom is coordinated tetrahedrally by four oxygen atoms and each oxygen atom is coordinated linearly by two silicon atoms. The linearity of the Si—O—Si linkage indicates a high degree of ionic character and in quartz (another modification of SiO$_2$) the Si—O—Si bond angle at room temperature is less than 180°. Table 22 lists the radius ratios of several MX$_2$ structures and the structure type in which each occurs under normal conditions; it is noteworthy that many of the MX and MX$_2$

Table 22 Radius Ratios of Some MX$_2$ Structures

'Fluorite'		'Rutile'		'Cristobalite'
CaF$_2$ 0·73	CdF$_2$ 0·71	MgF$_2$ 0·48	MnO$_2$ 0·57	BeF$_2$ 0·23
SrF$_2$ 0·83	HgF$_2$ 0·81	MnF$_2$ 0·59	SnO$_2$ 0·51	SiO$_2$ 0·29
BaF$_2$ 0·99		FeF$_2$ 0·59	TiO$_2$ 0·49	GeO$_2$ 0·38
Li$_2$O 0·43	Li$_2$S 0·17	CoF$_2$ 0·53	GeO$_2$ 0·38	
Na$_2$O 0·68	Rb$_2$S 0·80	NiF$_2$ 0·51		
K$_2$O 0·95		ZnF$_2$ 0·54		
Rb$_2$O 1·06				
Li$_2$Se 0·16	Li$_2$Te 0·14			
Rb$_2$Se 0·75	K$_2$Te 0·60			

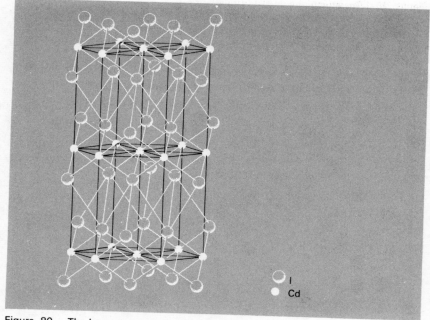

Figure 80. The layer structure type of CdI$_2$ (cadmium iodide).

structures undergo polymorphic transformations under different conditions of temperature and pressure.

In general, the MX_2 structures are in better agreement with the radius ratio deductions than are the MX structures, which may at first sight seem surprising as the polarization in the MX_2 structures might be expected to be greater on account of the presence of smaller and more highly charged cations. However, remembering the curves of fig. 76 and considering the Madelung constants of these structures it is reasonable to conclude that the lattice energies of MX_2 structures exhibit greater numerical differences than those between the 'CsCl' and 'NaCl' types:

	'Fluorite'	'Rutile'	'Cristobalite'
A	5·04	9·64	8·24

Thus the small energy terms which are important in deciding between 'CsCl' and 'NaCl' are without great structural effect in the MX_2 series.

Strong polarization leads to the development of layer lattices such as those of 'CdI$_2$' (fig. 80) and 'MoS$_2$' (fig. 81). The asymmetry of the coordination is evident: weak forces act across the composite layers [I—Cd—I] and [S—Mo—S] and the crystals exhibit good cleavage along planes parallel to these layers. Molybdenum disulphide

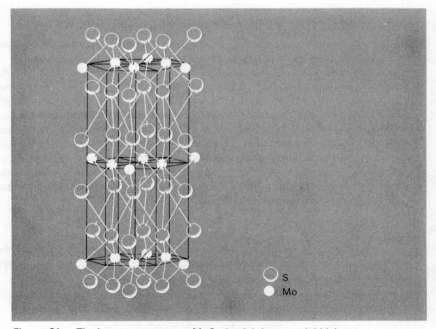

Figure 81. The layer structure type MoS_2 (molybdenum sulphide).

has lubricant properties on account of this particular feature, and can be compared with graphite (fig. 25).

Further polarization leads to discrete molecules being formed which are held together in the solid state by van der Waals forces and the structures have the properties associated with such forces (e.g. low melting and boiling points, low mechanical strength, etc.). Two examples are mercuric chloride and carbon dioxide (fig. 82). The atomic orbitals in $HgCl_2$ and CO_2 overlap to a large extent and covalent bonds

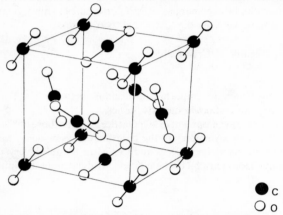

●c
○o

Figure 82.   The crystal structure of carbon dioxide.

are formed. We might consider that extreme polarization in ionic structures leads to covalent bond formation but this picture is only qualitative.

Ionic crystals are formed between cations and complex anions such as SO_4^{2-}, CO_3^{2-} and NO_3^-, while complex cations such as $\{Co(NH_3)_6\}^{3+}$ and $\{Cu(H_2O)_4\}^{2+}$ may also be involved in ionic structures. The complex ions have shapes and sizes which remain approximately constant throughout a wide range of structures (some are shown in fig. 83). One of these compounds is illustrated in fig. 3 where the tetrahedral SO_4^{2-} groups (one of them outlined) can be seen. Cohesion in this structure is obtained by strong electrostatic linkages between the Ca^{2+} ions and the oxygen atoms of the SO_4^{2-} groups, each Ca^{2+} ion being coordinated by eight such oxygen neighbours whilst each oxygen is linked with two Ca^{2+} ions and one sulphur atom. The coordination of each sulphur atom is tetrahedral.

4.3.6   *Hydrogen-bonded structures*

The structural effects of the hydrogen bond (see chapter 2) are far-reaching. We may begin by considering the anomalous properties of water in relation to the other hydrides of the same periodic group:

	H_2O	H_2S	H_2Se	H_2Te
m.p. (°C.)	0	−83	−63	−48
b.p. (°C.)	100	−62	−43	−4

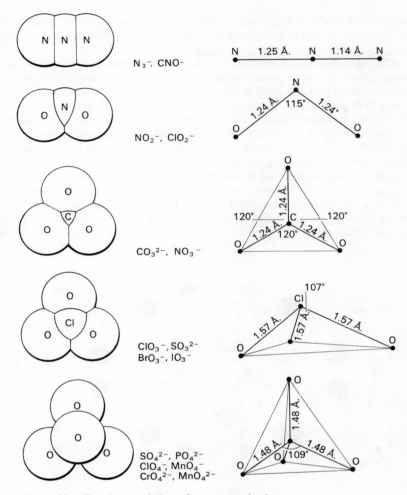

Figure 83. The shapes of sizes of some complex ions.

With the exception of water, these compounds show an increase in melting point and boiling point with a rise in molecular weight (a usual trend), but the difference between the melting point and boiling point is much larger in water than in the other hydrides. For example, in the solid state ice (fig. 1) has a very much less tightly packed structure than hydrogen sulphide, with its cubic close-packed structure. In ice, each water molecule is coordinated by four other molecules and has an effective radius of 1·38 Å. The O—H bonds in the water molecule (heavy lines in the figure) are of length 0·96 Å., the H—Ô—H bond angle being 104·5° with the hydrogen atoms positioned unsymmetrically along each O—O line. The resulting hydrogen-bonded system is responsible for the high degree of structure in liquid water and ice, the 'openness' of the ice crystal leading to a volume contraction on melting to form a more closely packed liquid.

Ammonium fluoride and ammonium hydrogen difluoride exhibit strong hydrogen bonding, unlike the other ammonium halides of coordination number eight, and the HF_2^- ion in NH_4HF_2, is itself hydrogen bonded and linked to the NH_4^+ ion by hydrogen bonds in addition to the ionic forces expected for such structures. Since the ammonium ion has a tetrahedral configuration, this is imposed upon the whole structure, both NH_4F and NH_4HF_2 having tetrahedrally coordinated arrangements, but in KHF_2 only the HF_2^- ion is hydrogen bonded and this is linked electrostatically to the potassium ions to give a higher coordination.

Hydrogen bonding is present in most hydrates. Fig. 84 illustrates a typical hydrate structure, $CaSO_4 . 2H_2O$, in which each Ca^{2+} ion is coordinated by six oxygen atoms from SO_4^{2-} groups (the structure of which is indicated) and by two oxygen atoms in water molecules, so that it is eight-coordinated. The structure is a type of layer structure, each water molecule linking a Ca^{2+} ion to one oxygen in the same 'layer' and

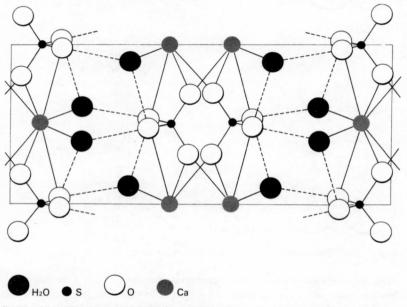

● H_2O ● S   ○ O   ● Ca

Figure 84.   The structure of gypsum, $CaSO_4 2H_2O$ (H atoms are not shown).

also to an oxygen atom in the next 'layer'. The cohesion of this structure in one direction is due to hydrogen bonding (shown by dotted lines in fig. 84), but the gypsum crystal exhibits a perfect cleavage and we find that the cleavage plane ruptures the weaker hydrogen bonds in the structure.

Only a few crystal structures have been discussed in order to amplify the earlier description of interatomic forces in chemical compounds, and to introduce a classification of these structures based upon the type of interactions present. It will be evident that a wealth of structural information is now available and for further study the reader is directed to the recent works of Evans* and of Bragg and Claringbull.†

4·4 The liquid state

The theory of the liquid state is much less well developed than that of the gaseous state (with its molecular chaos) or of the solid state (with its characteristic extreme regularity). Models and mathematical functions can often be envisaged for extreme ranges of certain properties but not for their intermediate values, and approximations made in the extreme cases may not be sufficiently accurate for the intermediate case. Liquids likewise represent a sort of compromise, in this instance between order and disorder.

Similarity to the solid state is apparent in the way that molecules are packed in a liquid. Cohesive forces strong enough to lead to a condensed state of matter do exist, but the appreciable translational energy of the molecules inhibits long-range order. In the solid state, by comparison, the kinetic energy of the molecules is negligible because although atoms or ions vibrate about their mean positions, free movement is prevented by strong and well defined interatomic forces.

The arrangement of the molecules in a liquid somewhat resembles that found in a gas, with molecules clustering together to form localized partially ordered groups which continually disperse and re-form. In other words, the molecules of a gas may be replaced by clusters of molecules in a liquid, so that certain distances of approach (those within the cluster) are more probable than others despite the fact that the range of distances within a given volume is very variable.

Liquids represent a state of higher internal energy and of lower degree of order than crystalline solids. The cohesion in a liquid may be due to ionic forces (in molten electrolytes), to metallic forces (in molten metals), to hydrogen bonding (in water, for example), or to van der Waals forces (in organic liquids); in some cases more than one of these forces may operate.

4·4·1 *Disorder in liquids*

All substances that do not decompose on heating form liquids, providing that the external pressure is sufficiently great. A crystal at its melting point and the liquid at the same temperature are in chemical equilibrium, but energetically the crystalline state is more favourable than that of the liquid. To procure melting, the enthalpy (latent heat) of fusion must be added to the system. The equilibrium situation is determined by the free energy change for the process and the increased disorder on melting

* Evans, R. C. (1964), *Crystal chemistry*, Cambridge University Press, 2nd Edn.
† Bragg, W. L. and Claringbull, G. F. (1965), *Crystal structures of minerals (The crystalline state, vol. IV)*, Bell.

causes the entropic term $T\Delta S$ to overcome the enthalpy change, causing the crystal to melt when the following relationship has been established:

$$T\{S \text{ (liq.)} - S \text{ (cryst.)}\} \geqslant H \text{ (liq.)} - H \text{ (cryst.)}. \tag{4.73}$$

The sharpness of a melting point indicates discontinuity between the solid state and the liquid state. In a gas the energy distribution of the molecules is given by the Boltzmann (classical) equation (**4.44**), but in a solid energy changes are quantized and when melting takes place enough energy must be supplied for the whole crystal to melt, otherwise some of it remains as a solid in equilibrium with the liquid at the melting point.

The transition between a liquid and a gas is not so marked. Due to its relatively high vapour pressure a liquid may be evaporated isothermally, vapour pressure data being expressed by the empirical equation

$$\ln p = a + b \ln T + \frac{c}{T}. \tag{4.74}$$

If the vapour obeys the gas laws, the molar heat of vaporization is given by:

$$L_T = \alpha + \beta RT. \tag{4.75}$$

The approximate values of β are 1·5, 2·5, 3·5 and 4·5 for liquids composed of monatomic, diatomic, triatomic and tetratomic molecules respectively. The term α is the molar heat of vaporization extrapolated to $T = 0°$, so that $\frac{L_V}{RT}$ is a constant; this relationship is known as Trouton's rule and is obeyed moderately well. Not surprisingly, liquids seem to obey both Boltzmann and quantized conditions in differing circumstances, but the approximate constancy of Trouton's rule indicates that a definite amount of energy must be expended to evaporate one mole of a liquid even though it evaporates continuously.

4·4·2 *Compressibility*

Liquids are generally more compressible than solids but much less compressible than gases. The compressibility β measures the relative decrease in volume with increase in applied external pressure and varies with temperature according to the approximate equation

$$\beta = \beta_0 \exp(bT). \tag{4.76}$$

For n-pentane and mercury, b has the values $7·97 \times 10^{-3}$ per deg. and $1·37 \times 10^{-3}$ per deg. respectively.

Although a solid and its melt are in chemical equilibrium, the discontinuity between these two states of matter is emphasized by a marked difference in their compressibilities.

The variation of the compressibility of a liquid with pressure is indicated in fig. 85. The decrease is rapid at low pressures and at 1000 atm. the compressibility has fallen to about one-half of its value at 1 atm.

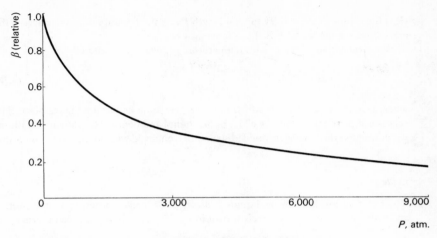

Figure 85. Variation of compressibility coefficient β with pressure.

4·4·3 Liquid flow

The fact that liquids flow under applied stress does not imply the absence of inter-atomic forces, but rather demonstrates their inability to maintain a fixed shape, as in a solid. The viscosity, η, of a liquid may be obtained from studies on the rate of flow through capillary tubes:

$$\eta = \frac{\pi R^4 P}{8 l V_t}. \tag{4.77}$$

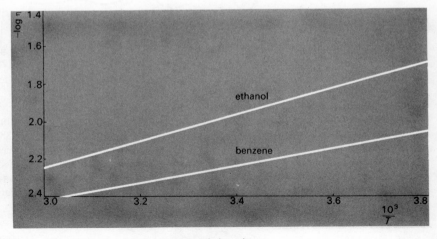

Figure 86. Temperature dependence of viscosity, η.

123   The states of matter

(R is the radius of a capillary tube of length l, P is the pressure difference across the ends of the capillary and V_t is the volume flow per second.)

The variation of viscosity with temperature is given approximately by

$$\eta = A \exp\left(\frac{-\xi}{RT}\right) \tag{4.78}$$

where ξ is an energy barrier which must be overcome before flow takes place. The relationship is demonstrated well by both ethanol and benzene (fig. 86) but it fails for water because the hydrogen-bonded structure is changed with change in temperature.

4·4·4   Evidence for structure

X-ray diffraction studies on liquids indicate a degree of ordering in the atomic arrangement. A typical pattern is shown in fig. 87 and is interpretable in terms of a

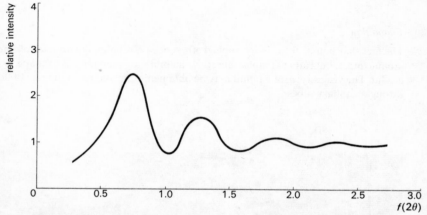

Figure 87.   Intensity of X-ray diffraction as a function of the scattering angle 2θ, for liquid Hg at 25°C.

radial distribution function, $p(r)$, such that the probability of finding another atom distant between r and $(r+dr)$ from any one atom is given by $4\pi r^2 p(r)\, dr$ (fig. 88). Evidently there is considerable order in liquids, and a principal difference between liquids and solids emerges from this study: in a solid, the structural unit (an array of atoms) is repeated periodically in three dimensions by the translations of a Bravais lattice, but in a liquid there is no regular repetition of this nature. These features are implied in the terms short-range order and long-range order.

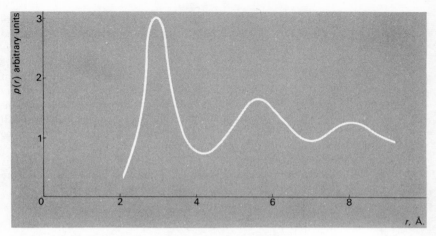

Figure 88. Radial distribution function for liquid Hg, 25°C.

4·4·5 *Structure models*

The cohesive forces operating in the liquid state are of prime importance in deciding its structure and an estimate of their magnitude is given by the internal pressure, P_i.

For an ideal gas P_i is zero, since by definition the internal energy of a gas is independent of its volume. For a real gas, however, forces of attraction exist between the molecules and an internal cohesive pressure results for which the term $\frac{a}{V^2}$ in the van der Waals equation of state for a gas attempts to account. In table 23, the magnitudes of the internal pressures for a number of gases and liquids are compared.

Table 23   Internal Pressures at 25°C. and
1 Atmosphere External Pressure

Gas	P_i atm.	Liquid	P_i atm.
(ideal)	0	$n\text{-}C_7H_{14}$	2 510
H_2	0·0005	CCl_4	3 310
O_2	0·0027	C_6H_6	3 640
CO_2	0·0072	CS_2	3 670
H_2O	0·0109	H_2O	13 200
Hg	0·0162	Hg	20 000

The internal pressure of a liquid varies much more rapidly with external pressure than does that of a gas. Thus, whereas a moderately simple extension of the ideal equation of state of a gas explains many of its properties, no such simple equation holds for a liquid.

A theory of the liquid state has to account for many diverse factors; these include the general decrease in enthalpy, entropy and volume in forming a solid, the viscosity and its variation with temperature, the compressibility of liquids, isothermal evaporation and the X-ray evidence of localized structure. No single theory has emerged yet to account satisfactorily for all the features of the liquid state.

Eyring considered a free space theory. The free space in a liquid is the volume which is not occupied by the molecules themselves. At ordinary temperatures, about 3 per cent of free space exists. This figure may be deduced from the compressibility studies already discussed. Between 1 atm. and 1000 atm., the large decrease in compressibility corresponds to a reduction in volume by 3 per cent. The high initial fall in the compressibility coefficient, β, may be interpreted as a removal of the free space in the liquid. After this has occurred, the liquid is much less compressible.

Eyring's liquid model is illustrated in fig. 89. The vapour above the liquid contains relatively few molecules, moving about completely at random. In the liquid itself, the

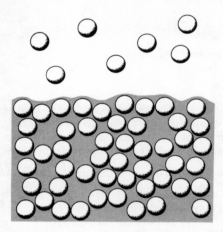

Figure 89. Eyring's model for the liquid state.

space is mostly filled and the molecules move about at random, singly or in clusters. If the temperature is increased, molecules pass into the vapour and 'holes' in the liquid increase in number. At the critical temperature, the density of the liquid should equal that of the vapour. Hence, the average density should remain constant. In practice, a small decrease in the average density with temperature is observed, so that

$$D_{av.} = D_0 - \alpha T. \tag{4.79}$$

D_0 is a limiting density at $T = 0°$, and α is $\dfrac{dD_{av.}}{dT}$. This relationship was discovered in 1886 by Cailletet and Mathias and is known as the law of rectilinear diameters. For n-pentane, $D_0 = 0\cdot3231$ and $\alpha = 0\cdot00046$, leading to fig. 90: X is the average density at 130° and XY represents the small decrease in the average density with increase in temperature.

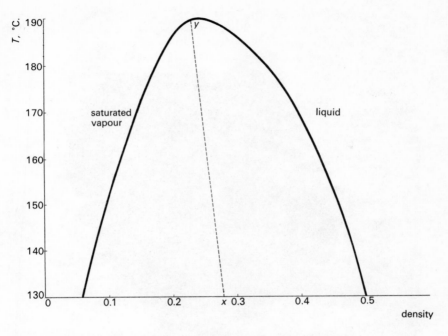

Figure 90.   Density change at the vapour–liquid transition point, for *n*-pentane.

The holes in the liquid may be of molecular size. A molecule adjacent to a vacant space would have 'gas-like' properties, whereas a molecule adjacent to other molecules would experience forces similar to those in a solid. Eyring and Ree now consider the equation of state for a liquid in terms of 'gas-like' and 'solid-like' functions.

Bernal considered the structure of a liquid in terms of the packing of molecules. X-ray evidence had shown the existence of five-fold coordination in liquids. Bernal arranged five spheres around one sphere and then added other spheres in an ordered array. A single point of abnormal coordination in several hundred spheres produced long range disorder in the model of the liquid.

Recently, Bernal concluded that the particles in a liquid are in a close-packed array or *heap* (fig. 91). Each molecule is in contact with many others but not in a regular manner. The coordination numbers are distributed between 5 and 12 with an average at about 8·5. This distribution of coordination is another fundamental structural difference between liquids and solids.

In a close-packed solid, the arrangement is called a *pile* (fig. 92). In contradistinction to the heap, a pile is a regular arrangement and it exhibits the single coordination number of 12, as in metal structures A1 and A3. The density of closest random packing is about 64 per cent of the total volume occupied. For loose packing it is reduced to 60 per cent and for close packing in a crystal it is 74 per cent.

Figure 91. A random close-packed heap of spheres (after Bernal).

A characteristic feature of liquids is their ability to dissolve substances to form an extensive range of homogeneous mixtures. This can be understood by considering the structures formed from equal spheres. If a larger sphere were introduced into the pile, a dislocation would result which would extend throughout the structure. In the heap, however, the effect of a similar impurity is likely to be less structure-breaking since the heap already contains many such dislocations.

Problems

1. The van der Waals constants, a and b, of a gas are related to its critical temperature, T_c°, and critical pressure, P_c, by the equations:

$$a = \frac{27R^2 T_c}{64 P_c}, \qquad b = \frac{RT_c}{8 P_c}.$$

Figure 92. A regular pile of spheres (after Bernal).

Calculate the critical temperature and the critical pressure for each of the gases listed in table 11.

2. Calculate the Joule–Thomson coefficient, and the inversion temperature, for gaseous ammonia.

3. At 25°C. the ratio $\dfrac{C_P}{C_V}$ for water vapour is 1·32. Show that the value for this ratio decreases to about 1·16 at temperatures for which molecular vibration is fully developed.

4. What are the Miller indices of planes in a crystal which makes the following intercepts on the x-, y- and z-axes respectively?

(i)	$\dfrac{a}{2}$	b	$-\dfrac{c}{3}$
(ii)	a	$\|b$	$c/4$
(iii)	$\|a$	$\|b$	$-c$
(iv)	$2a$	$-b$	$\|c$
(v)	$-\dfrac{a}{3}$	$-b$	$\dfrac{c}{2}$
(vi)	$\dfrac{a}{2}$	$2b$	$-\dfrac{3c}{2}$

5. What are the relative densities of atoms on the planes (100), (110), (111) and (032) in a body-centred cubic structure, assuming that the atoms occupy lattice point sites?

6. (a) Show that the volume occupied per sphere of radius r in a hexagonal close packed array of such spheres is $5.66r^3$.

(b) Show that the radius-ratio limits for a 6-coordinated MX ionic structure are 0·732 and 0·414.

7. Using the ionic radii in Appendix B, calculate the length of the unit cell edge in NaBr and in CsCl. Allow 0·333 per cent decrease in the radii for departure from additivity, and in addition, in CsCl, the radii must be increased by 3·00 per cent to account for the change in 6-coordination (Appendix B) to 8-coordination.

8. The latent heats of vaporization, L_T, at the boiling point, $T°$, for benzene, mercury and water are as follows:

	benzene	mercury	water
L_T, kcal. mole^{-1}	7·50	14·20	9·70
T, °K.	353	630	373

Calculate the Trouton's rule constants for these liquids and comment on the results.

Chapter 5
Chemical equilibrium

It is well-known from qualitative analysis* that 'insoluble' barium sulphate can be converted to barium carbonate by boiling it with a solution of sodium carbonate. The fraction of the barium sulphate so converted depends upon the concentration of the sodium carbonate solution: it is a mass effect as pointed out first by Rose in 1842. We shall consider next this effect in detail.

5·1   **The law of mass action**

The equation for the precipitation of silver chloride may be written as in (**5.1**); this

$$Ag^+ + Cl^- \rightarrow AgCl \tag{5.1}$$

reaction is sensibly complete. Not all reactions take place to the same extent, however. The esterification of acetic acid by ethanol is represented by equation (**5.2**); the

$$CH_3CO_2H + EtOH \rightleftharpoons CH_3CO_2Et + H_2O \tag{5.2}$$

double arrow indicates the reversible nature of this reaction. Strictly, the precipitation of silver chloride should be written as in (**5.3**), but the concentrations of Ag^+

$$Ag^+ + Cl^- \rightleftharpoons AgCl \tag{5.3}$$

and of Cl^- ions at equilibrium are small, about 10^{-5} mole litre^{-1}, and the reaction is regarded as complete for practical purposes. The extent of reactions will be studied in this chapter.

$$CH_3CO_2H + EtOH \rightarrow products \tag{5.4}$$

Consider again the reaction expressed by (**5.2**). The forward reaction may be written as in (**5.4**), and takes place at a certain rate. The factors determining the rate of a reaction were enunciated by Guldberg and Waage (1864–67); in modern terminology: *the rate of a chemical reaction is proportional to the product of the activities of the reacting species in the rate-determining step of the reaction at a given temperature.* The concept of a rate-determining step is explained in chapter 8.

The rate of esterification is given by equation (**5.5**), since the rate-determining step is that represented by the equation (**5.4**)

$$R_e \propto a(CH_3CO_2H) \cdot a(EtOH) \tag{5.5}$$

or $$R_e = k_e \cdot a(CH_3CO_2H) \cdot a(EtOH). \tag{5.6}$$

---

* See for example Ladd, M. F. C., and Lee, W. H. (1962), *Qualitative inorganic analysis*, Cleaver-Hume Press.

In a similar way, the rate-determining step of the backward reaction – the ester hydrolysis – is given by the right-to-left reaction in equation (5.2), and the rate of hydrolysis is given by (5.7)

$$R_h = k_h \cdot a(CH_3CO_2Et) \cdot a(H_2O). \tag{5.7}$$

In equations (5.6) and (5.7), k_e and k_h are the rate constants for the forward and the backward reactions, respectively.

During the course of the reaction, the concentrations of acid and alcohol decrease, and the rate of the forward reaction, as expressed by equation (5.6), decreases correspondingly (fig. 93); k_e, the rate constant, remains unchanged at a given temperature.

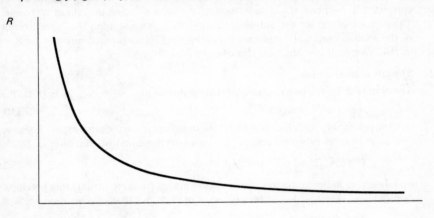

Figure 93.   The variation of the rate of a reaction (R) with time (t).

Thus, the rate of reaction changes with time; it may be defined at any instant by $\dfrac{-d\text{B}}{dt}$, where $-d\text{B}$ represents the decrease in concentration of one of the reacting species B during the time interval dt. Alternatively, the rate of reaction could be represented by $\dfrac{d\text{L}}{dt}$, where L is a product species.

When the system is at equilibrium, both reactions are proceeding with equal rates, i.e. $R_e = R_h$. Thus, we can write

$$K = \frac{k_e}{k_h} = \frac{a(CH_3CO_2Et) \cdot a(H_2O)}{a(CH_3CO_2H) \cdot a(EtOH)}. \tag{5.8}$$

K is the *equilibrium constant*, at a particular temperature.

The activity a of a chemical species is a thermodynamic concept, a full discussion of which will be found in the companion volume, in this series, on thermodynamics. We may note briefly here that the activity is an idealized concentration, so defined that as the concentration (c) tends to zero, the activity (a) tends to c. The activity is regarded as the product of the concentration and the activity coefficient (f), i.e.

$$a = c.f. \tag{5.9}$$

Thus, as c tends to 0, f tends to 1. For our present purpose we shall replace activities by molarities (moles per litre), represented by [ ], choosing examples for discussion in which this can be accepted without appreciable error.

The 'dynamic' approach to equilibrium which we have illustrated is useful in that it introduces the idea of a *mobile* equilibrium, in which both the forward and reverse reactions continue, but with equal rates. The difficulty in this treatment is to decide which are the rate-determining steps of the reactions; nevertheless, the result obtained, equation (5.8), is valid in all cases. The state of equilibrium cannot be determined by the mechanism by which it is established, so that any convenient and plausible mechanism may be assumed *in order to obtain an expression for the equilibrium constant*.

Consider the general reaction of equation (5.10)

$$aA + bB \rightleftharpoons lL + mM. \tag{5.10}$$

If the activity coefficients are taken as unity, the equilibrium constant for this reaction is given by equation (5.11); $[B]^b$ represents the bth power of the molar concentration of species B. Thus $bB = B + B + B \ldots b$ times; hence the product of the concentrations [B] is $[B]^b$, and the power b is introduced.

$$K = \frac{[L]^l[M]^m}{[A]^a[B]^b}. \tag{5.11}$$

This same expression may be derived, without consideration of the mechanism of reaction, by purely thermodynamic arguments – again, this is discussed in the volume on thermodynamics.

5·2   **Criterion for equilibrium**

A system is in equilibrium when the temperature and pressure of the system are constant, and there is no resultant change in the distribution of substances within the system, with the passage of time. Early attempts to explain the tendency for reactions to occur were expressed in terms of the 'affinities' of the reactants. The word affinity has no clear meaning in this context. Van't Hoff (1883) proposed that the tendency for a reaction to occur should be measured by a quantity now called the *free energy decrease* accompanying the reaction. At constant temperature and pressure, a process can take place in an *isolated* system (i.e. one which cannot exchange matter or energy with an adjacent system) only in the direction of a decrease in free energy (i.e. ΔG negative). Whether or not a reaction which has a negative value of ΔG *will* take place at a measurable rate depends upon how readily it may acquire the necessary activation energy; this will be discussed in more detail in the chapter on reaction kinetics. The following example illustrates this point. The standard free energy decrease accompanying the formation of sulphur dioxide from sulphur and oxygen is -72 kcal.

mole^{-1}; this is a spontaneous reaction. However, in order for it to be carried out, the sulphur has to be heated to initiate the reaction. Sulphur does not react in oxygen at 25°C.

The free energy of a system at equilibrium, at a given temperature and pressure, is a minimum; thus, one thermodynamic condition for equilibrium is $(\Delta G)_{T,P} = 0$. The two ideas that $(\Delta G)_{T,P}$ is negative for a spontaneous reaction and that $(\Delta G)_{T,P}$ is zero at equilibrium are of fundamental importance in the study of physical chemistry.

For our further study of equilibria in chemical systems, it will be convenient to make the subdivisions (i) homogeneous equilibria and (ii) heterogeneous equilibria.

5·3   Homogeneous equilibria

Reactions in homogeneous systems take place between molecules or ions and may be represented by chemical equations. Examples of such reactions have been given in (5.1) and (5.2). These systems can be studied by the law of mass action and a number of them will be considered.

5·3·1   *Gaseous systems – no change in the total number of molecules*

Consider the reaction of equation (5.13).

$$H_2 + I_2 \rightleftharpoons 2HI. \tag{5.13}$$

From (5.11), the equilibrium constant for this reaction may be written as in (5.14).

$$K = \frac{[HI]^2}{[H_2][I_2]}. \tag{5.14}$$

Let a mixture of a moles of H_2 and b moles of I_2 be heated until equilibrium is attained, at a given temperature. If y moles of H_2 are used in forming HI, then at equilibrium $(a-y)$ moles of H_2 remain; similarly $(b-y)$ moles of I_2 remain at equilibrium. $2y$ moles of HI are produced; the total number of moles present initially and at equilibrium is the same, $(a+b)$. In considering gaseous reactions, it is possible to express the concentrations by the corresponding partial pressures. Thus, equation (5.14) may be reformulated by (5.15). If P is the total pressure, then the partial pressures of the

$$K_p = \frac{p^2(HI)}{p(H_2) \cdot p(I_2)} \tag{5.15}$$

components of the system at equilibrium are as follows:

$$p(HI) = \frac{2y \cdot P}{(a+b)}; \qquad p(H_2) = \frac{(a-y) \cdot P}{(a+b)}; \qquad p(I_2) = \frac{(b-y) \cdot P}{(a+b)}.$$

(Note that $\sum_i p_i = P$). From equation (5.15), K_p may be written as in (5.16)

$$K_p = \frac{\left\{\frac{2y}{(a+b)}\right\}^2 \cdot P^2}{\left\{\frac{(a-y)}{(a+b)}\right\} \cdot P \cdot \left\{\frac{(b-y)}{(a+b)}\right\} \cdot P}$$

$$= \frac{4y^2}{(a-y)(b-y)}. \tag{5.16}$$

Equation (5.16) contains no term referring to the total pressure or to the volume of the system. The equilibrium composition in a homogeneous gas reaction in which the total number of molecules is constant, is independent of the volume and also of the total pressure. Consequently, the relative amount of HI formed is independent of the total pressure. The data in table 24 relates to a study of the system at 457·6°C.

Table 24   The Hydrogen–Iodine Equilibrium

$10^3[H_2]$, mole litre^{-1}	$10^3[I_2]$, mole litre^{-1}	$10^3[HI]$, mole litre^{-1}	K, equation (5.14)
5·617	0·5936	12·70	48·4*
4·580	0·9733	14·86	49·5*
3·841	1·524	16·87	48·6*
1·433	1·433	10·00	48·7†
1·696	1·696	11·81	48·5†
4·213	4·213	29·43	48·8†

* Equilibrium approached from H_2 and I_2.
† Equilibrium approached from HI.

The values of K, at the given temperature, are sensibly constant although equilibrium was approached from both the 'products' and the 'reactants' sides. Taking 48·8 as an average value for K at 457·6°, and the value 60·8 at 393·8°, the change in heat content (ΔH) of the system over the given temperature range may be calculated with equation (5.17) given here without proof.

$$\log_{10}\frac{(K_p)_{T_2}}{(K_p)_{T_1}} = \frac{-\Delta H}{2\cdot303\,R}\left(\frac{1}{T_2} - \frac{1}{T_1}\right) \tag{5.17}$$

The temperatures T_1 and T_2 are in °K. and R is 1·987 cal. mole^{-1} deg.$^{-1}$. Thus, $\Delta H = -3,785$ cal. mole^{-1} H_2 (or I_2). Note that K decreases with an increase in temperature, corresponding to a negative value of ΔH for the formation of hydrogen iodide; it is exothermic. It is usual to discuss the heat content (enthalpy) change *of the system*; accordingly, heat evolved is equivalent to a decrease in enthalpy (ΔH negative) for the system.

The reaction of nitrogen and oxygen to form nitric oxide under suitable conditions is endothermic, equation (5.18).

$$N_2 + O_2 \rightleftharpoons 2NO \qquad (\Delta H \text{ positive}) \tag{5.18}$$

The equilibrium constant is given by equation (**5.19**) and its variation with tempera-

$$K_p = \frac{p^2(NO)}{p(N_2) \cdot p(O_2)} \tag{5.19}$$

ture has been found experimentally to be represented approximately by equation (**5.20**).

$$\log_{10} K_p = \frac{-9{,}554}{T} + 1 \cdot 09. \tag{5.20}$$

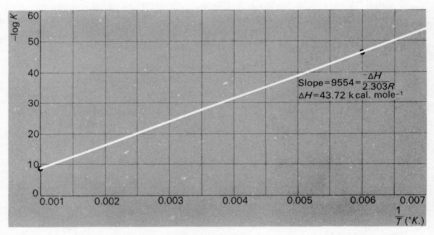

Figure 94.   The variation of K with temperature for the nitric oxide equilibrium.

Comparison with equation (**5.17**) shows that the formation of NO is endothermic. The variation of $\log_{10} K_p$ with $\frac{1}{T}$ is linear and the slope of the line is $\frac{-\Delta H}{2 \cdot 303 \, R}$. Fig. 94 shows the plot of equation (**5.20**) for nitric oxide; ΔH is $43 \cdot 72$ kcal. mole^{-1}.

5·3·2   *Gaseous systems – change in the total number of molecules*

Consider the gas phase reaction between nitrogen and hydrogen:

$$N_2 + 3H_2 \rightleftharpoons 2NH_3. \tag{5.21}$$

This reaction forms the basis of the industrial synthesis of ammonia. Let there be initially a moles of N_2 and b moles of H_2 in the system. At equilibrium, let y moles of nitrogen be converted to ammonia. The number of moles of each species is as follows:

$$
\begin{array}{lll}
 & \textit{Initially} & \textit{Equilibrium} \\
N_2 & a & (a-y) \\
H_2 & b & (b-3y) \\
NH_3 & 0 & 2y.
\end{array}
$$

Number of moles of each species

The total number of moles at equilibrium is $(a+b-2y)$. K_p is given by equation (5.22).

$$
K_p = \frac{p^2(NH_3)}{p(N_2) \cdot p^3(H_2)}. \tag{5.22}
$$

In contrast to the hydrogen–iodine reaction, the equilibrium composition for the nitrogen–hydrogen reaction depends upon the total pressure, P. Substituting the equilibrium concentrations into equation (5.22), K_p may be written as in (5.23).

$$
K_p = \frac{4y^2(a+b-2y)^2}{P^2(a-y)(b-3y)^3}. \tag{5.23}
$$

The data in table 25 relates to the nitrogen–hydrogen reaction.

Table 25   The Nitrogen–Hydrogen Equilibrium $\left(\dfrac{a}{b} = \dfrac{1}{3}\right)$

P(atm.)	10	50	100	10	50	100
T(°K.)	Percentage NH_3 formed			Equilibrium constant, $10^4 K_p$		
673	3·85	15·27	25·12	1·64	1·72	1·90
723	2·0	9·2	16·4	0·43	0·48	0·53
773	1·2	5·6	10·4	0·15	0·15	0·16

Clearly, an increase in pressure increases the yield of ammonia, but an increase in temperature decreases the yield of ammonia. The formation of ammonia is exothermic, unlike that of nitric oxide.

5·4   **The principle of mobile equilibrium**

This principle, usually known as Le Chatelier's principle, was developed independently by Le Chatelier (1885) and Braun (1886). It may be stated: *if a change of temperature, pressure or composition is impressed upon a system at equilibrium, the system will tend to adjust itself so as to nullify the change.*

This principle is a consequence of the second law of thermodynamics and may be applied to all systems at equilibrium. We have illustrated its application with equations (5.13) and (5.21), for example. The effects of changes in pressure and in temperature upon the position of equilibrium should not be confused with their effects upon the rate of reaction (or the rate of attainment of equilibrium). As discussed in the chapter on kinetics, an increase in temperature or pressure almost always increases the rate of a chemical reaction.

We consider again the nitrogen–oxygen and the nitrogen–hydrogen reactions which are re-stated, for convenience, in equations (5.24) and (5.25).

$$N_2 + O_2 \rightleftharpoons 2NO \qquad \Delta H \text{ positive} \qquad (5.24)$$

$$N_2 + 3H_2 \rightleftharpoons 2NH_3 \qquad \Delta H \text{ positive} \qquad (5.25)$$

The nitrogen–oxygen reaction is endothermic but there is no change in the total number of molecules. From the le Chatelier–Braun principle, a change in pressure has no effect upon the position of equilibrium. An increase in temperature increases the rates of both the forward and backward reactions, and favours the formation of nitric oxide, the endothermic reaction; decreasing the temperature retards the rates of both reactions and increases the concentrations of nitrogen and oxygen in the equilibrium mixture. These conclusions are in agreement with the variation of K_p, equation (5.19), with temperature illustrated in fig. 94.

In the equilibrium of equation (5.25), changes both in pressure and in temperature will affect the composition of the equilibrium mixture. Since the reaction is exothermic, an increase in temperature favours the reaction which will absorb heat, that is the decomposition of ammonia into nitrogen and hydrogen; in this case K_p, equation (5.22), decreases with an increase in temperature. An increase in total pressure favours the reaction which is accompanied by a decrease in volume, that is the formation of ammonia. From equation (5.23), if the total pressure (P) is increased, then since K_p is constant at constant temperature, y must increase. These effects have been illustrated quantitatively by the data in table 25.

5·5 **Liquid systems**

The esterification of acetic acid by ethanol was discussed at the beginning of this chapter. We consider it further as an example of a homogeneous liquid equilibrium. If the system is ideal, that is Raoult's law (chapter 6) is applicable, then the activities in equation (5.8) may be replaced by the corresponding number of moles, n, of each species, leading to (5.26).

$$K = \frac{n(CH_3CO_2H) \cdot n(H_2O)}{n(CH_3CO_2H) \cdot n(EtOH)}. \qquad (5.26)$$

If there are present initially a moles of acetic acid and b moles of ethanol, and if y moles of ester are formed, then the concentrations are as follows:

	Number of moles of each species	
	Initially	*Equilibrium*
CH_3CO_2H	a	$a-y$
EtOH	b	$b-y$
CH_3CO_2Et	0	y
H_2O	0	y

Hence, from equation (5.26) the equilibrium constant may be expressed by (5.27).

$$K = \frac{y^2}{(a-y)(b-y)}. \tag{5.27}$$

It should be noted that K may be calculated from (5.26) with the concentration of each species expressed in moles per litre. This leads to the same result for this reaction as there is no change in the total number of molecules. This procedure can be misleading in other types of reactions and should be avoided.

In table 26, data relating to the equilibrium in equation (5.26) have been listed. Certain variations in K may be noted; they could be due to experimental error and to departure from ideal behaviour.

Table 26 The Esterification of Acetic Acid with Ethanol at 100°C

a (moles)	b (moles)	y (moles)	K
1·00	0·19	0·18	4·0
1·00	0·32	0·29	3·9
1·00	0·48	0·41	4·1
1·00	1·00	0·67	4·1
1·00	2·00	0·85	4·2
1·00	8·00	0·97	4·5
			4·1 (Mean)

The equilibrium constant for this reaction has been found to vary little with change in temperature. Hence from the Le Chatelier–Braun principle the heat of reaction should be small; this has been confirmed experimentally.

5·6 Heterogeneous equilibria

The characteristic feature of a heterogeneous system is the presence of two or more *phases*. A phase is a homogeneous and physically distinct part of a system separated from other phases by a definite bounding surface. Ice, liquid water and steam are three phases in the water system. This system has one component; the number of *components* of a system at equilibrium is the smallest number of independently variable constituents required to express the composition of each phase present. Comparing equations (5.28) and (5.29) we note that the water system has one component

$$H_2O \text{ (cryst.)} \rightleftharpoons H_2O \text{ (liq.)} \rightleftharpoons H_2O \text{ (gas)} \tag{5.28}$$

$$CaCO_3 \text{ (cryst.)} \rightleftharpoons CaO \text{ (cryst.)} + CO_2 \text{ (gas)} \tag{5.29}$$

and three phases but the calcium carbonate system has two components and three phases. For if we select certain masses of $CaCO_3$ and CaO in (5.29), the mass of CO_2 is determined by the equation and is not independently variable. In the reaction between iron and steam, equation (5.30), three components must be chosen, Fe, H_2O,

$$3Fe \text{ (cryst.)} + 4H_2O \text{ (gas)} \rightleftharpoons Fe_3O_4 \text{ (cryst.)} + 4H_2 \text{ (gas)} \tag{5.30}$$

and H_2 for example. Again, if ammonium chloride is vaporized in vacuo, the system consists of one component. If ammonia gas or hydrogen chloride gas is admitted to the system, there are two components because the vapour no longer has a composition representative of the solid ammonium chloride in terms of equation (5.31).

$$NH_4Cl\,(cryst.) \rightleftharpoons NH_3\,(gas) + HCl\,(gas).\qquad(5.31)$$

A third quantity is needed to describe a heterogeneous system completely, namely the *number of degrees of freedom*. The number of degrees of freedom of a system is the number of variable properties, such as temperature, pressure and composition, which must be specified in order to define completely each phase in a system at equilibrium. In a system of one component, for example the water system, each phase has two degrees of freedom; it is bivariant. Fig. 95 illustrates the water system.

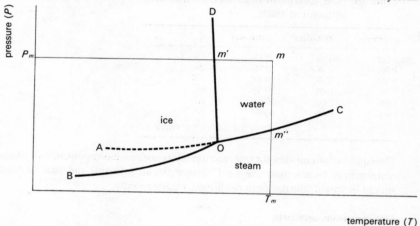

Figure 95. The ice–water–steam equilibrium diagram.

Any given point such as m needs both the temperature and pressure at that point to be stated in order to specify it completely. At points such as m' and m'', water is in equilibrium with ice and steam respectively and we have two-phase systems. It is then necessary to specify only T or P; the system along the lines OA, OB, OC and OD is univariant. The three phases co-exist at the triple point O, and the system is invariant at this point.

The relationship between the number of phases (p), the number of components (c) and the number of degrees of freedom (f) is expressed by the phase rule, equation (5.32).

$$p + f = c + 2.\qquad(5.32)$$

We consider next the equilibrium in equation (5.29) in more detail. The law of mass action is applicable strictly to homogeneous systems but may be extended to heterogeneous systems by assuming that the activity of each solid phase is constant; if the pure solid is chosen as the standard state, its activity is unity. The equilibrium constant for (5.29) is given by equation (5.33).

$$K = \frac{a(CO_2) \cdot a(CaO)}{a(CaCO_3)}. \tag{5.33}$$

Assuming the standard state for the solids, K may be written as in (**5.34**); the activity of carbon dioxide may be replaced by its partial pressure without appreciable error.

$$K = a(CO_2) = p(CO_2). \tag{5.34}$$

The constancy of the activity of a solid at any given temperature results from its constant vapour pressure; it is independent of the number of moles of solid present. An alternative point of view is to imagine that the heterogeneous reaction takes place homogeneously in the gas phase. Thus, we are led to equation (**5.35**).

$$K = \frac{p(CaO) \cdot p(CO_2)}{p(CaCO_3)}. \tag{5.35}$$

The vapours of $CaCO_3$ and of CaO are in equilibrium with the solids $CaCO_3$ and CaO respectively. Hence $p(CaCO_3)$ and $p(CaO)$ are constant and independent of the amounts of solids present. Again, equation (**5.34**) follows. The equilibrium dissociation pressure of carbon dioxide in this system varies from about 1 mm. at 800°K. to about 3000 mm. at 1300°K. Since ΔH is positive for this reaction, an increase in temperature increases the percentage decomposition of calcium carbonate at equilibrium.

The activity of a solid in contact with a liquid phase saturated with the solid is a constant at a given temperature. Consider the reaction between barium sulphate and sodium carbonate solution, with which we began this chapter, given by equation (**5.36**).

$$BaSO_4 \text{ (cryst.)} + CO_3^{2-} \text{ (aq.)} \rightleftharpoons BaCO_3 \text{ (cryst.)} + SO_4^{2-} \text{ (aq.)} \tag{5.36}$$

The terms in the expression for the equilibrium constant of this reaction which involve the solids may be omitted and assuming that molar concentrations may replace activities, we obtain (**5.37**).

$$K = \frac{[SO_4^{2-}]}{[CO_3^{2-}]}. \tag{5.37}$$

The data in table 27 relate to equilibrium (**5.36**); the figures in column 2 refer to the concentrations of added sodium sulphate. The agreement in the values of K for

Table 27   The Barium Sulphate–Sodium Carbonate
Equilibrium at 25°C.

| Initial concentrations (mole l.$^{-1}$) | | Equilibrium concentrations (mole l.$^{-1}$) | | |
$[CO_3^{2-}]$	$[SO_4^{2-}]$	$[CO_3^{2-}]$	$[SO_4^{2-}]$	K
0·200	0·000	0·0395	0·161	4·07
0·250	0·000	0·050	0·200	4·00
0·350	0·000	0·072	0·278	3·86
0·250	0·025	0·055	0·220	4·00
0·300	0·025	0·066	0·259	3·93
0·200	0·050	0·050	0·200	4·00

different concentrations is very good bearing in mind the approximations made in the treatment. Closely related systems lead next to a discussion on ionic equilibria.

5·7 Ionic equilibria

We have discussed homogeneous equilibria in terms of the law of mass action and the conditions under which heterogeneous equilibria also may be interpreted in the same terms. These two divisions will not be made explicitly in the following study of ionic equilibria.

Consider again equation (5.1). Silver chloride is a sparingly soluble electrolyte. 'Sparingly soluble' is a term difficult to define exactly; it can be applied to those substances the concentrations of which at saturation are so low that their activities may be replaced by molar concentrations without sensible error. This replacement is permissible usually for ionic concentrations of 10^{-4} mole $l.^{-1}$, or less. Silver chloride in saturated solution may be thought of in terms of equation (5.38). If in a litre of saturated solution, s moles of AgCl dissociates, then s moles of each of the species Ag^+ and Cl^- are formed.

$$AgCl \rightleftharpoons Ag^+ + Cl^-. \tag{5.38}$$
(solid)   (ions in saturated solution)

The equilibrium constant is given by (5.39):

$$K = \frac{a(Ag^+)a(Cl^-)}{a(AgCl)} \tag{5.39}$$

as discussed above, $a(AgCl)$ is a constant and the ionic activities may be replaced by their molar concentrations, leading to equation (5.40):

$$K' = S = [Ag^+][Cl^-] \tag{5.40}$$

S is the *solubility product* of silver chloride; it is the product of the molar concentrations of the ions at saturation and at a given temperature, for such sparingly soluble electrolytes. The general case of an electrolyte A_xB_y is represented by equation (5.41).

$$A_xB_y \rightleftharpoons xA^{y+} + yB^{x-} \tag{5.41}$$
(solid)   (ions in saturated solution)

The equation for S, developed as before, is (5.42), if A_xB_y is sparingly soluble.

$$S(A_xB_y) = [A^{y+}]^x[B^{x-}]^y \tag{5.42}$$

If the solubility of the electrolyte is s mole $l.^{-1}$, then at equilibrium there are $x . s$ gram-ion $l.^{-1}$ of A^{y+} and $y . s$ gram-ion $l.^{-1}$ of B^{x-}. Substituting these concentrations into equation (5.42) we obtain (5.43).

$$S(A_xB_y) = (x . s)^x(y . s)^y$$
$$= (x^x . y^y)s^{(x+y)} \tag{5.43}$$

The solubility is thus expressed by (5.44).

$$s(A_xB_y) = \left\{\frac{1}{x^x \cdot y^y} \cdot S(A_xB_y)\right\}^{\frac{1}{x+y}} \tag{5.44}$$

In the case of silver chloride, $x = y = 1$ and $s(AgCl) = \sqrt{[S(AgCl)]}$. If $S(AgCl)$ is 1.7×10^{-10} at 25°C., $s = 1.3 \times 10^{-5}$ mole l.$^{-1}$ The formula weight of silver chloride is 143.3 and thus $s(AgCl)$ may be stated as 0.0019 g. l.$^{-1}$, at 25°C.

The so-called 'common-ion effect' is an application of the solubility product principle and does not really merit a separate title. Several good examples of this effect are afforded by classical qualitative analysis. Consider the separation of the ions Fe^{3+}, Al^{3+} and Cr^{3+} (group III). The hydroxides of the cations of groups III to V and of Mg can be precipitated by ammonia:

$$Al^{3+} + 3OH^- \rightleftharpoons Al(OH)_3 \tag{5.45}$$

$$Mg^{2+} + 2OH^- \rightleftharpoons Mg(OH)_2. \tag{5.46}$$

The equilibrium between ammonia and water is written as in equation (5.47).

$$NH_3 + H_2O \rightleftharpoons NH_4^+ + OH^- \tag{5.47}$$

Nuclear magnetic resonance studies of the rate of isotope exchange in the NH_4^+ ion suggest that, in water, the ammonia molecule is hydrogen-bonded to three water molecules; there is no evidence in favour of the existence of 'NH_4OH'. The equilibrium constant for equation (5.47) – the dissociation constant (K_b) for the base – is given by (5.48).

$$K_b = \frac{[NH_4^+][OH^-]}{[NH_3]} \tag{5.48}$$

Since K_b is constant, at a given temperature, an increase in the concentration of ammonium ions produces a corresponding decrease in the concentration of hydroxyl ions. In these circumstances, there are insufficient hydroxyl ions to precipitate the hydroxides of the cations of groups IV and V and of magnesium. The hydroxides of the cations of group III are precipitated under these conditions; their solubility products are lower – see Appendix C.

In considering solubility product, we point out two common errors. The use of sodium chloride and of similar electrolytes of high solubility to demonstrate the solubility product principle is incorrect. From equation (5.49),

$$NaCl \rightleftharpoons Na^+ + Cl^- \tag{5.49}$$
(solid)   (ions in saturated solution)

we can formulate the equilibrium constant for this reaction in terms of activities, equation (5.50).

$$K = \frac{a(Na^+) \cdot a(Cl^-)}{a(NaCl)} \tag{5.50}$$

This equation is thermodynamically exact; its application requires a knowledge of the activities of the species at saturation. The solubility of sodium chloride is about 6 mole l.$^{-1}$; at this concentration it is not permissible to replace activities by concentrations.

The common-ion effect is often invoked to explain chemical phenomena in an oversimplified manner. For example, the action of hydrogen chloride gas upon saturated sodium chloride solution is well-known; sodium chloride is precipitated. This is a poor example of common-ion action; indeed, common-ion action may hardly apply at all. The same precipitation of sodium chloride can be brought about by passing hydrogen bromide gas or hydrogen nitrate gas into the solution. The precipitation is due mainly to the hydration of the hydrogen ion. The ions H^+ and Na^+ are competing for water molecules: the free energy of hydration* of a hydrogen ion is about four times greater than that for a sodium ion. Thus, hydrogen ions are solvated by water molecules at the expense of the sodium chloride which is then precipitated.

5·7·1   *Ionic strength*

Equations such as (**5.39**) suggest that the solubility of electrolytes is affected only by the addition of ions which are common to the salt under examination. The data for silver bromate recorded in table 28 show that this is not true. Evidently, the solubility

Table 28   The Solubility of Silver Bromate in the Presence of Potassium Nitrate, at 25°C.

$[KNO_3]$	$[AgBrO_3]$	I
0·0000	0·0083	0·0083
0·0260	0·0090	0·0350
0·0470	0·0095	0·0565
0·1000	0·0103	0·1103
0·1394	0·0106	0·1500

of silver bromate increases with the increase in concentration of potassium nitrate. Using equation (**5.9**) we can write the equilibrium constant for the silver bromate system as in (**5.51**).

$$K = \frac{a(Ag^+)a(BrO_3^-)}{a(AgBrO_3)} = \frac{[Ag^+][BrO_3^-] \cdot f(Ag^+)f(BrO_3^-)}{[AgBrO_3] \cdot f(AgBrO_3)}. \tag{5.51}$$

Experimentally, we can determine only the product $f_+ f_-$ and the mean ionic activity coefficient $f_\pm$ is given by equation (**5.52**).

$$f_\pm = \sqrt{f_+ f_-} \tag{5.52}$$

* The free energy of hydration of an ion is the decrease in free energy per g-ion for the process: M^{n+} (gas) + water → M^{n+} (hydrated ions).

We have defined the activity of a solid as unity; hence equation (5.51) becomes (5.53).

$$K = [Ag^+][BrO_3^-]f_\pm^2 \tag{5.53}$$

The value of $f_\pm$ depends upon the total *ionic strength* I of the solution, defined by equation (5.54).

$$I = \tfrac{1}{2}\sum_i c_i z_i^2. \tag{5.54}$$

c_i is the molar concentration of the ith ion of charge z_i. Thus, for potassium nitrate (and any other 1 : 1 electrolyte) the ionic strength of the solution is given by (5.55).

$$I = \tfrac{1}{2}[c(K^+)+c(NO_3^-)] = c(KNO_3). \tag{5.55}$$

The value of $f_\pm$ can be approximated for very dilute solutions by the Debye–Hückel equation, (5.56).

$$\log_{10}f_\pm = -0.509z_+z_-\sqrt{I}. \tag{5.56}$$

For the silver bromate–potassium nitrate system the relevant values of I are listed in table 28. Using equations (5.55) and (5.56), the data of table 29 were obtained. Since $f_\pm$ decreases with increasing I, and K is approximately constant at a given tempera-

Table 29 Mean Ionic Activity Coefficients and K for the System Silver Bromate–Potassium Nitrate at 25°C.

[KNO$_3$]	$\sqrt{I}$	z_+z_-	10^5S	$f_\pm$(5.56)	$f_\pm$(5.57)	10^5K^*
0·000	0·0911	1	6·89	0·899	0·912	5·72
0·0260	0·1871	1	8·14	0·804	0·845	5·81
0·0470	0·2377	1	9·03	0·757	0·817	5·90
0·1000	0·3321	1	10·6	0·678	0·778	6·32
0·1394	0·3873	1	11·3	0·635	0·764	6·40

* K calculated from (5.53), using $f_\pm$ (5.57).

ture, the solubility of silver bromate increases with increasing concentration of potassium nitrate, an unexpected result. The effect of the ionic strength of the saturated solution of silver bromate is evident at $c(KNO_3) = 0$. For salts of lower solubility than silver bromate, this effect is correspondingly less important. The solubility of silver chloride is about 1.3×10^{-5} mole l.$^{-1}$; for saturated silver chloride, $f_\pm = 0.996$. This demonstrates that as $c \to 0$, so $f_\pm \to 1$, as already remarked. The values of $f_\pm$ may be calculated by equation (5.56) for concentrations up to about 0·005 mole l.$^{-1}$ The calculation may be extended to concentrations up to 0·1 molar by using Davies's empirical equation (5.57).

$$\log_{10}f_\pm = -0.50z_+z_-\left\{\frac{\sqrt{I}}{1+\sqrt{I}}-0.3I\right\} \tag{5.57}$$

We consider next a system involving two sparingly soluble electrolytes, with an ion in common. A practical example is afforded by the Mohr titration, in which Cl$^-$

ions are determined by titration with Ag^+, using CrO_4^{2-} as an indicator, in neutral solution.

$$AgCl \rightleftharpoons Ag^+ + Cl^- \qquad S(AgCl) = 1\cdot7 \times 10^{-10} \qquad (5.58)$$

$$Ag_2CrO_4 \rightleftharpoons 2Ag^+ + CrO_4^{2-} \qquad S(Ag_2CrO_4) = 1\cdot9 \times 10^{-12}. \qquad (5.59)$$

Although the solubility product of silver chromate is the lower, silver chloride is precipitated first – its solubility is the lower:

$$s(AgCl) = \sqrt{[S(AgCl)]} = 1\cdot3 \times 10^{-5} \text{ molar}$$
$$= 1\cdot9 \times 10^{-3} \text{ g l.}^{-1}$$

$$s(Ag_2CrO_4) = \left\{ \frac{S(Ag_2CrO_4)}{4} \right\}^{\frac{1}{3}} = 7\cdot5 \times 10^{-5} \text{ molar}$$
$$= 2\cdot5 \times 10^{-2} \text{ g l.}^{-1}$$

Both of the equilibria in equations (5.58) and (5.59) are satisfied simultaneously in the analytical system. The concentration of silver ion is given by (5.60).

$$[Ag^+] = \frac{S(AgCl)}{[Cl^-]} = \left\{ \frac{S(Ag_2CrO_4)}{[CrO_4^{2-}]} \right\}^{\frac{1}{3}} \qquad (5.60)$$

Thus, no silver chromate will be precipitated until $[Cl^-] = 1\cdot2 \times 10^{-4}. \sqrt{[CrO_4^{2-}]}$; if, as usual, $[CrO_4^{2-}] = 10^{-2}$ approximately, the precipitation of silver chloride is quantitatively complete.

Gross inaccuracy would result if the titration were carried out in the presence of acid. Further equilibria must then be considered:

$$CrO_4^{2-} + H^+ \rightleftharpoons HCrO_4^- \qquad (5.61)$$

$$2HCrO_4^- \rightleftharpoons H_2O + Cr_2O_7^{2-} \qquad (5.62)$$

The formation of the ions $HCrO_4^-$ and $Cr_2O_7^{2-}$ in the presence of H^+ ions cause more Ag_2CrO_4 to dissociate, since $S(Ag_2CrO_4)$ is constant, at a given temperature. This is the rationale for the statement that 'all dichromates are soluble'. The enhancement of the solubilities of silver acetate by nitric acid and of barium sulphate by sulphuric acid are due to the establishment of similar equilibria.

If the solubility of silver chloride in varying concentrations of chloride ion is measured, it will be found that the solubility decreases at first, then passes through a minimum and finally increases, with increasing $[Cl^-]$, fig. 96. Common-ion action alone, curve I, predicts that $s \propto \dfrac{1}{[Cl^-]}$. The inclusion of the mean ionic activity coefficient, calculated from the ionic strength using equations (5.56) and (5.57), into the calculation of s produces curve II with a decrease in slope at the higher concentrations of Cl^-; the effect of the common ion cannot be overcome by ionic strength corrections. Neither curve I nor curve II represents the measured solubility, curve III. A further explanation could be the formation of complex ions, in which silver ions are taken into solution as an anionic complex, equation (5.63).

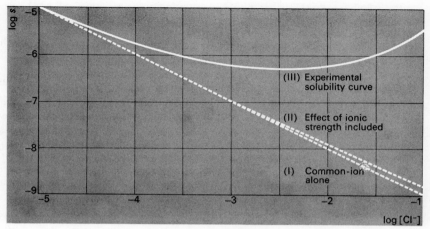

Figure 96. The solubility of AgCl in varying concentrations of Cl⁻ ion.

$$Ag^+ + 2Cl^- \rightleftharpoons \{AgCl_2\}^-. \tag{5.63}$$

There is no reason to suppose that molecules of AgCl are formed in solution.

5.7.2 *Acid–base equilibria*

Water is ionized to a small but finite extent in accordance with equation (5.64).

$$2H_2O \rightleftharpoons H_3O^+ + OH^- \tag{5.64}$$

The hydrogen ion is always hydrated by water, so that H_3O^+ is a more precise designation than H^+. For general purposes, however, the simpler designation is acceptable, and the equilibrium constant is given by equation (5.65).

$$K = \frac{a(H^+) \cdot a(OH^-)}{a(H_2O)}. \tag{5.65}$$

In dilute solutions, water is in excess, and its concentration (and activity) does not change appreciably with change of solute concentration; we may write equation (5.66),

$$K \cdot [H_2O] = [H^+][OH^-] \tag{5.66}$$

in which $[H_2O]$ is approximately $55 \cdot 6$ mole l.$^{-1}$, at 25°C. Under these conditions, $K = 1 \cdot 80 \times 10^{-16}$ and thus $K[H_2O] = 1 \cdot 00 \times 10^{-14}$. This quantity is known as the ionic product for water and is expressed by:

$$K_w(25°C.) = [H^+][OH^-] = 1 \cdot 00 \times 10^{-14}. \tag{5.67}$$

From (5.64), $[H^+] = [OH^-]$ and from (5.67), each is equal to 10^{-7}.

It is usual to express $[H^+]$ and $[OH^-]$ according to the pH scale. pH may be defined by equation (5.68).

$$pH = -\log_{10}[H^+]; \quad pOH = -\log_{10}[OH^-] \tag{5.68}$$

We adopt the notation pK, defined in a similar manner by equation (5.69).

$$pK = -\log_{10} K. \tag{5.69}$$

An aqueous solution having a pH of 7 at 25°C. is neutral, i.e. $[H^+] = [OH^-]$; if pH > 7, the solution is alkaline $- [OH^-] > [H^+] -$ and if pH < 7, the solution is acid $- [H^+] > [OH^-]$. Pure water is a neutral solution; its pH is 7, which is also its pOH. From equation (5.67) we can write (5.70), for dilute aqueous solutions.

$$pH + pOH = 14. \tag{5.70}$$

This expresses the electroneutrality, or charge balance, of aqueous solutions. In a general form, this concept may be formulated by equation (5.71).

$$a[A^{a+}] + b[B^{b+}] + c[C^{c+}] + \ldots = l[L^{l-}] + m[M^{m-}] + n[N^{n-}] + \ldots \tag{5.71}$$

It is convenient to classify electrolytes as *strong* or *weak*. A strong electrolyte is highly dissociated in dilute solution, for example HCl, Na_2SO_4 or NH_4NO_3. A weak electrolyte is only slightly dissociated in solution, for example HF, CH_3CO_2H, NH_3 or C_5H_5N (pyridine). Most, but not all, salts are strong electrolytes; $HgCl_2$ is one of the exceptions. It is noteworthy that the solvent is important in determining the strength of an electrolyte. Thus, HCl is a strong electrolyte in water but a weak electrolyte in glacial acetic acid. This is due to the very different abilities of the two solvents to accept a proton.

$$HCl + H_2O \rightleftharpoons H_3O^+ + Cl^- \tag{5.72}$$

$$HCl + CH_3CO_2H \rightleftharpoons CH_3CO_2H_2^+ + Cl^-. \tag{5.73}$$

The terms strong and weak are not synonymous with concentrated and dilute respectively, and should not be so used.

We consider next the relationship between the pH of a strong acid or a strong base and its stoichiometric concentration. If we assume complete dissociation of an acid in water, then if its concentration is c mole $l.^{-1}$, the concentration of H^+ due to the added acid is also c mole $l.^{-1}$ The following equations may be set up:

$$[H^+][OH^-] = K_w \tag{5.74}$$

$$[H^+]_{total} = [X^-] + [OH^-] \text{ (electroneutrality)} \tag{5.75}$$

$$= c + [OH^-]. \tag{5.76}$$

From equations (5.74) and (5.76) we obtain (5.77) and (5.78):

$$[H^+]^2 - c[H^+] - K_w = 0 \tag{5.77}$$

$$[H^+] = \frac{c}{2} \pm \sqrt{\left\{ \left(\frac{c}{2} \right)^2 + K_w \right\}}. \tag{5.78}$$

If $c^2 \gg 10^{-14}$, then K_w in equation (5.78) is negligible with respect to $\left(\dfrac{c}{2}\right)^2$, so that

$$[H^+] = c \tag{5.79}$$

$$pH = -\log_{10} c \tag{5.80}$$

$[H^+]$ is given by equation (5.79) and pH by (5.80). If $c^2 \ll 10^{-14}$, then $[H^+]$ is given by equation (5.81) and pH by (5.82). Fig. 97 shows the variation of pH with $[H^+]$

$$[H^+] = \sqrt{K_w} \tag{5.81}$$

$$pH = \tfrac{1}{2} pK_w. \tag{5.82}$$

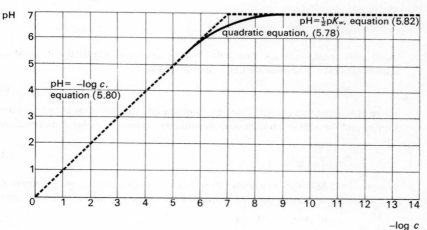

Figure 97.   pH of a strong acid as a function of concentration.

for a strong acid. It is convenient to write equations (5.77) in the form of (5.83) in order

$$c = [H^+] - \frac{K_w}{[H^+]} \tag{5.83}$$

to obtain this curve. The graph shows clearly that in calculating the pH of a strong acid, the contribution to the total hydrogen ion concentration from the ionization of water may be neglected until c is less than about 10^{-6} mole l.$^{-1}$

Examples
   (i) Calculate the pH for 0·005 N HCl.

   $c = 0.005$, assuming complete dissociation.

   From equation (5.68)
   pH $= -\log_{10} 0.005 = \overline{3}.6990 = -2.3010$
   pH $= 2.30.$

(ii) Calculate the pH for 10^{-7} molar nitric acid.
From equation (**4.78**)

$$[H^+] = 0.5 \times 10^{-7} \pm \sqrt{(0.25 \times 10^{-14} + 1.00 \times 10^{-14})}$$
$$= 1.62 \times 10^{-7} \text{ (the negative root was ignored)}$$
$$\underline{pH = 6.79.}$$

(iii) Calculate the pH for 0.01 N NaOH, assuming complete dissociation.

$$[OH^-] = 0.01$$

$$[H^+] = \frac{K_w}{[OH^-]} = 10^{-12}$$

$$\underline{pH = 12.00.}$$

Weak acids, weak bases and their salts. A weak acid is incompletely dissociated; its equilibrium may be represented by equation (**5.84**),

$$HA \rightleftharpoons H^+ + A^- \tag{5.84}$$

where HA is the weak acid. Since the acid is weak, the law of mass action may be applied and the equilibrium constant formulated in terms of molar concentrations

$$K_a = \frac{[H^+][A^-]}{[HA]} \tag{5.85}$$

by equation (**5.85**). K_a is the dissociation constant of the acid, at a given temperature. The following equations may be written for an aqueous solution of a weak acid:

$$K_a[HA] = [H^+][A^-] \tag{5.86}$$

$$K_w = [H^+][OH^-] \tag{5.87}$$

$$[H^+] = [A^-] + [OH^-] \text{ (electroneutrality)} \tag{5.88}$$

$$[A^-] + [HA] = c \text{ (mass balance).} \tag{5.89}$$

c is the total molar concentration of HA considered. The general solution is given by equation (**5.90**). Certain simplifying assumptions can be made for this system. Since

$$[H^+] = \frac{cK_a}{[H^+] + K_a} + \frac{K_w}{[H^+]} \tag{5.90}$$

the solution is acidic, $[OH^-]$ is very much less than $[A^-]$. Hence from equations (**5.88**) and (**5.86**), (**5.91**) and (**5.92**) may be derived.

$$[H^+] = [A^-] \tag{5.91}$$

$$K_a = \frac{[H^+]^2}{c - [H^+]} \tag{5.92}$$

If further, we assume that because the acid is weak, $[H^+]$ is small compared with c, then from (**5.92**) we derive equations (**5.93**) and (**5.94**).

$$\sqrt{K_a c} = [\text{H}^+] \tag{5.93}$$

$$\text{pH} = \tfrac{1}{2}\text{p}K_a - \tfrac{1}{2}\log_{10} c \tag{5.94}$$

For acetic acid, $K_a = 1\cdot8 \times 10^{-5}$ and $\text{p}K_a$ is $4\cdot75$. The variation of pH with c is illustrated by fig. 98. In order to calculate these curves, equation (5.90) and (5.92) are conveniently re-cast in terms of c, in the manner of (5.83). The circumstances requiring

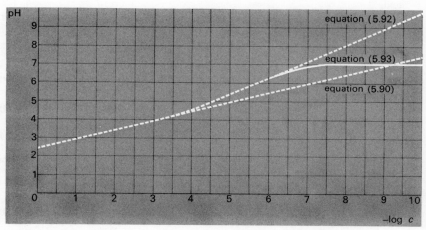

Figure 98.   Variation of pH of acetic acid with acid concentration (c).

the accurate formulation of the dependence of pH upon concentration can be appreciated readily from the curves.

The system weak base–water can be treated in a similar manner. We shall consider ammonia and pyridine (Py) as examples of weak bases. The general base can be

$$\text{NH}_3 + \text{H}_2\text{O} \rightleftharpoons \text{NH}_4^+ + \text{OH}^- \tag{5.95}$$

$$\text{Py} + \text{H}_2\text{O} \rightleftharpoons \text{PyH}^+ + \text{OH}^-. \tag{5.96}$$

represented by equation (5.97). Equations for $[\text{OH}^-]$ and $[\text{H}^+]$, corresponding to

$$\text{B} + \text{H}_2\text{O} \rightleftharpoons \text{BH}^+ + \text{OH}^-. \tag{5.97}$$

(5.90), (5.92) and (5.93) can be derived readily. Considering $0\cdot1$ molar ammonia solution, we may use (5.98) to deduce that the pH of the solution is $11\cdot13$. The more

$$[\text{OH}^-]^2 = 0\cdot1\, K_b. \tag{5.98}$$

accurate equation (5.99) leads to a pH of $11\cdot12$ for the same solution of concentration

$$K_b = \frac{[\text{OH}^-]^2}{c - [\text{OH}^-]} \tag{5.99}$$

$c = 0\cdot1$ mole l.$^{-1}$

151   **Chemical equilibrium**

Salt hydrolysis. The salts of a strong base and a weak acid and of a strong acid and a weak base are both hydrolyzed by water and the resulting solutions are alkaline

$$A^- + H_2O \rightleftharpoons HA + OH^- \tag{5.100}$$

$$BH^+ + H_2O \rightleftharpoons B + H_3O^+ \tag{5.101}$$

and acidic respectively. Evidently, A^- acts as a weak base and BH^+ acts as a weak acid.

The Brønsted–Lowry definition of acids and bases incorporates this more general implication: *an acid is a proton donor and a base is a proton acceptor.* The removal of a proton from any acid produces its conjugate base; e.g. the A^- species is the conjugate base of the acid HA. Consider the equilibrium in equation (5.102):

$$NH_4^+ + H_2O \rightleftharpoons NH_3 + H_3O^+ \tag{5.102}$$

$$K = \frac{[NH_3][H_3O^+]}{[NH_4^+][H_2O]}. \tag{5.103}$$

The equilibrium constant, given by equation (5.103), may be related to K_w and K_b by multiplying the right-hand side of equation (5.103) by $\dfrac{[OH^-]}{[OH^-]}$. From equations (5.48) and (5.67) we can deduce (5.104).

$$K_h = K[H_2O] = \frac{[NH_3][H_2O][H^+][OH^-]}{[NH_4^+][OH^-]} = \frac{K_w}{K_b} \tag{5.104}$$

K_h has been called the hydrolysis constant of the 'acid' NH_4^+. In a similar manner the hydrolysis constant of the 'base' Ac^- (acetate), equation (5.105), is given by (5.106).

$$Ac^- + H_2O \rightleftharpoons HAc + OH^- \tag{5.105}$$

$$K_h = \frac{K_w}{K_a}. \tag{5.106}$$

Example. The pK_a of formic acid (HFo) is 3·75. What is the pH of a 0·001 molar solution of sodium formate?

$$Fo^- + H_2O \rightleftharpoons HFo + OH^- \tag{5.107}$$

We can construct five equations to represent this system:

$$K_a[HFo] = [H^+][Fo^-] \tag{5.108}$$

$$K_w = [H^+][OH^-] \tag{5.109}$$

$$[Na^+] = 0·001 \tag{5.110}$$

$$[Fo^-] + [HFo] = 0·001 \text{ (mass balance)} \tag{5.111}$$

$$[H^+] + [Na^+] = [OH^-] + [Fo^-] \quad \text{(electroneutrality).} \tag{5.112}$$

From (**5.110**) to (**5.112**), the equation (**5.113**) may be written. Certain simplifications

$$[H^+]+[HFo] = [OH^-] \tag{5.113}$$

may be introduced: since the solution is basic, $[H^+]$ is very much less than $[Fo^-]$. Hence, from equation (**5.113**) we may write (**5.114**). Again the concentration of HFo

$$[HFo] = [OH^-]. \tag{5.114}$$

is very much less than that of Fo^-, and thus, from (**5.111**) we may equate $[Fo^-]$ to 0·001. Finally, from equation (**5.107**) we formulate (**5.115**):

$$K_h = \frac{K_w}{K_a} = K[H_2O] = \frac{[H^+][OH^-][HFo]}{[H^+][Fo^-]} \tag{5.115}$$

$$K_h = \frac{[OH^-]^2}{0\cdot001}. \tag{5.116}$$

$$pK_w - pK_a = 2pOH + \log_{10}(0\cdot001)$$

$$pH = 14 - (7\cdot00 - 1\cdot875 + 1\cdot5)$$

$$= 7\cdot37(5).$$

The full calculation of the pH of this system is obtained by solving equations (**5.108**) to (**5.112**).

$$c = \frac{K_a K_w}{[H^+]^2} - [H^+] + \frac{K_w}{[H^+]} - K_a \tag{5.117}$$

If $[H^+] \ll \dfrac{K_a K_w}{[H^+]^2}$, we can rewrite (**5.117**) as a quadratic in $[H^+]$:

$$(c + K_a)[H^+]^2 - K_w[H^+] - K_a K_w = 0 \tag{5.118}$$

which may be solved for $[H^+]$. Hence, pH $= 7\cdot01(2)$.

5·7·3   *Buffer solutions*

A study of weak electrolytes leads to a consideration of buffer solutions. In many chemical and biological investigations, it is often necessary to maintain a nearly constant pH during the course of a reaction which may produce, or may utilize, hydrogen ions. In these circumstances, the reaction is carried out in a buffer solution. A buffer solution contains a weak base and its salt, or a weak acid and its salt. In terms of the Brønsted–Lowry definition of acid and base, we conclude that a buffer solution is a mixture of a weak acid and its conjugate base or of a weak base and its conjugate acid. Two well-known examples are the systems NH_4^+–NH_3 and HAc–Ac^-. Buffer solutions permit the addition of small amounts of strong acid or strong base to them with only very slight change in the pH of the mixture. We consider first the system HAc–Ac^-.

Let the solution have the concentration 0·05 molar in both acetic acid and sodium acetate; $K_a = 1\cdot8 \times 10^{-5}$. Equations similar to (**5.108**) to (**5.112**) may be set up for this system. Again, we may make certain simplifications leading to the equations (5.119) to (5.121).

$$[Ac^-] = [HAc] = 0\cdot05 \tag{5.119}$$

$$[H^+] = K_a = 1\cdot8 \times 10^{-5} \tag{5.120}$$

$$pH = pK_a = 4\cdot74(5) \tag{5.121}$$

Consider next the addition of 1 ml. of N HCl to 100 ml. of the buffer solution. H^+ ions from the HCl will react with Ac^- ions from the dissociated sodium acetate to give HAc (non-ionized). Since $0\cdot001$ g-ion of H^+ is added the values of $[Ac^-]$ and $[HAc]$ are decreased and increased respectively by $0\cdot001$ mole. In addition the volume of solution has increased from 100 ml. to 101 ml. The new concentrations of Ac^- and HAc are given by equations (5.122) and (5.123).

$$[Ac^-] = (0\cdot050 - 0\cdot001) \times \frac{100}{101} = 0\cdot0485 \tag{5.122}$$

$$[HAc] = (0\cdot050 + 0\cdot001) \times \frac{100}{101} = 0\cdot0504. \tag{5.123}$$

Using equation (5.85), the pH of the solution is given by:

$$pH = pK_a - \log_{10}\frac{0\cdot0504}{0\cdot0485} = 4\cdot62(8). \tag{5.124}$$

We see that $\Delta pH = -0\cdot017$ units. If there had been no buffer action, the pH would have been that of a solution of $0\cdot001$ mole of HCl in 101 ml., that is of $0\cdot0099$ molar and the pH = 2. Equation (5.124) may be generalized as (5.125);

$$pH = pK_a + \log_{10}\frac{[\text{salt}]}{[\text{acid}]} \tag{5.125}$$

in this form it is often known as Henderson's equation. For the system BH^+-B, a similar equation, (5.126), may be derived leading to (5.127).

$$pOH = pK_b + \log_{10}\frac{[\text{salt}]}{[\text{base}]} \tag{5.126}$$

$$pH = pK_w - pK_b - \log_{10}\frac{[\text{salt}]}{[\text{base}]} \tag{5.127}$$

The simple equations apply well, within the hydrogen ion concentration ranges 10^{-3} to 10^{-6} and 10^{-8} to 10^{-11} respectively. Equation (5.125), for example, suggests that the pH is independent of concentration as long as the ratio [salt]/[acid] is a constant. This cannot be true at extreme dilution, since pH $\rightarrow 7\cdot00$ as the concentrations tend to zero.

The Van Slyke buffer index. The capacity of a buffer to resist the addition of strong acid or strong base can be measured by the amount of strong acid or strong base required to produce a given change in pH. The Van Slyke *buffer index* β is given by equation (5.128).

$$\beta = -\frac{dC_a}{d\text{pH}} = \frac{dC_b}{d\text{pH}} \tag{5.128}$$

The addition of C_a mole of strong acid to one litre of buffer solution decreases the pH and increases the acid component of the system by dC_a mole at the expense of the conjugate base. Without proof here, the equation for β developed in terms of a weak acid and its salt is given by (5.129).

$$\beta = 2\cdot303\left\{\frac{K_w}{[\text{H}^+]} + [\text{H}^+] + \frac{cK_a[\text{H}^+]}{(K_a + [\text{H}^+])^2}\right\} \tag{5.129}$$

The first two terms on the right-hand side of equation (5.129) are due to the buffering action of water; the third term is due to the acid–conjugate base pair. In the previous example of a buffer system, we selected HAc and NaAc of the same concentration, 0·05 molar. Thus, c in equation (5.129), which represents the total acetate concentration is 0·1 molar. Hence $\beta = -\frac{dC_a}{d\text{pH}} = -\frac{\Delta C_a}{\Delta\text{pH}}$. From (5.129), $\beta = 0\cdot576 \times 10^{-2}$ and $\Delta\text{pH} = -0\cdot017$, in good agreement with the previous result. The equation for β developed for a weak base and its salt is given by (5.130). The same result may be obtained from equation (5.129) using K_b in place of K_a, and $[\text{OH}^-]$ in place of $[\text{H}^+]$.

$$\beta = 2\cdot303\left\{\frac{K_w}{[\text{H}^+]} + [\text{H}^+] - \frac{cK_b^2}{\left(\frac{K_w}{[\text{H}^+]} + K_b\right)^2} + \frac{cK_b}{\left(\frac{K_w}{[\text{H}^+]} + K_b\right)}\right\} \tag{5.130}$$

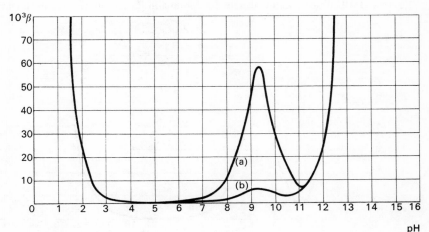

Figure 99. Buffer index for (a) 0·05N NH_3–0·05 N HCl, (b) 0·005 N NH_3–0·005 N HCl.

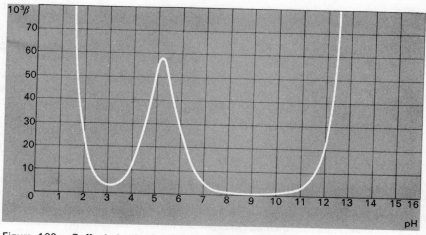

Figure 100. Buffer index for 0·05 N Pyridine–0·05 N HCl.

The variation of β with pH is illustrated by figs. 99 to 102: ammonia, pyridine, acetic acid and phenol are represented at various concentrations c. The maximum useful buffer capacity occurs at the pK_a or the pK_b of the system under consideration; at these values of pH, the concentrations of salt and acid or of salt and base respectively are equal. A ten-fold decrease in the salt concentration produces about a ten-fold decrease in the value of β. Minimum buffer action is found in the pH regions corresponding to the acid and the conjugate base. For example, with 0·05 molar acetic acid and 0·05 molar sodium acetate, the minima in β occur at pH 3·03 for the acid,

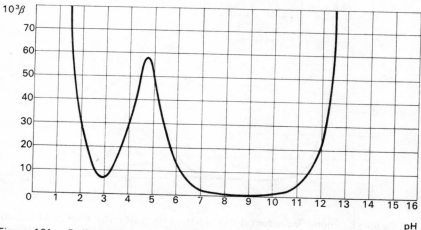

Figure 101. Buffer index for 0·05 N HAc–0·05 N NaOH.

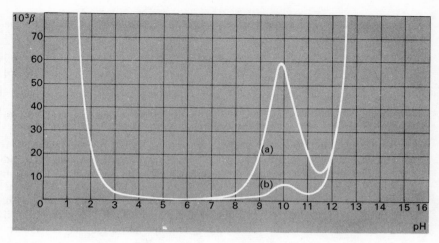

Figure 102. Buffer index for (a) 0.05 N C_6H_5OH–0.05 N NaOH (b) 0.005 N C_6H_5OH–0.005 N NaOH.

HAc, and at pH 8.72 for the conjugate base, Ac^-. A 0.05 molar solution of acetic acid has a buffer index of about 5×10^{-3} and a 0.05 molar solution of sodium acetate has a buffer index of 2×10^{-5}. The pH of a solution of sodium acetate is thus very sensitive to the presence of atmospheric carbon dioxide, which would invalidate its accurate measurement. The system HAc–Ac^- cannot provide a solution of pH outside the approximate range 3 to 9, unless strong acid or strong base is added. This is indicated by the rapid rise in β outside these limits (fig. 101). Similar deductions may be made in respect of the other systems from the curves in figs. 99, 100 and 102.

5·7·4 *Weak acid–weak base*

If the acid and the base forming a salt are both weak, for example ammonium acetate, then both the acid and the conjugate base interact with the solvent, as shown by equations (**5.131**) and (**5.132**).

$$NH_4^+ + H_2O \rightleftharpoons H_3O^+ + NH_3 \qquad \textbf{(5.131)}$$

$$Ac^- + H_2O \rightleftharpoons OH^- + HAc. \qquad \textbf{(5.132)}$$

These equilibria may be combined to give (**5.133**), or more simply (**5.134**).

$$NH_4^+ + Ac^- + 2H_2O \rightleftharpoons H_3O^+ + NH_3 + OH^- + HAc \qquad \textbf{(5.133)}$$

$$NH_4^+ + Ac^- \rightleftharpoons NH_3 + HAc \qquad \textbf{(5.134)}$$

Assuming dilute solutions, the equilibrium constant for (**5.134**) may be formulated by equation (**5.135**). From equations (**5.48**), (**5.67**) and (**5.85**, A = Ac), (**5.136**) may be derived.

$$K_h = \frac{[NH_3][HAc]}{[NH_4^+][Ac^-]} \tag{5.135}$$

$$K_h = \frac{K_w}{K_a K_b} \tag{5.136}$$

Let the original concentration of the salt, ammonium acetate in this example, be c mole l.$^{-1}$ In general, the degrees of dissociation of the conjugate base and of the acid will be different; in this example they are assumed equal, say α. From equation (**5.135**) the concentrations of NH_3 and of HAc are equal, and equal to αc, and the concentrations of NH_4^+ and of Ac^- are equal and equal to $(1-\alpha)c$. Thus, from (**5.136**), equation (**5.137**) is derived. Certain further approximations may now be made: if $\alpha \ll 1$, then $(1-\alpha) \rightarrow 1$; α is now equal to $\sqrt{K_h}$, and equation (**5.138**) may be deduced.

$$K_h = \frac{\alpha^2 c^2}{(1-\alpha)c} = \frac{\alpha^2 c}{(1-\alpha)}. \tag{5.137}$$

$$pH = \tfrac{1}{2}pK_w + \tfrac{1}{2}pK_a - \tfrac{1}{2}pK_b \tag{5.138}$$

For acetic acid and for ammonium acetate, $K_a \simeq K_b$, and so the pH of a solution of ammonium acetate is approximately 7·0, although hydrolysis has taken place.

From equation (**5.138**), it seems that the pH is independent of the concentration of the solution. This is strictly true only if the solutions are dilute, and if they are neutral. If $K_a < K_b$, the solution is alkaline, and if $K_a > K_b$, the solution is acid.

5·7·5 *Dibasic acids*

A dibasic acid can dissociate in two stages and two dissociation constants determine the composition of the system at equilibrium. We will consider the general case of an acid H_2A, which dissociates according to equation (**5.139**) and (**5.140**).

$$H_2A \rightleftharpoons H^+ + HA^- \tag{5.139}$$

$$HA^- \rightleftharpoons H^+ + A^{2-} \tag{5.140}$$

Five equations may be written to represent this system, (**5.141**) to (**5.145**),

$$K_1[H_2A] = [H^+][HA^-] \tag{5.141}$$

$$K_2[HA^-] = [H^+][A^{2-}] \tag{5.142}$$

$$K_w = [H^+][OH^-] \tag{5.143}$$

$$c = [H_2A] + [HA^-] + [A^{2-}] \qquad \text{mass balance} \tag{5.144}$$

$$[H^+] = [HA^-] + 2[A^{2-}] + [OH^-] \qquad \text{electroneutrality} \tag{5.145}$$

and may be solved by the following stages:

$$c - [H^+] = [H_2A] - [OH^-] - [A^{2-}] \tag{5.146}$$

$$[H_2A] = c - [H^+] + \frac{K_w}{[H^+]} + [A^{2-}] \tag{5.147}$$

$$= c - [H^+] + \frac{K_w}{[H^+]} + \frac{K_2[HA^-]}{[H^+]} \tag{5.148}$$

$$= \frac{[H^+][HA^-]}{K_1} \tag{5.149}$$

$$[HA^-] = \frac{\left(c - [H^+] + \dfrac{K_w}{[H^+]}\right)}{\left(\dfrac{[H^+]}{K_1} - \dfrac{K_2}{[H^+]}\right)} \tag{5.150}$$

$$[A^{2-}] = \frac{K_2}{[H^+]} \frac{\left(c - [H^+] + \dfrac{K_w}{[H^+]}\right)}{\left(\dfrac{[H^+]}{K_1} - \dfrac{K_2}{[H^+]}\right)} \tag{5.151}$$

$$[H^+] = \frac{\left(c - [H^+] + \dfrac{K_w}{[H^+]}\right)}{\left(\dfrac{[H^+]}{K_1} - \dfrac{K_2}{[H^+]}\right)} + \frac{2K_2\left(c - [H^+] + \dfrac{K_w}{[H^+]}\right)}{[H^+]\left(\dfrac{[H^+]}{K_1} - \dfrac{K_2}{[H^+]}\right)} + \frac{K_w}{[H^+]} \tag{5.152}$$

$$c = \left([H^+] - \frac{K_w}{[H^+]}\right) \left\{ 1 + \frac{\left(\dfrac{[H^+]}{K_1} - \dfrac{K_2}{[H^+]}\right)}{\left(1 + \dfrac{2K_2}{[H^+]}\right)} \right\}. \tag{5.153}$$

The results of the application of equation (5.153) to the dibasic acids carbonic acid and oxalic acid, are shown in table 30, where the total acid concentration, c, is listed as a function of pH. If K_2 is much less than K_1 and if pH is less than about 5·5, then

Table 30 Evaluation of Equation (5.153) for Carbonic Acid and for Oxalic Acid, at 25°C.

Carbonic acid		Oxalic acid	
pH	c (mole l.$^{-1}$)	pH	c (mole l.$^{-1}$)
		1	$2{\cdot}69 \times 10^{-1}$
		2	$1{\cdot}16 \times 10^{-2}$
3	$2{\cdot}33$	3	$9{\cdot}58 \times 10^{-4}$
4	$2{\cdot}34 \times 10^{-2}$	4	$7{\cdot}20 \times 10^{-5}$
5	$2{\cdot}43 \times 10^{-4}$	5	$5{\cdot}36 \times 10^{-6}$
6	$3{\cdot}29 \times 10^{-6}$	6	$4{\cdot}99 \times 10^{-7}$
7	$0{\cdot}00$	7	$0{\cdot}00$

equation (**5.153**) may be approximated by (**5.154**). This equation is similar to (**5.92**)

$$c = [H^+]. \left\{ 1 + \frac{[H^+]}{K_1} \right\}$$ (5.154)

with $K_1 = K_a$; the dibasic acid is now effectively a monobasic acid. This simplification can be applied to carbonic acid but not to oxalic acid below a concentration of 10^{-2} mole l.$^{-1}$, as table 31 shows. The dissociation constants used are listed in Appendix C.

Table 31 Evaluation of Equation (**5.154**) for Carbonic Acid and for Oxalic Acid, at 25°C.

Carbonic acid		Oxalic acid	
pH	c (mole l.$^{-1}$)	pH	c (mole l.$^{-1}$)
		1	$2 \cdot 69 \times 10^{-1}$
		2	$1 \cdot 17 \times 10^{-2}$
3	$2 \cdot 33$	3	$1 \cdot 02 \times 10^{-3}$
4	$2 \cdot 34 \times 10^{-2}$	4	$1 \cdot 00 \times 10^{-4}$
5	$2 \cdot 43 \times 10^{-4}$	5	$1 \cdot 00 \times 10^{-5}$
6	$3 \cdot 32 \times 10^{-6}$	6	$1 \cdot 00 \times 10^{-6}$
7	$(1 \cdot 23 \times 10^{-7})$	7	$(1 \cdot 00 \times 10^{-7})$

5·7·6 *Indicators*

An acid-base indicator is a weak acid or a weak base, and is slightly dissociated in solution. The acid and its conjugate base (or the base and its conjugate acid) are differently coloured. This dissociation can be represented by equations such as (**5.155**) and (**5.156**)

$$HIn \rightleftharpoons H^+ + In^-$$ (5.155)

$$InOH \rightleftharpoons OH^- + In^+$$ (5.156)

where HIn represents a weak acid indicator, such as methyl red, and InOH represents a weak base indicator, such as phenolphthalein. We shall consider the first of these in more detail.

The equilibrium constant for (**5.155**) is given by equation (**5.157**).

$$K_{In} = \frac{[H^+][In^-]}{[HIn]}$$ (5.157)

We see that $[H^+]$, and thus pH, governs the ratio of $[In^-]/[HIn]$ for the system. In the case of methyl red, HIn is the red form and In^- is the yellow form. If a fraction α of the total indicator present is dissociated, then the hydrogen ion concentration, from equation (**5.157**), is given by (**5.158**).

$$[H^+] = K_{In} \frac{(1-\alpha)}{\alpha}$$ (5.158)

If we assume that when α is less than 0·09, the In^- colour is just not visible to the eye, then the lowest hydrogen ion concentration at which In^- can be detected is given by equation (**5.159**).

$$[H^+] = K_{In}\frac{0·91}{0·09} \approx 10K_{In} \qquad (5.159)$$

The corresponding pH is $pK_{In} - 1$. Further, when 91 per cent of the indicator is dissociated, the colour due to HIn is just not visible to the eye. In this circumstance we can deduce that $pH = pK_{In} + 1$. With these working assumptions we derive the pH range of an acid-base indicator as $pK_{In} \pm 1$. In table 32 a number of acid-base indicators are listed. The pH ranges have been determined experimentally, using buffer solutions. They compare favourably with the values of $pK_{In} \pm 1$.

Table 32 Data for Acid-Base Indicators

	pH range	pK_{In}
Methyl orange	2·9–4·0	3·7
Bromophenol blue	3·0–3·6	4·0
Bromocresol green	3·8–5·4	4·7
Methyl red	4·4–6·0	5·1
Bromothymol blue	6·0–7·6	7·0
Phenol red	6·8–8·4	7·6
Phenolphthalein	8·3–10·0	9·4
Thymolphthalein	9·3–10·5	9·9

5·7·7   *Titrations*

The changes in pH during the titration of an acid with a base can be calculated by means of equations already developed. Attention is drawn to figs. 97 and 98, with the relevant theory. We shall consider the titrations of acids and bases of different strengths in solutions of initial concentrations of 1 N and 0·01 N.

Strong acid–strong base. The titration curves of 50 ml. of N HCl with N NaOH and of 50 ml. of 0·01 N HCl with 0·01 N NaOH are shown in fig. 103. The pH of the system changes rapidly in the neighbourhood of the equivalence point (in this case, neutrality – pH = 7). For practical purposes, the pH changes rapidly from 3 to 11 and from 5 to 9, for the N and 0·01 N solutions respectively. Suitable indicators for the titrations are shown on the figure. We can see that the use of methyl orange with the 0·01 N solutions would lead to an erroneous result; the colour change of the indicator would occur before the equivalence point.

Weak acids and bases. We shall consider the pairs acetic acid–sodium hydroxide ($K_a = 1·8 \times 10^{-5}$) and pyridine–hydrochloric acid ($K_b = 1·7 \times 10^{-9}$). The titration curves are illustrated in fig. 104.

On addition of 0·1 N NaOH to 0·1 N acetic acid, the pH increases sharply at first. The slope then decreases; the pH is now passing through the buffer working-range. A

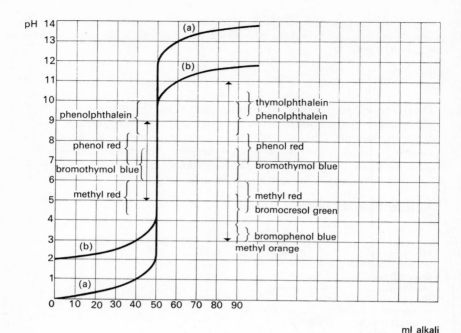

Figure 103. pH titration curves for strong acid–strong base (a) 1 N solutions, (b) 0·01 N solutions.

rapid change in pH occurs between 7·5 and 9·5 and indicators such as phenolphthalein or thymolphthalein would be suitable for this titration. For concentrations other than 0·1 N, the change in pH about the equivalence point must be evaluated; a shortening of this range, for example with 0·01 N solutions, would mean that phenolphthalein was the most suitable indicator. Continued addition of NaOH, after the equivalence point has been reached, produces only a slow increase in the pH of the solution – a solution of sodium hydroxide is effectively a buffer solution. The buffer index curve for this system (fig. 101) should be studied in conjunction with fig. 104.

The system 0·1 N pyridine–0·1 N HCl shows a rapid decrease from pH 9 with addition of acid. Again, the slope of the curve decreases through the buffer working range; fig. 100 can be studied with this titration curve. The change at the equivalence point is not very marked and no indicator is quite satisfactory for this titration; the best indicator is benzylaniline-azobenzene.

The system weak acid–weak base has not been considered in this section. It is of little importance in titrimetric analysis because the change in pH at the equivalence is so gradual that no indicator is useful. Such a titration would not be performed with an indicator. However, it may be performed conductimetrically (ch. 7).

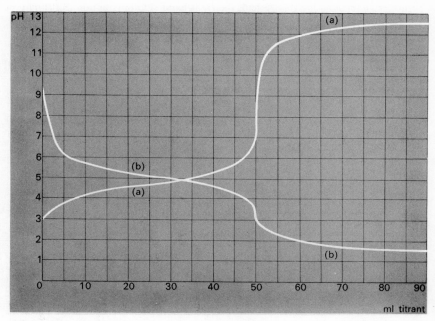

Figure 104. pH titration curves for 0·1 N solutions (a) weak acid (acetic acid)—strong base, (b) weak base (pyridine)—strong acid.

Problems

1. The following data refer to the equilibrium $N_2O_4 \rightleftharpoons 2NO_2$ at 25°C. and 35°C. Deduce an expression for K_p, evaluate K_p at both temperatures, and calculate ΔH for the reaction in the given temperature interval, using equation (5.17).

Initial concentration of N_2O_4 in mole $l.^{-1}(c)$	Total pressure in atm (P)	
	25°C.	35°C.
$6·28 \times 10^{-3}$	0·212	0·238
$1·26 \times 10^{-2}$	0·394	0·440
$1·98 \times 10^{-2}$	0·600	0·662

2. The following data refer to the $CaCO_3$ equilibrium, equation (5.29):

Interval	$p(CO_2)$ (mm.)	$T(°C.)$
1 ... {	$7·32 \times 10^{-2}$	500
2 ... {	$1·84$	600
{	$2·22 \times 10^1$	700
{	$1·67 \times 10^2$	800
4 ... {	$7·93 \times 10^3$	900
5 ... {	$2·94 \times 10^4$	1000

Since $K_p \propto p(CO_2)$ for this system, the right-hand side of equation (5.17) may be written as $\log_{10}\left(\dfrac{p_2}{p_1}\right)$. Calculate ΔH in the five temperature intervals and plot against $\dfrac{1}{T}$ (taken at the middle of the interval). Determine ΔH at 975°C. If the variation of ΔH with temperature may be represented by the equation

$$\Delta H = a + bT + cT^2,$$

find values for a, b and c, for the given temperature range. The best solution is given by the method of least-squares:

$$\Sigma_T(a + bT + cT^2 - \Delta H) = 0$$

$$\Sigma_T(aT + bT^2 + cT^3 - T\,\Delta H) = 0$$

$$\Sigma_T(aT^2 + bT^3 + cT^4 - T^2\,\Delta H) = 0.$$

Each summation is taken over the five values of ΔH with the corresponding temperature at the middle of the interval, e.g.

$$\Sigma_T(a + bT + cT^2 - \Delta H) = (a + 550b + (550)^2 c - \Delta H)$$

$$+ (a + 650b + (650)^2 c - \Delta H)$$

$$+ \ldots \text{etc.}$$

From these three equations, a, b, and c may be found.

3. The dissociation of ammonium carbamate may be represented by the equation:

$$NH_4CO_2NH_2 \text{ (cryst.)} \rightleftharpoons 2NH_3 \text{ (gas)} + CO_2 \text{ (gas)}.$$

ΔH for the forward reaction is negative. What changes in (a) the positions of equilibrium, and (b) the rate of attainment of equilibrium, would be expected for the following alteration of conditions: (I) decrease in pressure, (II) increase in temperature, (III) increase in $[NH_3]$, and (IV) increase in $[CO_2]$?

4. Draw the pH–titration curve for the system 0·1N pyridine–0·1N HCl. Calculate the pH initially and after the addition of 5, 10, 12·5, 20, 24, 25, 26, 28 and 30 ml. of acid to 25 ml. of the pyridine solution.

5. Calculate the solubility of $BaSO_4$, given that $S(BaSO_4) = 1·06 \times 10^{-10}$, in (i) 10^{-3} molar Na_2SO_4 and (ii) 10^{-2} molar $NaCl$.

6. Solve the quadratic equation $ax^2 + bx + c = 0$, with $a = 1$, $b = 123$ and $c = -200$, (i) using the equation

$$x = \frac{-b \pm \sqrt{(b^2 - 4ac)}}{2a},$$

(ii) by successive approximations using the equation in the form $x = -\left(\dfrac{c}{b}\right) - \left(\dfrac{a}{b}\right)x^2$, both with four-figure tables of logarithms. For the first approximation in (ii), let x

on the right-hand side be $-\left(\dfrac{c}{b}\right)$. Compare the results and check the validity of (ii) by calculating the square root in (i) with seven-figure tables. Note the usefulness of (ii) when $4ac \ll b^2$.

7. Calculate the pH of the following solutions: (i) 0·01 molar NaOH, (ii) 0·005 normal H_2SO_4, (iii) 1 ml. 2N HCl in 500 ml. water, (iv) $1\cdot0 \times 10^{-9}$ molar $Ba(OH)_2$.

8. The values of K_w for water at 0°C., 25°C. and 60°C. are $1\cdot2 \times 10^{-15}$, $1\cdot0 \times 10^{-14}$ and $9\cdot6 \times 10^{-14}$ respectively. Calculate the pH of water at each temperature. Use equation (**8.26**) to calculate the enthalpy of dissociation of a mole of water into its ions.

9. Determine the pH of the following solutions, using the dissociation constants in Appendix C: (i) 0·005 N acetic acid, (ii) 0·02 molar pyridine, (iii) 0·1 molar ammonium nitrate, (iv) 0·007 molar sodium sulphate, (v) 0·01 molar potassium cyanide, (vi) 1 molar sodium benzoate.

10. Calculate the pH of a solution which is 0·1 molar in formic acid and 0·2 molar in potassium formate. What is the change in pH on addition of 2 ml. N NaOH to 100 ml. of solution?

11. Calculate the pH of a 0·05 molar solution of phosphoric acid – it may be assumed that the third dissociation of H_3PO_4 is negligible.

12. By differentiating equation (**5.129**), find the condition for maximum and minimum values of β. Show that if c is much greater than $[H^+]$, then $[H^+] = K_a$ is one solution of the condition (it corresponds, in fact, to the maximum useful value of β).

Chapter 6
Physical properties of systems

The physical properties of any system may be classified generally into three main types: *additive*, *constitutive* and *colligative*.

An additive property is, for a given system, one which may be represented by the sum of the corresponding properties of its components. Mass is exactly additive but molar volume and ionic radii are only approximately additive properties. For example, the molar volume, V_m (molecular weight divided by the density) increases regularly by ΔV_m along a homologous series for each CH_2 group increment (for liquids and solids):

	CH_3OH	CH_3CH_2OH	$CH_3CH_2CH_2OH$		$CH_3CH_2CH_2CH_2OH$		
			n	iso	n	iso	tert
V_m (cm.^{3})	24·07	33·82	43·37	43·62	52·97	53·06	53·41
ΔV_m (cm.^{3})	9·75	9·68			9·65		

Again, the interionic distances, r_0, in ionic crystals are additive functions of the appropriate ionic radii:

	LiF	NaF	KF	RbF	CsF
r_0 (Å.)	2·005	2·310	2·665	2·815	3·005
Σr_i (Å.)	1·96	2·31	2·72	2·84	3·05
Δr (Å.)	−0·05	0·00	0·06	0·03	0·05

A constitutive property depends mainly upon the structural arrangement of atoms or molecules. The boiling point is an example of a constitutive property. The high boiling point of water, as compared to that of hydrogen sulphide for example, is due to the arrangement of the molecules in its hydrogen-bonded structure. Again, both the softness and lubricant property of graphite, and the hardness and abrasive property of diamond are intimately related to the arrangements of carbon atoms in each of these substances.

Colligative properties depend upon the number of molecules, or particles, in the system, rather than upon their nature. The pressure of an ideal gas at constant volume and constant temperature is one example of a colligative property.

In this chapter, we shall be concerned, at first, with the properties of dilute solutions. A solution is a homogeneous mixture consisting of one condensed phase and two or more components. In a binary solution, it is convenient to refer to the component in excess as the solvent, and to the other component as the solute. We shall see, however, that these two terms are completely interchangeable.

6·1 Vapour pressure and Raoult's law

In dealing with mixtures of miscible liquids or with solid–liquid systems, it is convenient to express the composition of the system in terms of the *mole fraction* of each component.

The mole fraction $x(A)$ of component A in a mixture containing $n(A)$ mole of species A, $n(B)$ mole of B etc. is given by

$$x(A) = \frac{n(A)}{n(A)+n(B)+\dots} = \frac{n(A)}{\sum_I n(I)}. \tag{6.1}$$

where the sum is taken over the I components.

From equation (6.1) it follows that

$$\frac{n(A)}{\sum_I n(I)}+\frac{n(B)}{\sum_I n(I)}+\dots+\frac{n(I)}{\sum_I n(I)} = 1. \tag{6.2}$$

We shall restrict our discussion mainly to two-component mixtures consisting of $n(A)$ mole of species A and $n(B)$ mole of species B. Hence

$$x(A) = \frac{n(A)}{n(A)+n(B)} \tag{6.3}$$

$$x(B) = \frac{n(B)}{n(A)+n(B)} \tag{6.4}$$

$$x(A)+x(B) = 1. \tag{6.5}$$

The vapour pressure of a solvent is lowered when a solute is dissolved in it. This fact was given a quantitative basis by Raoult (1887–88). He discovered that, *for ideal dilute solutions of solute B in a solvent A at a given temperature, the lowering of the vapour pressure of A was proportional to the mole fraction of A*; this may be regarded as a statement of Raoult's law. Hence

$$p(A) = \phi x(A). \tag{6.6}$$

For pure solvent, $x(A) = 1$ and so the constant ϕ may be identified with the vapour pressure of the pure solvent, $p^0(A)$. Thus

$$p(A) = p^0(A)x(A). \tag{6.7}$$

$p(A)$ is the partial vapour pressure of component A above the solution at the given temperature T. The following calculation explains further equation (6.7).

The vapour pressure of pure ethanol at 19°C. is 40·00 mm. and that of water at the same temperature is 16·48 mm. We may calculate the partial vapour pressures of ethanol and of water above a solution containing 2 g. of water and 50 g. of ethanol, at 19°C.

The number of moles of ethanol present is $\dfrac{50}{46\cdot07}$ = 1·085

The number of moles of water present is $\dfrac{2}{18\cdot02}$ = 0·1110

Using the previous nomenclature

$$x(\text{EtOH}) = \frac{n(\text{EtOH})}{n(\text{EtOH}) + n(\text{H}_2\text{O})} = \frac{1 \cdot 085}{1 \cdot 085 + 0 \cdot 1110} = 0 \cdot 9072$$

$$x(\text{H}_2\text{O}) = \frac{n(\text{H}_2\text{O})}{n(\text{EtOH}) + n(\text{H}_2\text{O})} = \frac{0 \cdot 1110}{1 \cdot 085 + 0 \cdot 1110} = 0 \cdot 0928$$

alternatively $x(\text{H}_2\text{O}) = 1 - x(\text{EtOH}) = 1 - 0 \cdot 9072 = 0 \cdot 0928$

Hence $p(\text{EtOH}) = p^0(\text{EtOH})x(\text{EtOH}) = 40 \cdot 00 \times 0 \cdot 9072 - = 36 \cdot 29$ mm.

and $p(\text{H}_2\text{O}) = p^0(\text{H}_2\text{O})x(\text{H}_2\text{O}) = 16 \cdot 48 \times 0 \cdot 0928 = 1 \cdot 529$ mm.

From equations **(6.5)** and **(6.7)**

$$p(\text{A}) = p^0(\text{A})\{1 - x(\text{B})\}$$

$$= . p^0(\text{A}) - p^0(\text{A})x(\text{B})$$

or $\dfrac{p^0(\text{A}) - p(\text{A})}{p^0(\text{A})} = \Delta p(\text{A}) = x(\text{B})$ **(6.8)**

Hence, the *relative* lowering of vapour pressure, $\Delta p(\text{A})$, is equal to the mole fraction of the *solute*, in dilute solution. This is an alternative statement of Raoult's law. In the above problem, the lowering of vapour pressure of ethanol by the addition of water implies a decrease in the *effective* concentration of ethanol in the system, i.e. a decrease in its activity.

If Raoult's law is obeyed throughout the whole composition range of a binary mixture, the system is said to behave ideally. The vapour pressure–composition curves

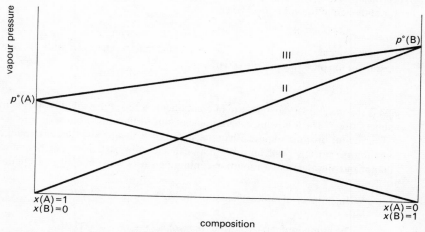

Figure 105. Vapour pressure–composition diagram for a binary ideal system.

for a binary ideal system are shown in fig. 105; the vapour pressure of pure B is shown as being greater than the vapour pressure of pure A. As the system is ideal, then from equation (6.7) the variations of both $p(A)$ and $p(B)$ with composition are straight lines, I and II, passing through the points $p^0(A)$ and $p^0(B)$ for $x(A)$ and $x(B)$ equal to unity, respectively.

From Dalton's law of partial pressures, the total pressure, P, at any composition is given by the sum $\{p(A) + p(B)\}$. Evidently, this is the straight line, III, joining the points $p^0(A)$ and $p^0(B)$. A limited number of pairs of liquids are known which exhibit this ideal behaviour. Examples are ethyl bromide–ethyl iodide at 30°C. and benzene–ethylene dichloride at 50°C.

Most pairs of liquids form non-ideal solutions. Sometimes the partial vapour pressure of component A is increased by adding the component B; a similar effect is then observed for the partial vapour pressure of component B. This behaviour is described as a positive deviation from Raoult's law and is illustrated by fig. 106. The total vapour

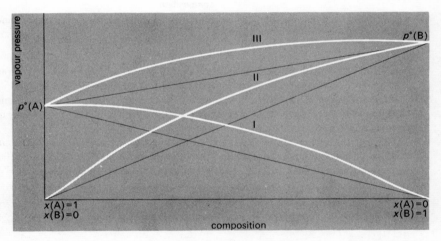

Figure 106. Vapour pressure–composition diagram for a binary system showing positive deviations from Raoult's law.

pressure is, at all compositions, greater than or equal to that corresponding to ideality. Positive deviations are exhibited by liquid mixtures in which the molecules repel each other and so enter the vapour phase more readily than in the pure liquids. The pairs of liquids n-pentane–ethanol and n-heptane–carbon tetrachloride are examples of this type of behaviour.

If the molecules of the liquids in a binary system tend to attract each other, then their escape into the vapour phase will be retarded. Negative deviations from Raoult's law ensue as in fig. 107. Examples of this type of behaviour are acetone–chloroform, and pyridine–acetic acid.

We see that the variations of total vapour pressure with composition tell us something about the interaction of the component molecules in a liquid mixture. It is

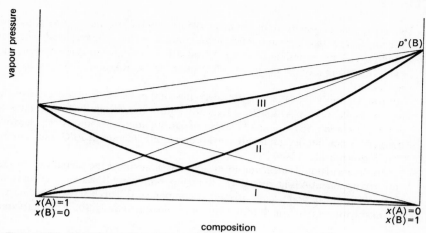

Figure 107. Vapour pressure–composition diagram for a binary system showing negative deviations from Raoult's law.

evident that two liquids in admixture both exhibit the same type of departure from ideality, at least over part of the range of composition, or none at all.

For a discussion of deviations from Raoult's law in general and of cases where one component shows both positive and negative deviations within different regions of composition see McGlashan, M. L., *J. Chem. Ed.*, vol. 10, 1963, p. 516.

The deviations from Raoult's law can be large; the total vapour pressure curve can then exhibit a maximum or a minimum. If we increase the deviations shown in fig. 106, then a maximum vapour pressure is attained (fig. 108). At the composition $x(A) = c$,

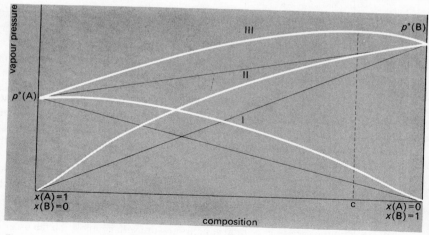

Figure 108. Enhanced positive deviations leading to a maximum vapour pressure.

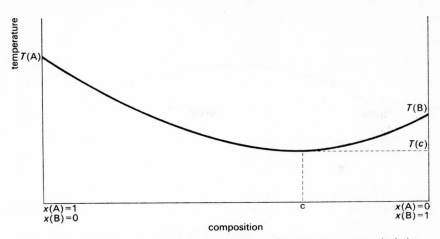

Figure 109.   A minimum boiling point due to large positive vapour pressure deviations.

the mixture has its highest vapour pressure, higher even than that of B, the more volatile of the two components.

Let us consider this situation from another point of view. The vapour pressure at each composition of the mixture will rise with increase in temperature until it attains the same pressure as that of its surroundings, say one atmosphere; the mixture then boils.

Now of all mixtures of A and B, that for which $x(A) = c$ will attain a pressure of one atmosphere at the lowest temperature. The component B attains atmospheric pressure at a higher temperature and component A at a higher temperature still. Hence the boiling point–composition curve for mixtures of A and B will exhibit a

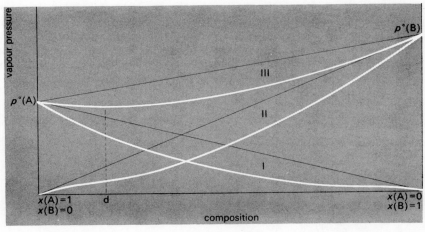

Figure 110.   Enhanced negative deviations leading to a minimum vapour pressure.

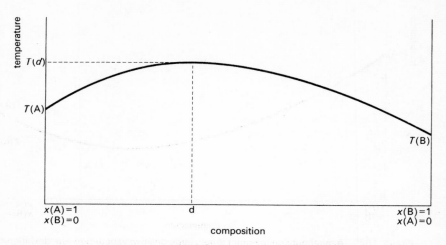

Figure 111. A maximum boiling point due to large negative vapour pressure deviations.

minimum boiling point, T_c, at the composition $x(A) = c$, (fig. 109). Pairs of liquids which show this behaviour are ethanol–water and ethyl acetate–water, for example.

If we consider enhancement of the negative deviations shown in fig. 107, then a minimum vapour pressure system can be obtained (fig. 110). Using the above argument, this would lead to a maximum in the boiling point–composition diagram (fig. 111). Examples of this type of behaviour are the systems hydrogen chloride–water and hydrogen nitrate–water. Appendix C tabulates additional data on maximum boiling point and minimum boiling point systems.

We could measure the lowering in vapour pressure in order to find the molecular weight of one component if we know the molecular weight of the other component. This method is followed most easily in a two-component system in which one component, the solute B, is non-volatile. The total vapour pressure is that of the other component, the solvent A. The following example illustrates the method. The vapour pressure of a solution of 15 g. of glucose, $C_6H_{12}O_6$, in 100 g. of water is 17·28 mm. at 20°C. At the same temperature, the vapour pressure of pure water is 17·54 mm.

From equation (**6.8**)

$$\frac{p^0(H_2O) - p}{p^0(H_2O)} = x(B) = \frac{n(B)}{n(A) + n(B)}$$

or, subtracting 1 from each side

$$\frac{p}{p^0(H_2O)} = \frac{n(A)}{n(A) + n(B)} = x(A)$$

$$\frac{17·28}{17·54} = \frac{\dfrac{100}{18·02}}{\dfrac{100}{18·02} + \dfrac{15}{M}}$$

where M is the molecular weight of glucose. Hence

$$\frac{1}{M} = \frac{5 \cdot 549 - 5 \cdot 467}{15(0 \cdot 9852)}$$

or $\qquad M = 180 \cdot 2.$

However, vapour pressures are not very easy to measure with accuracy. It is more convenient to measure experimentally certain related properties, such as freezing point depression or osmotic pressure.

6·1·1   Freezing-point depression

One result of the lowering of vapour pressure of a solvent by the addition of a non-volatile solute is that the freezing point of the solution is lowered, compared with that of the pure solvent. Blagden (1788) showed that the lowering of the freezing point generally was proportional to the solute concentration. Raoult (1878–86) established that equimolar solutions of different substances depressed the freezing point of a given solvent by the same amount, provided that the solutions formed were dilute and that the solute did not associate or dissociate in the solvent.

If we plot the vapour pressure–temperature curves for a pure solvent A in the vicinity of its melting point and a solution in A of an involatile solute B, we observe that the curve for the solution lies *below* that for the solvent (fig. 112). On this diagram,

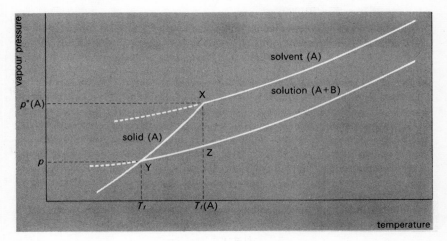

Figure 112.   Freezing point depression diagram for a binary system: solute involatile.

the freezing point of pure solvent is at $T_f(A)$; at X the liquid solvent and solid solvent are in equilibrium. The freezing point of the solution of B in A is at T_f; at this temperature the solution is in equilibrium with solid solvent. The freezing point

173   Physical properties of systems

depression, ΔT_f, is given by $T_f(A) - T_f$. The distance XZ is equal to the lowering of the vapour pressure, Δp, and is given by $p^0(A) - p$.

Since the interval ΔT_f is small and since the vapour pressure curves for solvent and dilute solution are nearly parallel at the freezing point, $\dfrac{YZ}{XZ}$ is constant or

$$\Delta T_f \propto \Delta p(A). \tag{6.9}$$

Using equation (6.8) we may write

$$\Delta T_f \propto x(B) \propto \frac{n(B)}{n(A) + n(B)} \propto \frac{\dfrac{w(B)}{M(B)}}{\dfrac{w(A)}{M(A)} + \dfrac{w(B)}{M(B)}}$$

where $w(A)$, $w(B)$, $M(A)$ and $M(B)$ are respectively the weights and molecular weights of the species A and B. If the solutions are dilute, $\dfrac{w(B)}{M(B)} \ll \dfrac{w(A)}{M(A)}$ and

$$\Delta T_f = \phi \frac{w(B)M(A)}{w(A)M(B)} \tag{6.11}$$

where ϕ is a proportionality constant. The *molal freezing point depression constant*, or the *molal cryoscopic constant*, K_f, may be defined as the freezing point depression in an ideal solution containing 1 mole of solute in 1000 g. solvent; thus

$$K_f = \frac{\phi M(A)}{1000} \tag{6.12}$$

and

$$\Delta T_f = \frac{K_f w(B) 1000}{M(B) w(A)}. \tag{6.13}$$

A more exact expression for (6.13) is

$$\Delta T_f = K_f \frac{\dfrac{w(B)}{M(B)}}{\dfrac{w(A)}{M(A)} + \dfrac{w(B)}{M(B)}} \left(1 + \frac{1000}{M(A)} \right). \tag{6.14}$$

We will examine equations (6.13) and (6.14) using the following problem:

1·8212 g. carbon tetrachloride in 100 g. benzene gave a freezing point depression of 0·603 C°.; K_f for benzene is 5·11.

Equation (6.13) $0 \cdot 603 = \dfrac{5 \cdot 11 \times 1 \cdot 8212 \times 1000}{M \times 100}$

whence $M = 154 \cdot 3$

Equation (6.14) $0 \cdot 603 = \dfrac{5 \cdot 11 \times \left(\dfrac{1 \cdot 8212}{M} \right)}{\left(\dfrac{100}{78 \cdot 11} \right) + \left(\dfrac{1 \cdot 8212}{M} \right)} \left(1 + \dfrac{1000}{78 \cdot 11} \right)$

whence $M = 152 \cdot 9$.

The difference between these two values is about 1 per cent; the true molecular weight is 153·8. Since experimental errors and departure from ideality limit the accuracy of the method, the short equation (6.13) is generally used.

The cryoscopic method for determining molecular weights will be described with reference to fig. 113.

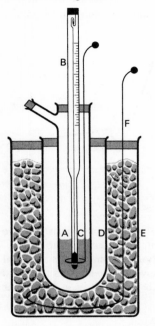

Figure 113. A Beckmann freezing point apparatus.

A weighed quantity of solvent whose cryoscopic constant is known is placed in the tube A and a Beckmann thermometer B, preset to the required temperature range, and a stirrer C are fitted. The tube is fitted into a wider tube D in order to provide an air space, to aid slow cooling. This assembly is contained in a vessel E in which a freezing mixture is placed. The freezing mixture should be at a temperature about 5 deg. below the f.p. of the solvent. Another stirrer F is provided; both stirrers have thermally insulated handles.

The temperature of the liquid is allowed to fall to about $\frac{1}{2}$ deg. below its freezing point. Vigorous stirring with the stirrer C induces crystallization and the temperature rises to the freezing point.

The solvent is allowed to melt and a weighed quantity of solute in the form of a pellet is added and dissolved; the new freezing point is determined and the molecular weight evaluated. The following points should be noted:

(i) The solution should be dilute.

(ii) The solute should not associate or dissociate in the solvent.

(iii) Pure solvent *only* must separate from solution.

(iv) Crystallization should commence at about $\frac{1}{2}$ deg. below the freezing point.

Figs. 114a and 114b illustrate supercooling with solvent and with solution. When a supercooled solvent crystallizes, the latent heat of fusion is released and the temperature rises rapidly to the freezing point and remains constant until complete

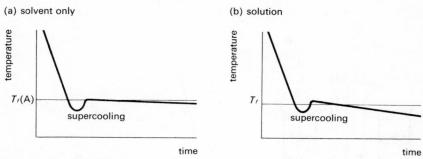

(a) solvent only

(b) solution

Figure 114. Supercooling.

melting has taken place. The system solid solvent–liquid solvent consists of two phases and one component; if the pressure is constant, the system is invariant.

In the case of solid solvent crystallizing from a solution, two phases exist again but there are two components; the condensed system is now univariant. After the initial rise to the freezing point, the temperature immediately begins to fall again. In practice, the plotting of 'cooling curves' is not necessary.

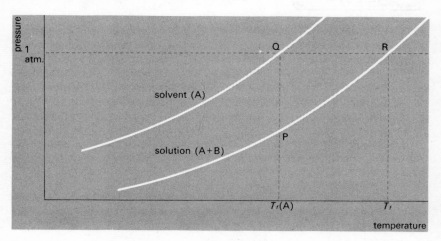

Figure 115. Boiling point elevation diagram for a binary system: solute involatile.

Boiling-point elevation

Fig. 115 illustrates the vapour pressure–temperature relationships for a solvent and for a solution, both near the boiling point. Again, we consider a dilute solution of an involatile solute B in a solvent A. The vapour pressure curve for the solvent lies above that for the solution at all temperatures. At a pressure of one atmosphere, the liquids boil.

The pure solvent boils at $T_b(A)$; the solution has a lower vapour pressure and hence a higher boiling point, T_b. The increase in boiling point, $T_b - T_b(A)$ is the boiling point elevation, ΔT_b, for the solution.

From fig. 115, $\Delta T_b = QR$. The vapour pressure lowering at $T_b(A)$ is equal to QP, and since ΔT_b is small and the curves are nearly parallel near the boiling point, for dilute solutions, $\dfrac{QR}{QP}$ is constant or

$$\Delta T_b = \phi \Delta p(A) \tag{6.15}$$

as before. We shall assume that $\dfrac{w(B)}{M(B)} \ll \dfrac{w(A)}{M(A)}$, and define a *molal boiling point eleva-tion constant* or *ebulliscopic constant*, K_b, as the boiling point elevation produced by an ideal solution contain 1 mole of the solute in 1000 g. of solvent. Thus

$$K_b = \phi \frac{M(A)}{1000} \quad \text{and}$$

$$\Delta T_b = \frac{w(B)1000}{M(B)w(A)}. \tag{6.16}$$

Example. 2·00 g. of urea dissolved in 125 g. of water produced a boiling point elevation of 0·139 C.° ; K_b for water is 0·52 C.°
From equation (5.16)

$$0·139 = \frac{0·52 \times 2·00 \times 1000}{M \times 125} \quad \text{whence } M = 59·86.$$

The true molecular weight for urea, $CO(NH_2)_2$, is 60·06.

6·1·3   *Osmosis and osmotic pressure*

It was discovered in the middle of the eighteenth century that if alcohol and water were separated by an animal membrane, e.g. a pig's bladder, the water passed through the membrane into the alcohol, but the alcohol did not pass through the membrane into the water. Subsequently, this property was observed with solutions in general. The essential property of the membrane is that it allows the passage of water (or solvent) molecules through it but not that of solute molecules, or ions; the term *semi-permeable* is used to describe these membranes.

A semi-permeable membrane can be formed in the walls of a porous pot by electro-lysing solutions of copper sulphate and potassium ferrocyanide which are separated

177   Physical properties of systems

by the pot (fig. 116). Copper ferrocyanide is formed in the pores of the pot and then acts as a good semi-permeable membrane.

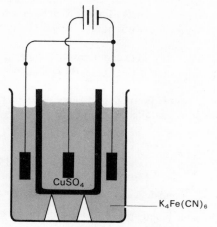

Figure 116.   Preparation of a semi-permeable membrane of $Cu_2Fe(CN)_6$.

Osmosis is the passage of solvent from a dilute solution through a semi-permeable membrane into a more concentrated solution. It can be demonstrated with the apparatus of fig. 117. As water enters the porous pot, the pressure rises; this is indicated by the difference in levels in the pressure gauge, M. Osmotic pressure can be *demonstrated* by this apparatus, but it cannot be *measured*, for the solution changes in concentration during the experiment. In the absence of an external pressure (in the

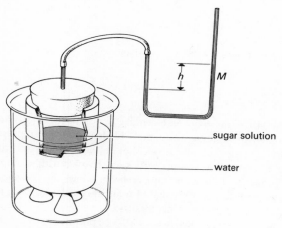

Figure 117.   Demonstration of osmosis.

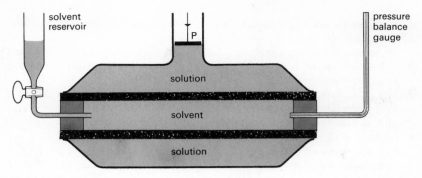

Figure 118. The Berkeley–Hartley apparatus.

case of fig. 117 a hydrostatic pressure), apparent osmosis could continue until the solutions on each side of the semi-permeable membrane have the same osmotic pressure, i.e. until they are *isotonic*.

The osmotic pressure may be defined as the external pressure which must be applied to a concentrated solution separated from a dilute solution by a semi-permeable membrane, at a particular temperature, to prevent osmosis taking place. Osmotic pressure may be measured using the Berkeley and Hartley apparatus (fig. 118). A

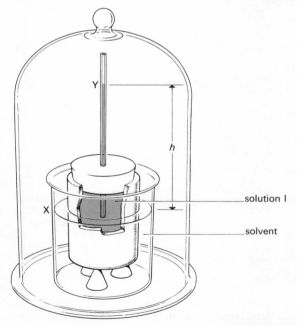

Figure 119. Relationship between osmotic pressure and vapour pressure lowering.

known variable external pressure, P, balances the osmotic pressure of the solution-solvent system.

The osmotic pressure of a solution is related to the lowering of vapour pressure of the component solvent. We consider here a descriptive treatment of this relationship.

The semi-permeable membrane (porous pot) separates a dilute solution I from a solution of slightly lower concentration II, fig. 119. The apparatus is confined at constant temperature and constant pressure under a bell-jar. When equilibrium is established, the osmotic pressure of the ambient solution is given approximately by the height, h, of the column of solution.

The vapour pressure of the solution at Y must be equal to that of the solvent at Y, assuming an involatile solute, at equilibrium. If the vapour pressure of the solvent at X is $p^0(A)$, that at Y is $p' = (p^0(A) - h\rho^0 g)$, where ρ^0 is the density of solvent vapour and g is the acceleration due to gravity. At a pressure $p^0(A)$ and a temperature T, the molar volume of the solvent vapour is $\dfrac{RT}{p^0(A)}$, assuming that the vapour behaves as an ideal gas, so that $\rho^0 = \dfrac{M p^0(A)}{RT}$, where M is the molecular weight of the solvent in the vapour phase. If the density of the solution is ρ, then the osmotic pressure π is approximately $h\rho g$; this is a good approximation if the solution is dilute. Eliminating hg:

$$\pi = \frac{\rho(p^0(A) - p')}{\rho^0} = \frac{\rho \Delta p}{\rho^0},$$

or

$$\frac{\Delta p}{p^0(A)} = \frac{M\pi}{\rho RT}. \tag{6.17}$$

From equation (6.8) $\dfrac{\Delta p}{p^0(A)} = x(B)$,

hence

$$M\pi \left\{ \frac{n(A) + n(B)}{\rho n(B)} \right\} = RT. \tag{6.18}$$

Since the solution is dilute, $n(A) + n(B) \simeq n(A)$ and $\dfrac{Mn(A)}{\rho nB}$ is V, the volume of solution per mole of solute B. Thus, $V = \dfrac{1}{c}$, where c is the concentration in mole l.$^{-1}$

Hence

$$\pi = cRT. \tag{6.19}$$

The equation of state for an ideal gas may be written

$$P = \frac{RT}{V}. \tag{6.20}$$

The similarity to (6.19) is evident. Hence, for a dilute solution, one mole dissolved in 22·4 l. produces an osmotic pressure of one atmosphere, at s.t.p.

Example. 0·450 g. of a sugar in 100 ml. solution exerts an osmotic pressure of 0·624 atmosphere at 20°C. We require to calculate the molecular weight of the sugar; $R = 0.0821$ l. atm. mole^{-1} deg.$^{-1}$

(i) $0.624 = \left(\dfrac{4·5}{M}\right) \times 0.082 \times 293·16$ whence $M = 173·3(5)$

or

(ii) at 20°C. 4·5 g. of the sugar in 1000 ml. exerts O.P. 0·624 atm.

at 0°C. $4·5 \times 22·4$ g. in 22400 ml. exerts O.P. $\dfrac{0·624 \times 273·16}{293·16}$ atm.

at 0°C. $\dfrac{4·5 \times 22·4 \times 293·16}{0·624 \times 273·16}$ g. in 22400 ml. exerts O.P. 1 atm.

whence $M = \dfrac{4·5 \times 22·4 \times 293·16}{0·624 \times 273·16} = 173·3(7).$

In the determination of molecular weights from colligative properties of solutions, it has been shown that the effect measured – depression of freezing point, elevation of boiling point or osmotic pressure – *decreases* as the molecular weight of the solute *increases.* Because of the accuracy with which a capillary rise, produced by a small osmotic pressure, can be measured, this method is most suitable for measuring the molecular weights of polymers in solution – particularly as polymers are often sparingly soluble, so that the solutions are very dilute (see problem 10, p. 208). A modern osmometer is shown in fig. 120.

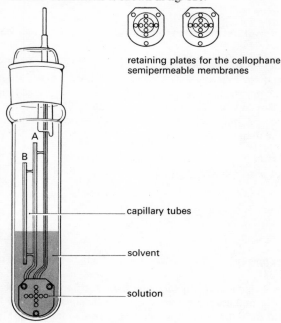

retaining plates for the cellophane
semipermeable membranes

capillary tubes

solvent

solution

Figure 120.   A modern osmometer.

6·2   Anomalous behaviour

A solution containing 0·35 g. of potassium chloride in 100 g. of water exhibits a freezing point depression of 0·143°C. We know that the 'molecular weight' of potassium chloride is 74·53 and, since the cryoscopic constant for water is 1·86°C., we can calculate the expected freezing point depression from equation (6.13). This gives a value of 0·087°C. Thus the observed depression is about 1·64 times greater than the expected value. The ratio

$$\frac{\text{observed f.p. depression}}{\text{calculated f.p. depression}}$$

is called the i factor, a term introduced by van't Hoff in 1886 to explain apparent anomalies, or departures from ideal behaviour.

Measurements of the i factors for a series of chlorides, at a given concentration, lead to the typical results in table 33.

Table 33 i Factors for Some Electrovalent Chlorides

	i	'α'
NaCl	1·90	0·90
$MgCl_2$	2·10	0·55
$LaCl_3$	1·24	0·08

These chlorides are electrovalent compounds and dissociate into ions in aqueous solution:

$$MCl_x \rightarrow M^{x+} + xCl^-. \tag{6.21}$$

If the initial concentration of the electrolyte is c mole l.$^{-1}$ and if we *assume* a degree of dissociation 'α', then at equilibrium the concentrations of the species in equation (6.21) are, in order, $c(1-\alpha)$, $c\alpha$ and $xc\alpha$. The total concentration of all three species is thus $c(1+x\alpha)$. Now the freezing point depression, and indeed any other colligative property, depends upon the total number of particles in solution. Hence

$$i = \frac{\text{total number of particles in solution, after dissociation}}{\text{total number of particles in solution, before dissociation}}.$$

In the derivation of equations (6.7), (6.8), (6.13), (6.16) and (6.19) the solute was considered neither to dissociate nor to associate. Thus

$$i = \frac{c(1+x\alpha)}{c} = 1 + x\alpha. \tag{6.22}$$

So from the value of i, an apparent degree of dissociation 'α' may be calculated; this quantity is listed in table 33.

We have seen in chapter 4, that ionic compounds, such as the chlorides in table 33, are ionized in the solid state, and upon dissolution in water the ions dissociate. We would expect at first that the i factors for sodium chloride, magnesium chloride and lanthanum chloride would be 2, 3 and 4 respectively.

The values of 'α' in table 33 suggest incomplete dissociation. This is not the true explanation; we did not begin with molecules of sodium chloride in the solid, and experimental evidence shows that there are no such molecules present in the solution.

At any finite concentration, a given ion experiences electrostatic forces due to the ions in its immediate neighbourhood. An ion develops about itself an 'atmosphere' of ions, of both signs but predominantly of opposite sign to that of the central reference ion. As a result, the ions are not entirely free to move, and so do not exert their full effect upon the lowering of solvent vapour pressure according to their mole fraction, as Raoult's law requires.

The extent of this interionic attraction increases with increasing concentration and with increasing ionic charge. The difference between this correct explanation and that of incomplete dissociation, for strong electrolytes, should be noted carefully, as both postulates imply the same type of anomaly in colligative properties.

Let us reconsider the solution of potassium chloride containing 0·35 g. in 100 g. of water. The molality of this solution is 0·047; the stoichiometric molalities of K^+ and of Cl^- ions are each 0·047. The properties of this solution show that the effective concentrations, or activities, of the ions are lower, due to interionic attraction. We express this fact by the mean ionic activity coefficient, which is 0·82 for potassium chloride at a stoichiometric concentration of 0·047 molal. Hence the effective concentration is only $0·047 \times 0·82$ molal i.e. 0·039 molal. From equation (**6.13**) we calculate the freezing point depression at the new effective concentration as 0·0716°C.

Hence i would be $\dfrac{0·143}{0·0716} = 1·997$, (i.e. approximately 2).

Some solutes become *associated* in solution. The aliphatic carboxylic acids show a strong tendency to form dimers by intermolecular hydrogen bonding:

$$R-C \overset{O-H\cdots\cdots O}{\underset{O\cdots\cdots H-O}{\Big\langle \quad \Big\rangle}} C-R.$$

This tendency is enhanced in non-polar solvents, such as benzene; presumably there is little solvent–solute interaction and the intermolecular hydrogen bonding predominates. *p*-Cresol and nitrobenzene are other examples of substances which associate in benzene or in toluene.

Association leads to i factors which are less than unity:

$$2RCO_2H \rightleftharpoons (RCO_2H)_2$$

initial concentration	c	0
equilibrium concentration	$c(1-\beta)$	$\dfrac{c\beta}{2}$

Hence
$$i = \frac{c(1-\beta)+\dfrac{c\beta}{2}}{c} = 1 - \frac{\beta}{2} \qquad (6.23)$$

where β is the degree of association.

Example. A solution of 1·425 g. of acetic acid in 100 g. benzene has a freezing point depression of 0·608°C. Since K_f for benzene is 5·11, the apparent molecular weight is 119·8. Thus as the true molecular weight of acetic acid is 60·05, this substance is almost completely dimerised at this concentration; i from equation (**6.23**) is 0·5, and β is unity.

So far we have considered the depression of freezing point of a liquid, the solvent. The melting point of a solid solvent is lowered in a similar manner, by dissolving a solute in it to form a *solid solution*. A solid solution, like a liquid solution, is completely homogeneous.

The cryoscopic constant for some solids is large and so a freezing point depression may be measured using a thermometer graduated in 0·1°C. This leads to a simple method for determining approximate molecular weights for organic compounds. Camphor has a cryoscopic constant of 40°C. (see Appendix C) and may be used for this purpose. Its melting point is 177°C. however, and camphene (m.p. 42·7°C., K_f 35°C.) may be preferred.

Example. 0·01 g. naphthalene mixed with 0·1 g. of camphene melted at 40·0°C. Thus

$$2·7 = \frac{35 \times 0·01 \times 1000}{M \times 0·1}$$

whence M, the molecular weight of naphthalene is 129·6 (true value of $M = 128·2$).

6·3 Distillation

If distillation is carried out isothermally, then the composition of the vapour and that of the liquid with which it is in equilibrium are the same, and may be determined from isothermal vapour pressure–composition curves, such as figure 106 or 107.

Usually, distillation is carried out at constant atmospheric pressure and the boiling point of a mixture varies as the composition changes. For a binary system which is nearly ideal, the boiling point will vary regularly with composition. If the deviations of the system from Raoult's law are large and a maximum or a minimum occurs in the vapour pressure–composition curve, then *azeotropic mixtures* will be obtained. We shall consider three examples of distillation.

6·3·1 *Regular increase in boiling point*

Fig. 121 illustrates the temperature–composition diagram for this system. From the kinetic theory of gases equation (**4.29**), for a binary ideal mixture

$$p(\text{A}) = \frac{2E_K}{3V}n(\text{A}) \tag{6.24}$$

$$p(\text{B}) = \frac{2E_K}{3V}n(\text{B}) \tag{6.25}$$

$$P = p(\text{A}) + p(\text{B}).$$

Hence from Dalton's law.

$$\frac{p(A)}{P} = \frac{n(A)}{\{n(A)+n(B)\}} = x(A)$$

and

$$\frac{p(B)}{P} = \frac{n(B)}{\{n(A)+n(B)\}} = x(B).$$

Thus

$$\frac{dp(A)}{dx(A)} = P = \frac{p(A)}{x(A)}$$

whence

$$\frac{dp(A)}{dx(A)} \cdot \frac{x(A)}{p(A)} = \frac{dp(B)}{dx(B)} \cdot \frac{x(B)}{p(B)}.$$

But

$$dx(A) = -dx(B)$$

hence

$$\frac{x(A)}{p(A)} \cdot \frac{dp(A)}{dx(A)} + \frac{x(B)}{p(B)} \cdot \frac{dp(B)}{dx(A)} = 0.$$

The total pressure P is, from Dalton's law, $p(A)+p(B)$. Hence

$$\frac{dP}{dx(A)} = \frac{dp(A)}{dx(A)} + \frac{dp(B)}{dx(A)}$$

$$= \frac{dp(A)}{dx(A)} \left\{ 1 - \frac{p(B)x(A)}{p(A)x(B)} \right\}. \tag{6.26}$$

Now

$$\frac{dp(B)}{dx(A)} = \frac{-dp(B)}{dx(B)},$$

and is negative. If $\dfrac{dP}{dx(A)}$ is positive,

$$\frac{p(A)x(B)}{p(B)x(A)} > 1, \quad \text{or} \quad \frac{p(A)}{p(B)} > \frac{x(A)}{x(B)}.$$

Hence, the vapour is richer in A than is the liquid from which it was vaporized. Similarly, if $\dfrac{dP}{dx(A)}$ is negative, the vapour is richer in B than is the liquid from which it was vaporized.

In the example of fig. 121, $\dfrac{dT_b}{dx(B)}$ is positive: Since, for the vapour, the temperature of boiling is inversely proportional to the pressure, it follows that $\dfrac{dP}{dx(B)}$ is negative, or $\dfrac{dP}{dx(A)}$ is positive. Hence, the vapour is richer in A than the liquid from which it was vaporized. Consider the liquid with composition c; it boils at the temperature $T(d)$ and the composition of the vapour is given by f. The composition f is richer in A than the composition c and the boiling point of the liquid rises. If the condensed vapour e,

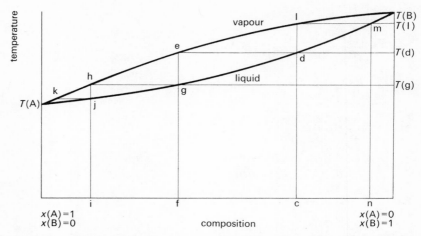

Figure 121. Temperature composition diagram for binary system: regular increase in boiling point.

which has the composition f, is redistilled, it boils at the temperature $T(g)$; the composition of the vapour is now given by i. Obviously, successive distillations will produce a small amount of the pure component, A.

If the original liquid, boiling at $T(d)$, is continuously distilled, the composition of the residual liquid is changed from that at c to pure B, the boiling point increasing regularly to $T(B)$. If the vapour of composition f were not allowed to escape but kept in equilibrium with the liquid, and boiling continued, the composition of the liquid would move to n, and that of the vapour to l. The boiling point is then $T(l)$; at this temperature, the whole of the original liquid is converted to vapour.

Fractional distillation implies a stepwise progression such as c, d, e, g, h, etc. leading to a pure component, A. A fractionating column is a device which enables this process to be achieved without the separation of each successive distillate. As vapour rises up a fractionating column it meets a downflow of liquid and becomes cooled. From fig. 121 we see that if the temperature of the vapour is lowered, it will partially condense giving a liquid richer in B and a vapour richer in A.

We may note that generally, the steeper the boiling point–composition curve, the greater the difference in composition between liquid and vapour at a boiling point. This can be seen to arise from the fact that $\dfrac{dP}{dx(A)}$ is inversely proportional to $\dfrac{dT}{dx(A)}$.

Examples of this type of system are oxygen–nitrogen (liquid air), acetone–water and chloroform–carbon tetrachloride.

6·3·2 *Maximum boiling point*

For a minimum or a maximum in the vapour pressure–composition curve, we require $\dfrac{dP}{dx(A)} = 0$. Hence, from equation (**6.26**)

$$\frac{p(A)}{p(B)} = \frac{x(A)}{x(B)}. \tag{6.27}$$

Fig. 122 illustrates a system of two components with a maximum boiling point (minimum vapour pressure). At the maximum, the composition of the vapour is the same as that of the liquid with which it is in equilibrium, equation (6.27).

A complete separation of the components A and B is not possible in this type of system. A liquid of composition c will boil at a temperature $T(d)$ when the com-

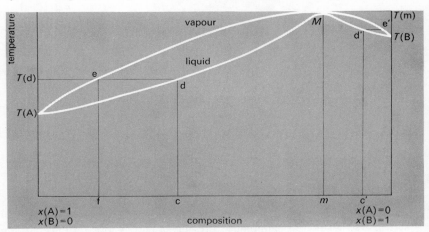

Figure 122. A maximum boiling point system.

position of its vapour is given by f. Fractionation of the distillate will give the pure component A. The composition of the liquid tends to the value m; at this composition it distils unchanged, at a temperature $T(m)$.

Again, if a composition such as c' is distilled, the pure component B may be obtained eventually and the liquid composition moves to m. Thus we may obtain in a pure state only that component which is present in excess of the composition of the *azeotropic* mixture m. Systems of this type are not common: a well-known example is the hydrogen chloride–water system:

P., mm.	b.p.,°C.	%HCl
400	92·08	21·235
500	97·58	20·916
600	102·21	20·638
700	106·42	20·360
760	108·58	20·222
800	110·01	20·155

A constant boiling point mixture of hydrogen chloride and water may be used as a primary standard in volumetric analysis.

6·3·3 Minimum boiling point

The condition $\dfrac{dP}{dx(A)} = 0$ describes also a minimum in the temperature–composition curve, fig. 123. From the previous reasoning, we may conclude that in this type of

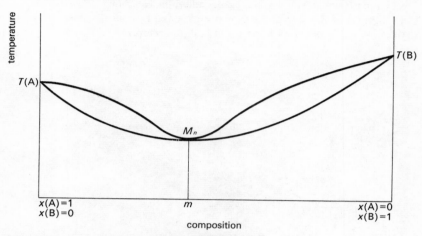

Figure 123. A minimum boiling point system.

system, fractionation would produce a residue of pure A with a distillate of composition m, or a residue of pure B with the same distillate, whichever component is present in the starting mixture in excess of the azeotropic composition m.

Examples of this type of behaviour are the systems ethyl acetate–water, ethyl acetate–ethanol and acetone–carbon tetrachloride.

6·4 Partially miscible liquids

If a little phenol or ether is added to an excess of water it will dissolve completely. Further addition of the organic compound will lead to the formation of two layers. One layer is water saturated with the organic compound, the other layer is the organic compound saturated with water. The two layers are in equilibrium and are called *conjugate solutions*.

The system phenol–water may be studied at atmospheric pressure. Since there are two components and generally three phases, application of the phase rule indicates one degree of freedom:

$$f = c - p + 2 = 1.$$

Temperature defines the system, fig. 124. At a given temperature the compositions of the liquid layers are fixed and are independent of the amounts of the two phases present. At any temperature T the conjugate solutions have the compositions a and b. As the temperature increases, the mutual solubilities increase: at the temperature T_e,

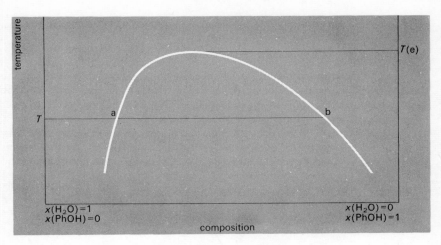

Figure 124. Portion of the phenol–water diagram.

the system is homogeneous at all compositions. This temperature is the (upper) *consolute temperature* or (upper) *critical solution temperature* for the system. In the case of phenol and water, the temperature is 66°C. and the composition is 66 per cent water.

The system nicotine–water, fig. 125, illustrates upper and lower critical solution temperatures at 208°C. and 61°C. respectively.

6·5   Immiscible liquids

Suppose we have a mixture of two almost completely immiscible liquids, for example

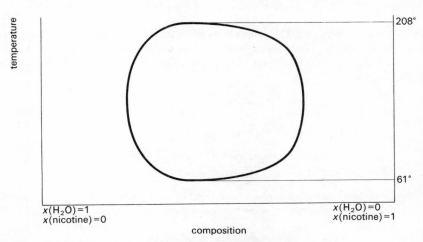

Figure 125.   The nicotine–water diagram (under pressure).

189   Physical properties of systems

aniline and water; at equilibrium, two liquid phases (conjugate solutions) and a vapour phase coexist. Applying the phase rule:

$$p+f = c+2 \quad \text{or} \quad f = 1.$$

The total vapour pressure is the sum of the separate vapour pressures of the two pure components, and depends upon temperature. The total pressure is independent of the composition of the mixture; addition of more aniline, or more water, merely changes the relative amounts of the two layers present without altering their compositions.

The vapour pressure–temperature curves for the aniline–water system are shown in fig. 126. The total vapour pressure is 760 mm. at $T(A+B) = 98.4°C$. At this temperature, the partial vapour pressures of aniline and of water are 42.4 mm. and

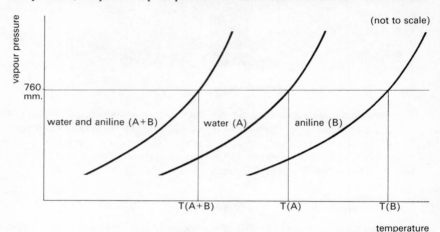

Figure 126. Vapour pressure-temperature curves for the aniline–water system.

717.6 mm. respectively. The proportions of aniline and of water in the vapour are in the ratio $42.2 : 717.6$, because both kinds of molecules possess the same kinetic energy, E_K, at a given temperature, and therefore from equation (5.24) exert the partial pressures

$$p(H_2O) = \frac{2E_K}{3} n(H_2O)$$

$$p(C_6H_5NH_2) = \frac{2E_K}{3} n(C_6H_5NH_2).$$

Hence $\quad \dfrac{n(H_2O)}{n(C_6H_5NH_2)} = \dfrac{p(H_2O)}{p(C_6H_5NH_2)}.$

Since the molecular weights of water and aniline are approximately 18 and 93 respectively, the relative weights of these molecules in the vapour are

$$\frac{w(H_2O)}{w(C_6H_5NH_2)} = \frac{717.6 \times 18}{42.4 \times 93} = 3.28.$$

Thus, if the vapour is condensed, the distillate contains about 23 per cent aniline.

This is the basis of steam distillation. To obtain a good yield by this method we require (i) a high partial vapour pressure of the organic compound and (ii) a high molecular weight of the organic compound. These two requirements are to some extent antithetical, as liquids with a high molecular weight usually have a low vapour pressure.

t, °C.	90	95	98	100
$p(C_6H_5NO_2)$, mm.	12·9	16·7	19·2	20·9
$p(H_2O)$, mm.	525·8	633·9	707·3	760·0
P, mm.	538·7	650·6	726·5	780·9

The molecular weights of nitrobenzene and of water are approximately 123 and 18 respectively. We require to determine the percentage by weight of nitrobenzene extracted by steam distillation. Fig. 127 shows the total pressure, P, plotted against

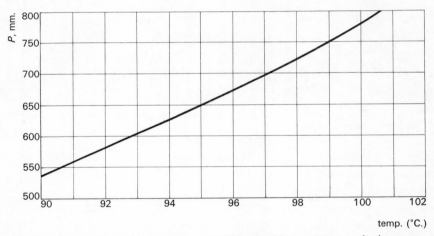

Figure 127. Variation of total vapour pressure P with temperature: nitrobenzene—water.

temperature; from this graph we deduce the boiling point of the mixture is 99·25°C. at 760 mm. In fig. 128, the partial vapour pressures of nitrobenzene and of water are plotted against temperature. At $t = 99·25$°C. the partial vapour pressures of water and of nitrobenzene and 741 mm. and 20·25 mm. respectively. Hence

$$\frac{w(H_2O)}{w(C_6H_5NO_2)} = \frac{741 \times 18}{20·25 \times 123} = 5·36$$

or about 15·7 per cent nitrobenzene in the steam-distillate.

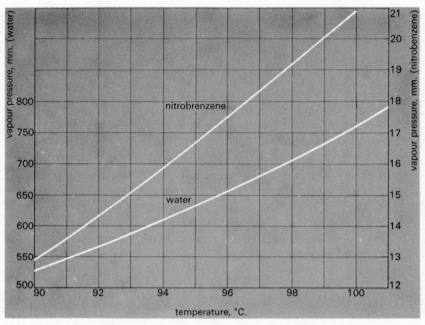

Figure 128. Variation of partial vapour pressures with temperature, for the nitro-benzene–water system.

6·5·1 *Solvent extraction*

Consider a solute which is soluble in two almost immiscible solvents, for example benzoic acid in water ether; in this, both layers, aqueous and ethereal, will contain some solute. At equilibrium, at a given temperature, there is a fixed ratio between the concentrations of the solute in the two layers, independent of the total present, provided that the solute is in the same molecular form in both solvents.

Let w_1 g. of solute of molecular weight M be contained in V_1 ml. of solution. Its initial molar concentration is thus $\dfrac{1000w_1}{M \times V_1}$. If this solution is shaken with V_2 ml. of a second and immiscible solvent, and w_2 g. of the solute passes into the second solvent from the first, then the molar concentrations in the two layers are

$$\text{Solvent } 1 : \frac{1000(w_1 - w_2)}{MV_1}$$

$$\text{Solvent } 2 : \frac{1000w_2}{MV_2}$$

The above proviso ensures that the molecular weight, M, is the same in both solvents.

The ratio of these concentrations is $\dfrac{(w_1 - w_2)V_2}{w_2 V_1}$, and is a constant, D, the *distribution coefficient*, for the system at a given temperature; this is the basis of the solvent extraction process.

Consider the extraction by ether of 100 ml. (V_2) of aqueous solution containing 5 g. (w_1) of solute A. We will assume that the ratio of the solute concentrations in ether and water is 10. If the solution is shaken with 15 ml. ether, w_2 g. of A will be extracted where

$$\frac{w_2}{5 - w_2} \times \frac{100}{15} = \frac{1}{10},$$

from which $w_2 = 3 \cdot 0$ g. If the extraction is repeated with a second 15 ml. portion of ether, the 2 g. of solute remaining in the aqueous layer is reduced to w_2'; since

$$\frac{w_2'}{2 - w_2'} \times \frac{100}{15} = \frac{1}{10},$$

$w_2' = 1 \cdot 2$ g. A third similar extraction reduces the concentration of solute in the aqueous layer to $0 \cdot 32$ g., i.e. a total of $4 \cdot 52$ g., or 94 per cent, has been extracted.

If the same extraction had been carried out, but adding the 45 ml. of ether in one portion, the amount of solute extracted from the aqueous layer would have been given by w_3, where

$$\frac{w_3}{5 - w_3} \times \frac{100}{45} = \frac{1}{10}.$$

from which $w_3 = 4 \cdot 1$ g., i.e. 82 per cent.

Evidently, it is always advantageous to extract with several small portions of solvent, rather than with one portion of the same total volume.

6·5·2 Distribution

The problem just considered is a particular example of the *distribution law*. For a system of two immiscible liquids, if a third substance is added, which is soluble in both liquids, then $c_1/c_2 = D$, where c_1 and c_2 are the molar concentrations of the solute in the two layers, at a given temperature. Consider the following data relating to the distribution of iodine between carbon tetrachloride (I) and water (II):

c (I)	c (II)	D
0·020	0·000235	85·1
0·040	0·000469	85·2
0·060	0·000703	85·4
0·080	0·000930	86·0
0·100	0·00114	87·5

The value of D is sensibly constant. A small drift with concentration is just noticeable; strictly the distribution law requires that the ratio of the *activities* of the solute in the two solvents is constant. If the solutions behave ideally, their activities may be replaced by mole fractions, and furthermore, if they are dilute, the ratio of the mole fractions is approximately the ratio of the corresponding molar concentrations.

We can use the distribution law to study equilibria in solution. For example:

$$I_2 \text{ (cryst.)} + I^- \text{ (aq.)} \rightleftharpoons I_3^- \text{ (aq.)}. \tag{6.26}$$

The tri-iodide equilibrium, equation (**6.26**), can be studied by finding a solvent (II), immiscible with water (I), in which one of the reactants is soluble; for example, carbon disulphide dissolves iodine and is immiscible with water. The equilibrium (**6.26**) exists in aqueous solution only and the ratio

$$\frac{[I_2] \text{ in aqueous layer}}{[I_2] \text{ in carbon disulphide layer}} = D.$$

Suppose we shake a solution of iodine in carbon disulphide with an aqueous solution of potassium iodide of concentration m. At equilibrium, let the total concentration of iodine be m_I in layer I and m_{II} in layer II; the concentration of iodide ions is zero in layer II.

Assuming the distribution law, the concentration of free iodine in layer I is Dm_{II} and that in the form of I_3^- is $m_I - Dm_{II}$. The concentration of free I^- in layer I is thus $m - (m_I - Dm_{II})$. Hence, if K is the equilibrium constant for equation (**6.26**):

$$K = \frac{[I_3^-]}{[I_2][I^-]} = \frac{m_I - Dm_{II}}{Dm_{II}(m - m_I + Dm_{II})}.$$

From a study of the tri-iodide equilibrium at 14°C., the value of K has been found, by this method, to be 955. K may be called the *stability constant* of the complex I_3^- ion.

6·6   **Molecular weights**

It is convenient to summarize in this chapter the methods available for the determination of molecular weights. These will be considered under two headings: (i) gases and volatile liquids and (ii) low-volatility liquids, and solids.

6·6·1   *Gases and volatile liquids*

The molecular weight of a gaseous substance can be determined directly from density measurements. The normal density of a gas is the mass of a specific volume at a given temperature and pressure; for example the density of oxygen is 1·4290 g. l.$^{-1}$ at s.t.p. The density per unit pressure is w/PV, where w is the mass of gas occupying V litre at s.t.p. This density would be constant at a given temperature if the gas behaved ideally. However, in practice, the value of w/PV changes with pressure, as may be inferred from fig. 129. The value $(w/PV)_0$ is the *limiting density* of the gas; for oxygen, it has the value 1·4276 g. l.$^{-1}$ Limiting densities are independent of pressure and can be compared without introducing errors due to non-ideality.

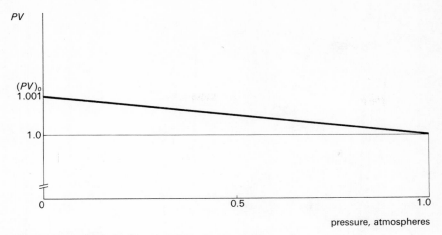

Figure 129. The limiting value of *PV* for real gases.

Regnault's method. A glass globe of about 1 l. capacity is evacuated and weighed, using another similar globe as a counterpoise. It is then filled with dry gas and reweighed. The volume of the globe may be determined by filling it with pure water and weighing, or the globe may be filled with hydrogen and weighed at the same temperature and pressure leading to the relative vapour density:

$$\text{density} = \frac{\text{mass of gas in globe}}{\text{volume of globe}}$$

$$\text{relative vapour density} = \frac{\text{mass of gas in globe}}{\text{mass of hydrogen in globe}}.$$

The molecular weight is *twice* the vapour density.

Dumas's method. In this method, a substance is vaporized completely at atmospheric pressure in a glass globe from which it displaces all the air. The globe is then sealed and weighed. Again, the volume of the globe must be determined, in order to calculate the density of the gas. A counterpoise globe must be used or alternatively, a buoyancy correction must be applied to the observed mass.

Victor Meyer's method. In this method, which is suitable for a volatile liquid, the liquid is vaporized rapidly and displaces its own volume of air, fig. 130. The vapour displaces a volume of air at the temperature, T, of the jacket. Provided that only air is displaced beyond the region of temperature T and that air obeys Charles's law, the volume of air measured at the ambient temperature, t, represents the volume of vapour formed, corrected to this temperature.

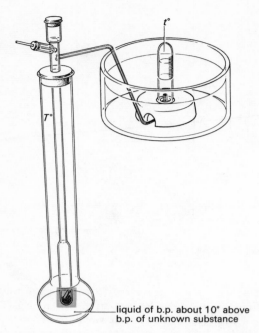

sand

liquid of b.p. about 10° above
b.p. of unknown substance

Figure 130.   Victor Meyer vapour density apparatus.

Example. 0·1475 g. chloroform were volatilized in a Victor Meyer apparatus and
30·1 ml. of air were collected over water at 17°C. and 755·1 mm. pressure. The vapour
pressure of water at 17°C. is 14·4 mm. and the density of hydrogen gas at s.t.p. is
0·000089 g. ml.$^{-1}$

Corrected pressure of air $= 755 \cdot 1 - 14 \cdot 4 = 740 \cdot 7$ mm.

$$\text{Volume of air at s.t.p.} = \frac{30 \cdot 1 \times 740 \cdot 7 \times 273 \cdot 16}{760 \times 290 \cdot 16}$$

$$= 27 \cdot 62 \text{ ml.}$$

$$\text{Density of vapour} = \frac{0 \cdot 1475}{27 \cdot 62} = 0 \cdot 00534 \text{ g. ml.}^{-1}$$

$$\text{Vapour density} \quad = \frac{0 \cdot 00534}{0 \cdot 000089} = 60 \cdot 00$$

Molecular weight $= 120 \cdot 0$
True molecular weight of chloroform $= 119 \cdot 38$

Anomalous vapour density results will be obtained if association or dissociation takes place in the vapour phase: e.g.

$$N_2O_4 \rightleftharpoons 2NO_2 \rightleftharpoons 2NO + O_2 \qquad \qquad \textbf{(6.27)}$$

$$2HI \rightleftharpoons H_2 + I_2. \qquad \qquad \textbf{(6.28)}$$

Consider the first part of the equilibria in equation (**6.27**). Initially, suppose that 1 mole of dinitrogen tetroxide is present; at equilibrium let a fraction α be dissociated. Then the number of moles has increased as a result of dissociation to $(1-\alpha) + 2\alpha = 1 + \alpha$. The mass of gas remains constant, and since density is inversely proportional to volume,

$$\frac{\text{vapour density after dissociation}}{\text{vapour density before dissociation}} = \frac{1}{1+\alpha}, \qquad \qquad \textbf{(6.29)}$$

an anomalous result will be obtained for the vapour density of N_2O_4.

In the equilibrium (**6.28**), there is no change in the total number of molecules after dissociation and hence no information about dissociation can be obtained from vapour density measurements.

Example. The vapour density of dinitrogen tetroxide at 26°C is 38. We will calculate the percentage of NO_2 molecules present at this temperature (i) by volume and (ii) by weight.

Assume one mole of N_2O_4 was present initially:

$$N_2O_4 \rightleftharpoons 2NO_2$$
$$(1-\alpha) \quad 2\alpha.$$

At equilibrium the total number of moles present is $(1+\alpha)$. The total volume is equal to $(1+\alpha) \times 22.4$ litre, and the volume of NO_2 is $2\alpha \times 22.4$. Hence

(i) $\%NO_2$ by volume $= \dfrac{2\alpha}{1+\alpha} \times 100.$

Now $\dfrac{1}{1+\alpha} = \dfrac{38}{46}$. Hence $\alpha = 0.21$ and $\%NO_2$ by volume $= \dfrac{42}{1.21} = 34.7$.

(ii) Total mass of gas $= 92$ g.

      Mass of $NO_2 = 2\alpha \times 46$ g.

$\%NO_2$ by weight $= \dfrac{92 \times \alpha \times 100}{92} = 21.0.$

(The cancellation of $M(N_2O_4)$ by $2M(NO_2)$ is peculiar to this problem.)

We have considered measurement of molecular weights by methods involving vapour pressure, freezing point depression, boiling point elevation and osmotic pressure. We add notes here on two modern physical methods.

6·6·2 Mass spectrometry

Traces of the vapour of the substance under examination are ionized by heating, or by electron bombardment in a mass spectrometer. The positive ions so formed are accelerated by an electric field of strength V volt. If the particle is singly charged, it acquires a kinetic energy given by

$$\tfrac{1}{2}mv^2 = Ve \tag{6.30}$$

where m and v are the molecular mass and velocity of the positive particle. The beam of ions is narrowed by passing through a slit system and is then introduced into a semi-circular magnetic field of strength H gauss. The radius of curvature, r, of the path of the moving particle is given by

$$\frac{e}{m} = \frac{v}{Hr}. \tag{6.31}$$

From equations (6.30) and (6.31)

$$\frac{e}{m} = \frac{2V}{H^2 r^2}. \tag{6.32}$$

Thus if H and V are constants, r is proportional to $(m/e)^{\frac{1}{2}}$, for a number of different ions. If the deflected beams are intercepted by a photographic plate, the position of a trace on the plate is directly related to the mass-to-charge ratio, or to the molecular weights of ions of similar charge. A very high degree of precision is attainable: for example, the molecular weight of an organic compound, euphenyl iodoacetate ($C_{32}H_{53}O_2I$), has been measured with an accuracy of 1 part in 10^6.

6·6·3 X-ray methods

From the relationship: density = mass/volume we can write

$$D_m = \frac{n \times M \times 1 \cdot 660 \times 10^{-24}}{V \times 10^{-24}}.$$

D_m is the measured density in g. cm.$^{-3}$, M is the molecular weight, n is the number of molecules in the unit cell of volume V Å.^{3} and $1 \cdot 660 \times 10^{-24}$ g. molecule^{-3} is the atomic mass unit. The volume of the unit cell is evaluated from the unit cell dimensions a, b and c; for an orthorhombic unit cell, $V = abc$. If M is known approximately, its accurate value may be obtained by X-ray methods; n is a positive integer. This technique is particularly useful for dealing with crystalline hydrates, since they can be examined directly in the solid state. The method is not absolute, however.

6·7 Simple eutectic mixtures and salt hydrates

We conclude this chapter with a short discussion on some simple hydrate systems, which are relevant to the subject matter of this chapter.

Consider the system potassium iodide–water, fig. 131. No compounds (i.e. no crystalline hydrates) are formed in this system. Ice separates from the solution along the line AC whereas along the line BC potassium iodide separates from solution. The line BC represents the solubility of potassium iodide in water at varying temperatures; its steepness indicates that the solubility of potassium iodide increases slowly with temperature. The line AC is the freezing point depression curve for potassium

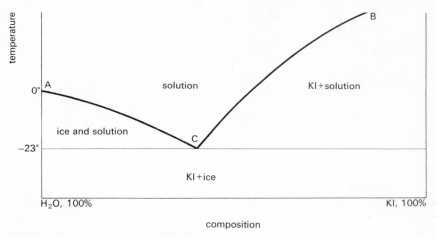

Figure 131. The KI–H₂O phase diagram.

iodide. The point C is a *eutectic* point; at this composition and temperature, a mixture of ice and potassium iodide separate out together and the temperature remains constant at −23°C. until all the liquid phase has disappeared.

It is important to note that the eutectic is a *mixture*. The phase rule may be expressed

$$p = c + 1 - f$$

since we are considering a condensed system at constant pressure. At C the system is invariant and since there are two components, there are three phases, i.e. solid potassium iodide, ice and solution.

A portion of the sodium sulphate–water system is shown in fig. 132. Several hydrates are formed in this system. Along the line AC ice is in equilibrium with liquid solution of varying composition, but along CB the solid phase present is sodium sulphate decahydrate. At B, a transition point is reached and crystals of *anhydrous* sodium sulphate separate out. The point B is called an *incongruent melting point*: the solid and the liquid obtained from it by melting do not have the same composition. B is an invariant point and sodium sulphate decahydrate, anhydrous sodium sulphate and liquid are in equilibrium here at a temperature of 32·4°C. The first portion of the curve BD shows a negative temperature coefficient of solubility.

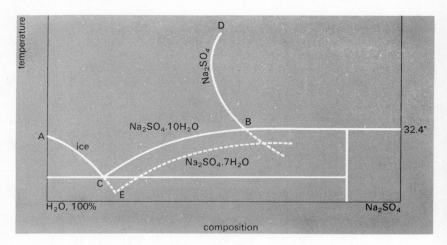

Figure 132.   A portion of the Na_2SO_4–H_2O phase diagram.

Fig. 133 shows a portion of the ferric chloride–water system. Again, several hydrates are formed. The line AB represents ice in equilibrium with solution, forming a eutectic at B with ferric chloride dodecahydrate. At the point C, the liquid and solid phases in equilibrium have the same composition; C is termed a *congruent melting point*. Another congruent melting point is shown at E. D represents the eutectic between ferric chloride dodecahydrate and ferric chloride heptahydrate.

The variation in vapour pressure above a salt hydrate is illustrated in fig. 134 with reference to copper sulphate, a much studied example, at 25°C.

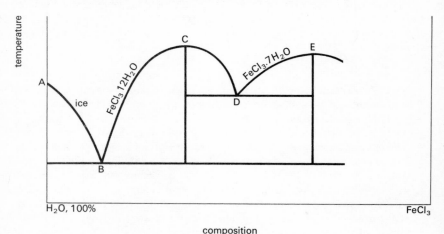

Figure 133.   Portion of the $FeCl_3$–H_2O phase diagram.

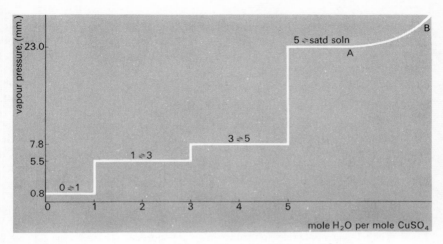

Figure 134. Isothermal (25°C) dehydration of the $CuSO_4$–H_2O system.

If a concentrated solution of copper sulphate is evaporated isothermally, the vapour pressure falls along the line BA. At the point A, the solution is saturated with respect to the pentahydrate which then crystallizes. The vapour pressure remains constant until all the saturated solution has crystallized. The phase rule indicates that this is correct:

$$p + f = c + 2, \quad \text{or} \quad f = 2 + 2 - 3 = 1.$$

Since there are three phases, the system is univariant along any horizontal line and is specified by the composition.

At 5 moles water per mole copper sulphate, the vapour pressure decreases sharply on further evaporation to 7·8 mm., at which pressure the trihydrate and pentahydrate are in equilibrium.

A study of diagrams such as fig. 134 shows how to 'dry' a hydrate to a true stoichiometric composition. In order to obtain a pure sample of copper sulphate pentahydrate, a sample containing water slightly in excess of the required composition, is confined over a mixture of the pentahydrate and trihydrate which are already in equilibrium. The excess moisture is absorbed by the trihydrate, the vapour pressure will equilibrate at 7·8 mm. and the stoichiometric composition, $CuSO_4 . 5H_2O$, will be attained. We may see from this discussion that a hydrate can rarely, if ever, be used as an analytical standard.

Problems

1. Explain the terms: mole fraction; colligative property; partial pressure; binary system; critical solution temperature; ideal solution; minimum boiling point composition; steam distillation.

2. The vapour pressure of water and of acetone at 39·5°C. are 54·30 mm. and 400·0 mm. respectively. Calculate the partial vapour pressures of both water and acetone in a solution containing 10 g. of water and 20 g. of acetone, at 39·5°C., assuming the system to be ideal.

3. The vapour pressure of ethanol at 19°C. is 40·00 mm. If 1·032 g. of a non-volatile substance M dissolved in 98·7 g. of ethanol produce a vapour pressure lowering of 0·432 mm., what is the molecular weight of the substance M?

4. An aqueous solution of a weak monobasic acid containing 0·1 g. in 21·7 g. of water freezes at $-0·187°C$. If the value of K_f for water is 1·86°C., what is the molecular weight of the monobasic acid?

5. Interpret fully the fact that a 0·1 molal solution of glucose has the same freezing point as a solution of calcium chloride containing 0·44 g. in 100 g. water.

6. A solution of 12·5 g. of urea in 170 g. of water gave a boiling point elevation of 0·63°C. Calculate the molecular weight of urea, taking $K_b = 0·52°C$. Derive any formula used.

7. The following data refer to the freezing point depressions of solutions of carbon tetrachloride, molecular weight 153·8, in benzene:

molality	0·1184	0·3499	0·8166
ΔT_f	0·603	1·761	4·005

In each case deduce an experimental value for K_f and comment upon the results obtained.

8. The following measurements of osmotic pressure, at 30°C., were made by Berkeley and Hartley (1906–9):

Molality (m) of sucrose solution	Osmotic pressure (π), atm.
0·590	15·48
1·081	29·72
1·662	48·81
2·396	74·94
3·331	111·87
4·178	148·46

The following data on the density of sucrose solutions have been measured subsequently:

Molality (m) of sucrose solution	Density (d), g. cm.$^{-3}$
0·000	0·996
0·325	1·034
0·730	1·077
1·252	1·122
1·701	1·160
2·550	1·224
4·660	1·340

Determine values for R at each concentration using the equation

$$\pi = cRT$$

where c is the concentration in mole l.$^{-1}$ To convert molality to molarity the following relationship is needed:

$$c = \frac{1000md}{1000+m}.$$

Extrapolate the results for R to the value $c = 0$; the units of R will be l. atm. mole^{-1} deg.$^{-1}$

9. The activity coefficient $f_{\pm}$ for 0·05 molal sodium chloride is 0·821. What would be the freezing point of an aqueous solution of sodium chloride at this concentration if K_f is 1·86°C?

10. A non-volatile solute of molecular weight 500 is dissolved in a solvent of cryoscopic constant 6·9, to form a saturated solution of molality 0·01. Calculate (i) the freezing point depression and (ii) the osmotic pressure at 25°C., assuming that the gram-molecular volume is 22·41.

Verify that, for a sparingly-soluble compound of high molecular weight, it is more practicable to determine the molecular weight from osmotic pressure measurements than from freezing point depression measurements. It may be assumed that a temperature change can be determined with an error of $\pm0·002°$ and that an osmotic pressure can be determined with an error of ±2 mm. Hg.

11. The freezing point depressions for p-cresol ($M = 108·1$) in benzene ($K_f = 5·11$) are 0·420° and 5·002° for solutions of molalities 0·0860 and 1·850 respectively. Calculate the degrees of association at the two concentrations.

12. 100 ml. of an aqueous solution of phenol containing 15 g. l.$^{-1}$ are shaken with (i) one 50 ml. portion of amyl alcohol and (ii) two 25 ml. portions of amyl alcohol. If the ratio of the concentration of phenol in water to that in amyl alcohol is $\frac{1}{16}$, calculate the total weights of phenol extracted in the processes (i) and (ii) above.

13. If a steam distillation of bromobenzene is carried out, the boiling point is found to be 96°C. at 770 mm. pressure. If the partial vapour pressure of water is 657·6 mm. at 96°C., calculate the weight percentage of bromobenzene in the steam distillate.

14. The antibiotic compound gliotoxin, $C_{13}H_{14}O_4N_2S_2 \cdot xH_2O$, crystallizes with a unit cell of volume 1451 Å.^{3}; its measured density is $1·543\pm0·01$ g. cm.$^{-3}$ Chemical evidence suggests a molecular weight of about 330. Determine (i) the number of molecules in the unit cell and (ii) the molecular weight, with probable limits of error.

Chapter 7
Electrochemistry

7·1   Electrolytic conduction

Two forms of electrical conduction are illustrated by figs. 135 and 136. In fig. 135, the current in the external circuit is carried through the conductors by electron flow; this process may be termed *electronic* conduction. It should be noted that the direc-

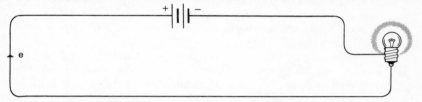

Figure 135.   Electronic conduction.

tion of electron flow is opposite to that of the conventional 'flow of current'. In fig. 136, the circuit is completed by two platinum electrodes dipping into a dilute aqueous solution of sulphuric acid. In this circuit, the current in the wires is carried as before, by electron flow, but in the solution, the current is carried by ion-transport; this

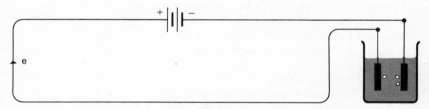

Figure 136.   Electronic conduction, with electrolytic conduction through the solution.

process may be termed *electrolytic* conduction. Chemical processes occur at the electrodes; in this example, hydrogen is evolved at the cathode (negative electrode) and oxygen is evolved at the anode (positive electrode). The use of the terms *anode* and *cathode* is best restricted to discussions of electrolysis.

Solutions which conduct electricity are termed electrolyte solutions and the substance producing these ions in solution is termed an electrolyte.

7·2 Faraday's laws of electrolysis

The decomposition of an electrolyte solution by an electric current is termed electrolysis. The quantitative aspect of electrolysis is governed by Faraday's laws of electrolysis. These are best summarized by equation (7.1): m is the mass in g. of an ion formed or discharged by passing a current of I amp. for t second; E is the chemical equivalent of the ion.

$$m = \frac{E(It)}{F}. \tag{7.1}$$

The product of I (amperes) and t (seconds) is the charge in coulomb. If $(It) = F$, then $m = E$. In other words, F coulomb is the charge required to form or discharge 1 g-equivalent of any ion. This charge is termed a faraday and is 96487 coulomb g-equivalent^{-1}.

The number of g-equivalents in 1 g-ion of any species is equal to $|z|$, the numerical charge on the ions of the given species. Since 1 g-ion contains N ions, the electric charge associated with a single ion is $\dfrac{|z|F}{N}$, where N is the Avogadro constant. For a singly charged ion, $|z| = 1$; hence $\dfrac{F}{N}$ represents the magnitude of the electronic charge in coulomb. This value is $1·602 \times 10^{-19}$ coulomb and is equal to $4·803 \times 10^{-10}$ e.s.u. of charge.

7·3 Electrolyte solutions

The basis of many modern studies of electrolyte solutions is embodied in the Arrhenius theory of 1887. It was then assumed that an acid, a base or a salt, upon dissolution, undergoes spontaneous dissociation to a greater or lesser degree, forming positive and negative ions: this is exemplified by equation (7.2).

$$MX \rightleftharpoons M^+ + X^- \tag{7.2}$$

The anions (negative ions) and cations (positive ions) are free to move independently, but, on application of an electric field, the resultant motions of the ions are towards the anode and the cathode respectively. The extent of dissociation is expressed by the degree of dissociation, α.

Consider an electrolyte which on dissociation forms γ ions per 'molecule' (in the case of ionic solids, the term 'molecule' should be interpreted as ion-pair). If the solution contains p molecules per litre, then, at equilibrium, there are $\gamma\alpha p$ ions and $p(1-\alpha)$ undissociated 'molecules' in one litre of solution. The total number of particles is thus $p(1-\alpha+\gamma)$. If there had been no dissociation, then one litre of solution would have contained p particles. The van't Hoff i factor is given by equation (7.3) and α by (7.4).

$$i = \frac{p(1-\alpha+\gamma\alpha)}{p} = 1-\alpha+\gamma\alpha \tag{7.3}$$

$$\alpha = \frac{i-1}{\gamma-1} \tag{7.4}$$

Arrhenius determined i from measurements of freezing-point depression, at various concentrations of electrolyte, and calculated α from equation (**7.4**). As it will be shown later, α may be derived also from measurements of electrical conductance. Results, similar to those obtained by Arrhenius, are listed in table 34 for hydrochloric acid and for acetic acid, in aqueous solutions.

Table 34 Degree of Dissociation for Hydrochloric Acid and for Acetic Acid, at 25°C.

c, g.-equiv. l.$^{-1}$	i	α, equation (**7.4**)	K	α, equation (**6.22**)	K
		HCl			
0·000	—	(1·00)	—	(1·00)	—
0·001	1·98	0·98	0·05	0·99	0·10
0·010	1·95	0·95	0·18	0·97	0·31
0·100	1·88	0·88	0·65	0·92	1·1
1·000	2·12	1·12	−10·5	0·78	2·8
		CH_3CO_2H			
0·000	—	(1·00)	—	(1·00)	—
0·001	—	—	—	0·13	$1·8 \times 10^{-5}$
0·010	—	—	—	0·04	$1·8 \times 10^{-5}$
0·100	1·02	0·02	$4·1 \times 10^{-5}$	0·01	$1·7 \times 10^{-5}$
1·000	0·96	(0·08)*	—	0·004	$1·4 \times 10^{-5}$

*Acetic acid is 8 per cent associated, as dimers, at a concentration of 1 molar.

The agreement in the two determinations of α for hydrochloric acid, at least up to a concentration of 0·001 g-equiv. l.$^{-1}$, was regarded as good supporting evidence for the Arrhenius theory. At higher concentrations, the agreement is poor and values of α greater than unity are obtained from the i factor. Furthermore, the equilibrium constant for equation (**7.2**), calculated according to the law of mass action, showed appreciable variation with concentration. On the other hand, for the weak electrolyte acetic acid, the values of the equilibrium constant show a very much smaller variation with concentration.

It may be noted that the Arrhenius theory pays no attention to the important role of the solvent. Later theories are much concerned with ion-solvent interaction, and the unique nature of water is recognized. In the example considered above, water was taken as the solvent; similar behaviour would be observed in a number of other solvents, such as ethanol or acetonitrile. In general, the electrical conductance of solutions depends upon the viscosity, the molecular weight and the dielectric constant of the solvent. It is the combination of low viscosity, low molecular weight and high dielectric constant that gives water its unique properties as an ionizing solvent.

7.4 Electrical conductance

The electrical conductance of an electrolyte solution may be treated in a manner similar to that of a metal: a specific conductance is defined as the reciprocal of the specific resistance (the resistance between opposite faces of a cm. cube of solution). The usual symbol for specific conductance is κ and the units are $\text{ohm}^{-1} \text{cm.}^{-1}$ (see equation **7.8**).

In order to study the effect of concentration on conductance for various electrolytes, we need to define the conductance of a fixed quantity of electrolyte at various concentrations: one g-equivalent is chosen. A 0·5 N solution contains 1 g-equivalent

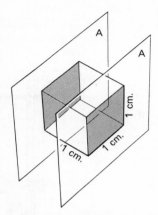

Figure 137.   Specific conductance and equivalent conductance.

in 2 l. of solution. If this solution were enclosed between two parallel electrodes placed 1 cm. apart, then the area of each electrode surface would be 2000 cm.² (fig. 137). Each cm.² of electrode forms one face of a 1 cm. cube of solution and the conductance between these faces is κ. Since there are 2000 such cubes, the conductance between the electrodes is 2000 or $\dfrac{1000}{0·5}$. This is the conductance of 1 g-equivalent of electrolyte at the concentration 0·5 N, i.e. it is the *equivalent conductance*, Λ. In general, a solution of concentration c g.-equiv. l.^{-1} has an equivalent conductance of $\dfrac{1000\kappa}{c}$, i.e.

$$\Lambda = \frac{1000\kappa}{c}. \tag{7.5}$$

The units of Λ are $\text{ohm}^{-1} \text{cm.}^{-1} \text{l. g-equiv.}^{-1}$

7·4·1   *Measurement of conductance*

The quantity which is measured directly is the resistance of a certain volume of solution. A conductance cell is placed in one arm of a Wheatstone bridge circuit (fig. 138). The variable resistance and variable capacitor are adjusted until no current flows through the headphones detector. At this balance point, the potential at S is equal to that at Q. Hence the resistance of the solution is given by equation (7.6).

$$R = \frac{R_2 R_5}{R_1} \tag{7.6}$$

An a.c. signal is essential and a frequency of 1000 Hz is generally used. The application of a d.c. potential to the circuit leads to electrolysis, and the electrodes become polarized, i.e. a counter e.m.f. is set up which opposes the flow of the current.

Because an alternating voltage is supplied to the bridge, both the conductance and the capacitance of the cell must be balanced, for zero current through the detector; the capacitance is balanced by adjustment of C_3, (fig. 138) in conjunction with R_3.

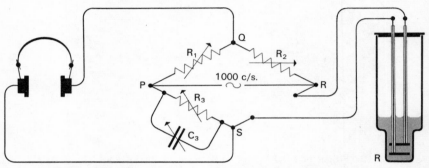

Figure 138. Wheatstone bridge circuit for the measurement of the resistance R of an electrolyte solution.

The specific resistance ρ is given by equation (7.7), and the specific conductance κ by (7.8):

$$\rho = R \cdot \frac{A}{l} \tag{7.7}$$

$$\kappa = \frac{1}{R} \cdot \frac{l}{A}. \tag{7.8}$$

The term (l/A) is the *cell-constant*; it is determined using a solution of known specific conductance. Potassium chloride solutions are generally used; the relevant data is given in table 35.

Table 35 Specific Conductance of Potassium Chloride in Aqueous Solution, κ in $ohm^{-1} cm.^{-1}$

c, g.-equiv./l.	18°C.	25°C.
0·010	0·001223	0·001411
0·100	0·01119	0·01289
1·000	0·09820	0·1117

This table indicates the need for strict temperature control while making conductance measurements: the conductance cell is placed in a thermostat maintained at a temperature constant to $\pm 0 \cdot 1°C$. or less.

The specific conductance measures the ease with which current flows through a solution. Solutions of different concentration have different specific conductances because each cm.[3] of the different solutions contains a different number of ions. Thus, the equivalent conductance, already defined by $\dfrac{1000\kappa}{c}$ is used to compare the current-carrying abilities of 1 g-equivalent of different electrolytes at various concentrations. It may be reiterated that by definition equivalent conductance, Λ, is the conductance of a solution contained by parallel electrodes 1 cm. apart, whose area is such that the volume of solution enclosed contains 1 g-equivalent of electrolyte. In practice, Λ is calculated from κ using equation (7.5).

7·5 The independent conductances of ions

Many precise measurements of equivalent conductance were made by Kohlrausch between 1870 and 1900. It was found empirically that a graphical plot of Λ against $\sqrt{c}$ approximated to a straight line at low concentration, for many electrolytes (fig. 139). These electrolytes are now termed strong electrolytes. The equivalent conductance of weak electrolytes, such as acetic acid or ammonia, approach the region of low concentration almost tangentially.

The curves for the strong electrolytes can be extrapolated to a limiting value at $\sqrt{c} = 0$, as shown by the dashed line in fig. 139. The extrapolated value is the *equivalent conductance at zero concentration*, Λ_0. This quantity may be regarded as a measure of the conductance of 1 g-equivalent of electrolyte in such a volume that the electrolyte is completely dissociated and in which the ions exert no attraction

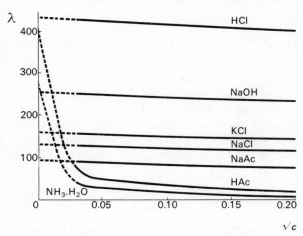

Figure 139. Equivalent conductance of electrolyte solution at 25°C.

upon one another. (If the dissociation constant of a weak acid or base is less than about 10^{-5}, complete dissociation will not occur in water even at zero concentration. The water provides a hydrogen ion concentration of 10^{-7}, so that, e.g. if $K_a = 10^{-5}$, $\alpha_{(c=0)} = 0.99$.) We may formulate Λ_0 by equation (7.9).

$$\Lambda_0 = \lim_{c \to 0} \Lambda = \lim_{c \to 0} \frac{1000\kappa}{c} \tag{7.9}$$

As $c \to 0$, κ also $\to 0$; this ratio has a finite value in the limit, which is expressed by Λ_0. This value is a characteristic of the electrolyte.

The concept of the equivalent conductance at zero concentration leads to the idea of independent conductance of ions. Table 36 lists values of Λ_0 for pairs of electrolytes

Table 36 Λ_0 for Electrolyte Pairs at 25 °C—Kohlrausch's law

	Λ_0		Λ_0	$\Lambda_0(KA) - \Lambda_0(NaA)$
KCl	150.0	NaCl	126.4	23.6
KNO_3	145.1	$NaNO_3$	121.5	23.6
KAc	115.3	NaAc	91.7	23.6
$\frac{1}{2}K_2SO_4$	153.5	$\frac{1}{2}Na_2SO_4$	129.9	23.6
				$\Lambda_0(MCl) - \Lambda_0(MNO_3)$
KCl	150.0	KNO_3	145.1	4.9
NaCl	126.4	$NaNO_3$	121.5	4.9
NH_4Cl	150.0	NH_4NO_3	145.1	4.9
$\frac{1}{2}CaCl_2$	135.5	$\frac{1}{2}Ca(NO_3)_2$	130.6	4.9

with a common cation or common anion. The difference in Λ_0 for each pair is independent of the anion or cation respectively. Kohlrausch postulated (1876) that each ion contributed a definite amount to the total conductance of a solution. This is exactly true only at zero concentration when there is no ionic interaction. The independent conductance of ions is summarized by equation (7.10)

$$\Lambda_0 = (\lambda_0^+) + (\lambda_0^-) \tag{7.10}$$

in which (λ_0^+) and (λ_0^-) are the conductances at zero concentration of the positive and the negative ions respectively.

7·6 **Transport numbers**

The current carried by an electrolyte solution during electrolysis is not necessarily shared equally between anions and cations. If (t_+) and (t_-) represent the fractions of the total current carried by the cations and anions respectively, i.e. their *transport numbers*, then their sum is unity, equation (7.11). In a solution containing $(m+n)$ ionic species, m being cationic and n being anionic, $\sum_m (t_+)_m + \sum_n (t_-)_n = 1$.

$$(t_+) + (t_-) = 1 \tag{7.11}$$

In metal conductors, the current is carried entirely by electron flow; in this case $(t_+) = 0$ and $(t_-) = 1$.

For an electrolyte solution, the method of measuring the transport number, t, due to Hittorf (1853) will be described. A suitable apparatus is illustrated by fig. 140.

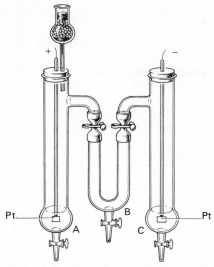

Figure 140. Hittorf's apparatus for the determination of transport numbers. (The clips are open during the experiment, and are closed when the contents of the outer compartments are removed for analysis, so as to prevent siphoning from the centre compartment.)

It consists of three compartments, A, B and C. The whole apparatus may be filled with a solution of silver nitrate ($AgNO_3$), for example, of known concentration c g.-equivalent per litre. If one faraday of charge is passed, the changes which occur are shown diagrammatically in fig. 141.

The number of equivalents of silver nitrate in the centre compartment B should remain unchanged throughout the experiment. In the cathode compartment C, the passage of one faraday produces changes due to the migration of ions and to the electrode reaction. The change in the number of equivalents of Ag^+ in C is $(t_+) - 1$ or $-(t_-)$ and the change in the number of equivalents of NO_3^- is also $-(t_-)$.

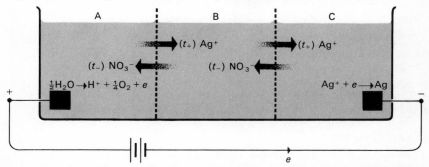

Figure 141. Schematic representation of a Hittorf experiment using silver nitrate, $AgNO_3$.

Similarly, the changes in the anode compartment A are $-(t_+)$ equivalents of Ag^+ per faraday of charge passed.

The net effects are the removal of (t_-) equivalents of silver nitrate from the cathode compartment and the removal of (t_+) equivalents of silver ions from the anode compartment. The change in the number of g.-equivalents in each compartment can be determined by analysis of the whole compartment and (t_+) and (t_-) can be evaluated.

In practice only a small fraction of a faraday is passed, e.g. 25 mA. for 2 hours or 180 coulomb. Suppose that under these conditions a loss of x g-equivalents occurs in the cathode compartment, then (t_-) is given by $\dfrac{xF}{180}$.

Analysis of the centre compartment confirms that no change in electrolyte concentration has occurred. This proves that the changes within the electrode compartments are confined to those compartments and have not been affected by diffusion into or out of the centre compartment. It should be noted that since the total change in equivalents is required, the entire contents of each compartment should be analysed.

The transport number gives the fraction of the total conductance contributed by a given ion. From equations (7.10) and (7.11) we may deduce (7.12) and (7.13).

$$(\lambda_0^+) = (t_0^+)\Lambda_0 \qquad\qquad\qquad (7.12)$$

$$(\lambda_0^-) = (t_0^-)\Lambda_0 \qquad\qquad\qquad (7.13)$$

(t_0^+) and $t_0^-)$ are the transport numbers of the cation and the anion respectively, extrapolated to zero concentration. Tables 37 and 38 list values of t and λ for different ions at various concentrations. The law of independent conductances of ions is true only at zero concentration and fails at high concentration when conductance and transport are properties of the electrolyte rather than of its component ions.

Table 37 Transport Numbers (t_+) and (t_-) at 25°C.

c, g-equiv. l.$^{-1}$	HCl	KCl	NaCl	NaOH	KNO$_3$
			(t_+)		
0·00	0·821	0·491	0·394	0·290	—
0·01	0·825	0·490	0·392	0·203	0·502
0·10	0·831	0·490	0·385	0·183	0·502
			(t_-)		
0·00	0·179	0·509	0·606	0·710	—
0·01	0·175	0·510	0·608	0·797	0·498
0·10	0·169	0·510	0·615	0·817	0·498

7·6·1   *Velocities of ions*

In table 38, values of u_0 are listed. These represent the ion mobilities, i.e. the absolute velocities of the ions in a potential gradient of 1 volt cm.$^{-1}$ The values were determined from the following calculations.

Table 38 Ion Conductances λ_0 and Ion Velocities u_0, at 25°C.

	(λ_0^+), ohm^{-1} cm.$^{-1}$	$10^4(u_0^+)$, cm. sec.$^{-1}$		(λ_0^-), ohm^{-1} cm.$^{-1}$	$10^4(u_0^-)$, cm. sec.$^{-1}$
H^+	350·0	36	OH^-	192·0	20
K^+	74·5	7·7	I^-	76·8	8·0
NH_4^+	74·5	7·7	Cl^-	75·5	7·8
Ag^+	63·5	6·6	NO_3^-	70·6	7·3
Na^+	50·9	5·3	Ac^-	40·8	4·2
Li^+	38·7	4·0	$\frac{1}{2}SO_4^{2-}$	79·0	8·2
$\frac{1}{2}Ca^{2+}$	60	6·2	$\frac{1}{4}Fe(CN)_6^{4-}$	111	11·5

Consider the cell implied by fig. 137. For an appreciable voltage (see 'overvoltage'), electrolyte solutions obey Ohm's law. Thus, if a current of I amp flows through a cell, which has a potential difference of V volts maintained between the electrodes, then the conductance of the cell is given by equation (7.14).

$$I = \frac{V}{R} = \Lambda V \tag{7.14}$$

At zero concentration, the current flow can be divided between anion and cation contributions. From equations (7.10) and (7.14) we can write (7.15) and (7.16).

$$I = \Lambda_0 V = (\lambda_0^+)V + (\lambda_0^-)V \tag{7.15}$$

$$= (I_+) + (I_-). \tag{7.16}$$

The electrodes enclose 1 g-equivalent of electrolyte in solution, i.e. there are $\frac{N}{(z_+)}$ cations and $\frac{N}{(z_-)}$ anions, where N is the Avogadro constant and (z_+) and (z_-) are the charges on the cations and the anions respectively. Let (u_+) and (u_-) represent the average velocities of the corresponding ions in a field of potential gradient of 1 volt cm.$^{-1}$

Fig. 137 is illustrated schematically by fig. 142. It may be seen that an anion or a cation crossing an imaginary boundary, B, in one second, must start at or within (u_-) cm. or (u_+) cm. respectively, from the boundary. In one second, $\frac{(u_+)N}{(z_+)}$ cations and $\frac{(u_-)N}{(z_-)}$ anions cross the boundary. The corresponding currents are $\frac{(z_+)e(u_+)N}{(z_+)}$ and $\frac{(z_-)e(u_-)N}{(z_-)}$. At zero concentration, and using equations (7.15) and (7.16) together with the fact that $N = \frac{F}{e}$, we obtain (7.17) and (7.18).

$$(I_+) = (\lambda_0^+)V = eN(u_0^+) = F(u_0^+) \tag{7.17}$$

$$(I_-) = (\lambda_0^-)V = eN(u_0^-) = F(u_0^-) \tag{7.18}$$

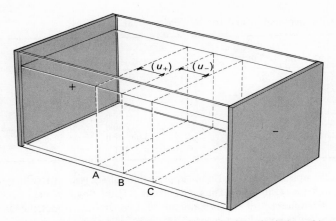

Figure 142.   Schematic diagram to illustrate the calculation of ion mobility.

If $V = 1$, we obtain equation (**7.19**) for the limiting ion velocities.

$$(u_0^+) = \frac{(\lambda_0^+)}{F}; \qquad (u_0^-) = \frac{(\lambda_0^-)}{F} \tag{7.19}$$

$$\Lambda_0 = F(u_0^+ + u_0^-) \tag{7.20}$$

The high mobilities for the hydrogen and the hydroxyl ions, compared with those of other ions, should be noted. It is considered that these values arise because of hydrogen ion (proton) *transfer* through the solvent. Water is a strongly hydrogen-bonded liquid and a possible transfer mechanism is illustrated by fig. 143. The 'transfer' of hydroxyl ions may be interpreted as the reverse movement of protons.

The change in velocity along the series K^+, Na^+, Li^+ is not that to be expected from a consideration of their ionic radii, table 39. The results indicate a greater degree of hydration for the smaller ions, so that Li^+ is effectively the largest cation. Comparing $Li^+(H_2O)_m$, $Na^+(H_2O)_n$ and $K^+(H_2O)_p$ where m, n and p are the numbers of water molecules which move with the ions (their primary hydration shells), we deduce that $m > n > p$.

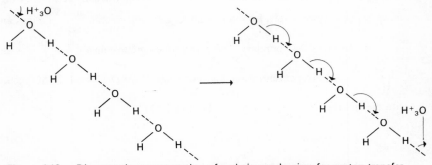

Figure 143.   Diagramatic representation of a chain mechanism for proton transfer.

Table 39   Radii (r) and Average Hydration Numbers ($\bar{\mu}$) of Some Ions

	r, Å	$\bar{\mu}$		r, Å	$\bar{\mu}$
Li^+	0·60	3·2	Cl^-	1·81	3·7
Na^+	0·95	4·4	Br^-	1·93	3·1
K^+	1·33	3·7	NO_3^-	1·2	2·5
Mg^{2+}	0·66	7·5	SO_4^{2-}	1·5	8·4

For a weak electrolyte the change in Λ with concentration c is due to the change in the degree of dissociation α of the electrolyte. As the concentration is reduced, α increases, and there are more ions present (Λ is always the conductance of one equivalent of the electrolyte). Since, as $c \to 0$, $\Lambda \to \Lambda_0$, the ratio $\dfrac{\Lambda}{\Lambda_0}$ gives the degree of dissociation at the concentration to which c refers.

For a strong electrolyte, Λ varies much less with concentration than for a weak electrolyte, and α is considered to be unity, at least in dilute solutions. The increase in Λ with decrease in concentration is now considered to be due to an increase in the velocities of the ions. According to the theory of Debye and Hückel (1923), oppositely-charged ions attract each other, and thus move less slowly under a potential gradient, at a finite concentration, than at almost zero concentration. Thus, the ratio $\dfrac{\Lambda}{\Lambda_0}$, for a strong electrolyte, is considered to represent $\dfrac{(u^+)+(u^-)}{\{(u_0^+)+(u_0^-)\}}$, where (u^+) and (u^-), apply to the same concentration as does Λ. The Debye-Hückel theory leads to the equation

$$\Lambda = \Lambda_0 - S\sqrt{c},$$

where S is a constant for a given electrolyte, solvent and temperature. Thus a plot of Λ against $\sqrt{c}$ should be linear, a suggestion first introduced by Kohlrausch (1898). For a uni-univalent electrolyte at 25°C. in water, $S = 0·228\Lambda_0 + 60·32$.

The changes in Λ, α and u with concentration are compared, for a weak and a strong electrolyte, in table 40.

Table 40

c, g-equiv. $l.^{-1}$	Λ_c	α	u^+	u^-
		CH_3CO_2H		
0·00	398	1·0	0·00363	0·000425
0·01	18·64	0·04	0·00362	0·000423
0·10	4·66	0·01	0·00359	0·000421
		NaCl		
0·0	126·5	1·0	0·000517	0·000795
0·01	118·5	1·0	0·000481	0·000747
0·10	106·7	1·0	0·000428	0·000680

7.7 Applications of conductance measurements

7·7·1 Determination of Λ_0 for a weak electrolyte

From fig. 139 it is evident that the value of Λ_0 for a weak electrolyte cannot be found by extrapolation of the measured values of equivalent conductance. Furthermore, conductance measurements cannot be carried out with accuracy at concentrations much below 10^{-4} g.-equivalent l.$^{-1}$

The law of independent ionic conductances can be used to determine Λ_0 for a weak electrolyte. This will be illustrated by reference to equations (**7.21**) to (**7.23**).

$$\Lambda_0(HAc) = \lambda_0(H^+) + \lambda_0(Ac^-) \tag{7.21}$$

$$\lambda_0(H^+) + \lambda_0(Ac^-) = \lambda_0(H^+) + \lambda_0(Cl^-) + \lambda_0(Na^+) + \lambda_0(Ac^-)$$
$$- \lambda_0(Na^+) - \lambda_0(Cl^-) \tag{7.22}$$

$$\lambda_0(H^+) + \lambda_0(Ac^-) = \Lambda_0(HCl) + \Lambda_0(NaAc) - \Lambda_0(NaCl)$$
$$= \Lambda_0(HAc) \tag{7.23}$$

Any weak electrolyte can be studied in a similar manner. It will be realized that the quantities on the right-hand side of equation (**7.23**) are all evaluated by extrapolation of the experimentally determined equivalent conductance data for the appropriate strong electrolytes.

Example. The values of Λ_0 for sodium hydroxide, sodium nitrate and ammonium nitrate are 242·9, 121·5 and 145·1, ohm^{-1} cm.$^{-1}$ l. g-equiv.$^{-1}$ respectively, at 25°C. In accordance with equation (**7.23**), the equivalent conductance at zero concentration for ammonia solution is $(242·9 + 145·1 - 121·5) = 266·5$ ohm^{-1} cm.$^{-1}$ l. g-equiv.$^{-1}$ at 25°C.

Ions such as NH_4^+ and Ac^- undergo hydrolysis in aqueous solution forming H^+ ions and OH^- ions respectively. The extent of this hydrolysis varies with concentration. Hence, in an accurate application of (**7.23**), the equivalent conductances of NH_4^+ and Ac^-, and of similarly hydrolysed ions, must be corrected at each concentration for the presence of H^+ and OH^- respectively, before extrapolation to zero concentration (see p.152).

7·7·2 Determination of the dissociation constant for a weak uni-univalent electrolyte

The Arrhenius theory of electrolytic conduction was outlined earlier and table 34 lists dissociation constants obtained from conductance measurements.

If all the ions of 1 g-equivalent of a weak electrolyte contribute to current flow, then the equivalent conductance is Λ_0, which is proportional to $(u_0^+) + (u_0^-)$. from equation (**7.20**). If at a given concentration, a fraction α of the electrolyte dissociates, the equivalent conductance, Λ, provided that the solution is sufficiently dilute for interionic attraction to be negligible, is proportional to $\alpha\{(u_0^+) + (u_0^-)\}$. Hence, α is given by the conductance ratio, equation (**7.24**).

$$\alpha = \frac{\Lambda}{\Lambda_0} \tag{7.24}$$

This proviso ensures that the ions have their limiting mobilities (u_0^+) and (u_0^-), at the given concentration.

In chapter 5, the expression for the equilibrium constant is discussed. For an equilibrium system such as (7.25), the equilibrium constant is given, in terms of concentrations, by equation (7.26). At equilibrium $[A^+] = \alpha c = [B^-]$, and $[AB] = c(1-\alpha)$; hence K is given also by (7.27), and using equation (7.24), by (7.28)

$$AB \rightleftharpoons A^+ + B^- \tag{7.25}$$

$$K = \frac{[A^+][B^-]}{[AB]} \tag{7.26}$$

$$K = \frac{\alpha^2 c}{1-\alpha} \tag{7.27}$$

$$K = \frac{c\Lambda^2}{\Lambda_0(\Lambda_0 - \Lambda)}. \tag{7.28}$$

From a set of conductance measurements over a range of concentration between 5×10^{-4} and 5×10^{-2} g-equiv. l.$^{-1}$ we can obtain α and K for a weak electrolyte without appreciable error, provided that $K_a > 10^{-5}$.

7·7·3   *Determination of solubility and solubility product*

If the solubility of a sparingly soluble electrolyte, such as calcium sulphate, is s g-equivalent l.$^{-1}$ and if the specific conductance of the saturated solution is κ_s, then the equivalent conductance is $\dfrac{1000\kappa_s}{s}$. If the solution is sufficiently dilute, $\Lambda \approx \Lambda_0$; hence, the solubility can be obtained from measurements of the specific conductance of the saturated solution. From table 38, $\Lambda_0(CaSO_4)$ is equal to 139·0 ohm^{-1} cm.$^{-1}$ l. g-equiv.$^{-1}$ At 25°C., the specific conductance of the saturated solution is 0·00416 ohm^{-1} cm^{-1}; the specific conductance of the water is $1·50 \times 10^{-6}$ ohm^{-1} cm.$^{-1}$, which is almost negligible *in this example*. The solubility of calcium sulphate is given by $\dfrac{1000(0·004158)}{\Lambda_0}$ which is 0·0299 g-equiv. l.$^{-1}$ The solubility in g. l.$^{-1}$ is $0·0299 \times 68·08 = 2·035$, where 68·08 is the equivalent (in this example, half-molecular) weight of calcium sulphate. The solubility in g-ion l.$^{-1}$ is $\dfrac{0·0299}{2}$, where 2 is the numerical charge on the ions. Hence, the solubility product of calcium sulphate is $(0·01495)^2 = 2·2(4) \times 10^{-4}$.

This value for the solubility product differs appreciably from that listed in Appendix C, which is $2·4 \times 10^{-5}$. Evidently, saturated calcium sulphate is not sufficiently dilute for activities to be replaced by concentrations. An approximate correction may be applied, using the Debye-Hückel limiting law to obtain the mean ionic activity coefficient, $f_\pm$ (chapter 5). Remembering that both ions are doubly charged, $f_\pm$ is evaluated as 0·317. Hence, the solubility product is given more accurately by $(0·01495)^2 \times (0·317)^2 = 2·2 \times 10^{-5}$, which agrees more closely with the true thermodynamic solubility product.

The above experimental method assumes the absence of hydrolysis or of complex ion formation.

7·7·4 *Determination of the charges on complex ions*

From the data in table 38, it may be seen that the average ion conductance per single charge, excluding H^+ and OH^-, is about 65 ohm^{-1} cm.$^{-1}$, at 25°C. and at zero concentration. It is convenient to work at a concentration of 2^{-10} mole l.$^{-1}$ (a dilution of 2^{10} or 1024 l. mole^{-1}); we may take $\Lambda(1024)$ as lying in the range 60 to 70 ohm^{-1} cm.$^{-1}$ The *molar* conductance is defined by $\dfrac{1000x}{m}$, where m is the electrolyte concentration in moles per litre. The molar conductances of different types of electrolytes is shown in table 41, and some examples of their use are listed in table 42. The molar conductance of the AB_2 electrolyte, for example, is explained by considering that it furnishes *one* A^{2+} ion and *two* B^- ions, or in all *four* times the *equivalent* conductance of a singly-charged ion.

Table 41 Molar Conductance Ranges for Different Types of Electrolytes at 25°C.

Electrolyte type	Molar conductance range, ohm^{-1} cm.$^{-1}$ l. mole^{-1}
AB	120–140
AB_2, A_2B	240–280
AB_3, A_3B	360–420
AB_4, A_4B	480–560

Table 42 Examples of Ionic Charge Determination, using Table 40

Complex compound	Molar conductance, Λ (1024)	Electrolyte type
$Pt(NH_3)_6Cl_4$	500	$A^{4+}B^-$
$K_3Co(NO_2)_6$	418	$A_3^+B^{3-}$
$[Co(NH_3)_3(NO_2)_3]$	1·5	Neutral complex (non-electrolyte)

7·7·5 *Conductance titrations*

A conductance titration is performed in a conductance cell. Readings of resistance (or of conductance) and of volume of titrant are recorded. Several examples will be considered (fig. 144).

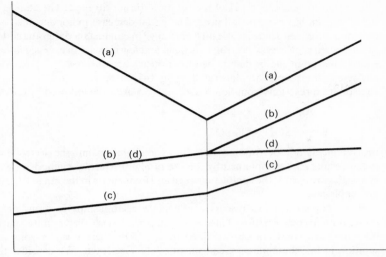

relative conductance

(a)

(a)

(b)

(d)

(b) (d)

(c)

(c)

volume of titrant

(a) Strong acid –strong base
(b) Weak acid ($pK_a \approx 5$) –strong base
(c) Weak acid ($pK_a \approx 10$) –strong base
(d) Weak acid ($pK_a \approx 5$) –weak base ($pK_b \approx 5$)

Figure 144.   Conductance titrations.

(a) If an alkali is added to a strong acid, the highly conducting hydrogen ions are replaced by cations of much lower conductance and the conductance of the solution decreases. Immediately after the equivalence point, the further addition of alkali introduces excess hydroxyl ions and the conductance increases, but not so steeply as the decrease before the equivalence point, since the conductance of OH^- is only about 0·55 times that of H^+.

(b) If an alkali is added to a weak acid ($pK_a \approx 5$), the conductance of the solution falls initially: the common ion formed represses the dissociation of the weak acid. With continued addition of alkali, the conductance rises. Both sodium ions and hydroxide ions are being added to the solution, but the OH^- ions are replaced by acetate ions in the reaction (**7.29**).

$$HAc + OH^- \rightleftharpoons Ac^- + H_2O . \qquad (7.29)$$

Immediately after the equivalence point, the conductance rises more rapidly because of the presence of excess hydroxyl ions.

(c) If the acid is very weak ($pK_a \approx 10$), the conductance rises throughout the titration; from the small equilibrium constant, it is clear that initially there are so few ions that the conductance of the solution is inappreciable.

(d) The conductance titration of a weak acid and a weak base is interesting. We have noted in chapter 4 that this titration cannot be performed by any process that relies upon the change in pH of the solution during titration. The change in conductance can, however, be followed. The initial decrease in conductance is due to common ion effect. There is little further change in conductance after the equivalence point, because the excess electrolyte is weak and few ions are in excess. However, the equivalence point can be determined from the change of slope.

These four examples are illustrated by fig. 144, curves (a) to (d).

Precipitation reactions, equations (7.30) and (7.31), can be followed by conductance

$$Ag^+ + Cl^- \rightarrow AgCl \qquad (7.30)$$

$$Ba^{2+} + SO_4^{2-} \rightarrow BaSO_4 \qquad (7.31)$$

measurements. Some errors may arise due to precipitation onto the electrode surfaces. Better results may be obtained by the use of high frequency methods in which the electrodes are *outside* the conductance cell and frequencies in the range 1 to 300 MHz are employed.

Many older textbooks discuss conductance relationships in terms of dilution rather than of concentration. Thus, zero concentration is called infinite dilution and the equivalent conductance is defined by $\Lambda = Kv$, where v is the volume of the solution in ml. containing 1 g-equivalent of the electrolyte. We consider that this treatment is undesirable: extrapolation of equivalent conductance to obtain Λ_0, for strong electrolytes, cannot be carried out satisfactorily when dilutions are plotted as zero concentration corresponds to infinite dilution. Furthermore, modern studies of electrolyte solutions discuss conductance in terms of ionic strength and hence, in terms of concentrations.

7·8   The e.m.f. of cells

All substances, even metals such as zinc and copper, have a tendency to dissolve in water. Metals dissolve to form cations, positive ions, in solution, and their valence electrons remain on the metal. The tendency of metals to dissolve is decreased, and may even be reversed, if ions of the same type as those derived from the metal are already present in solution.

Suppose that a zinc rod is placed in a 1 molar solution of zinc sulphate. Zinc tends to dissolve producing a few more Zn^{2+} ions in solution, and leaving the rod negatively charged with respect to the solution (fig. 145a). A potential difference is set up between the rod and the solution and an electrical double layer is formed.

If a rod of copper is placed in a 1 molar solution of copper sulphate, a few ions from the solution are deposited upon the copper rod, which becomes positively charged with respect to the solution (fig. 145b).

In general, the numbers of ions released or deposited in the circumstances described is very small. The tendencies mentioned above are soon reduced to zero by the potential differences which are established. Consider a zinc electrode. As the negative potential is developed on the rod, the rate at which zinc ions leave the rod to go into solution is reduced. On the other hand, as the rod becomes negatively charged, the rate at which Zn^{2+} ions from solution become deposited on the rod is increased. Equilibrium is soon established when the two rates become equal. The potential difference which is set up is precise, and depends upon the activity (or approximately,

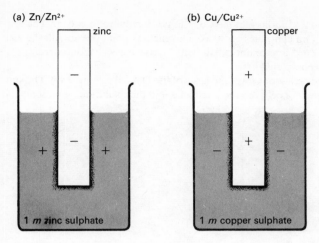

Figure 145.   Reversible electrode systems.

the concentration) of ions in solution and upon the temperature, for the given electrode.

If the two systems shown in fig. 145 are placed in electrical contact, without free mixing of the solutions, and if the electrodes are connected externally, then electron flow will take place in the external circuit (fig. 146). Electrons are transferred from zinc to copper through the external circuit. The electrode processes are given by equations (7.31) and (7.32);

$$Zn \rightarrow Zn^{2+} + 2e \qquad\qquad (7.32)$$

$$Cu^{2+} + 2e \rightarrow Cu \qquad\qquad (7.33)$$

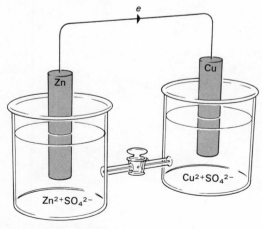

Figure 146.   An e.m.f. cell.

the zinc is oxidized to Zn^{2+} ions and the Cu^{2+} ions are reduced to copper. The process is spontaneous, and continues until, from a practical point of view, all the zinc has been oxidized to Zn^{2+} ions or until all the Cu^{2+} ions have been reduced to copper, whichever process is completed first.

The above electrode reactions form the basis of the Daniell cell (fig. 147). The sum of the potential differences between the electrodes and their solutions represents the

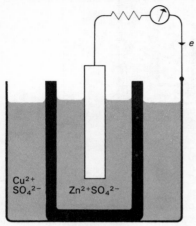

Figure 147.   A Daniell cell.

e.m.f. of the cell; in the present example, it is about 1·1 volt. In this context, e.m.f. has its usual meaning of potential difference between electrodes in the absence of ohmic voltage drop, i.e. on open circuit when no current flows.

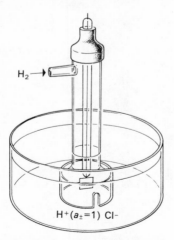

Figure 148.   A hydrogen electrode.

The e.m.f. of a cell is measured with a potentiometer or with a valve voltmeter. The potential difference between each electrode and the solution cannot be measured because there is no way of making contact with the solution without setting up another electrode potential difference.

For convenience, a reference electrode is defined. It is the standard hydrogen electrode (fig. 148), and consists of pure hydrogen gas at unit partial pressure in contact with a solution of hydrogen ions at unit activity. The hydrogen bubbles over the surface of a platinum electrode which has been coated with finely-divided platinum (platinum black); the potential difference between this electrode and the solution is chosen as 0·000 volt, at 25°C.

Using the hydrogen reference electrode, the potential difference of any other electrode system may be measured with respect to it. A *standard* electrode potential implies unit activity of the ions and a temperature of 25°C. This is illustrated for the zinc and copper electrode systems, separately, in fig. 149. It should be noted that

(a) Zn/Zn^{2+} (b) Cu/Cu^{2+}

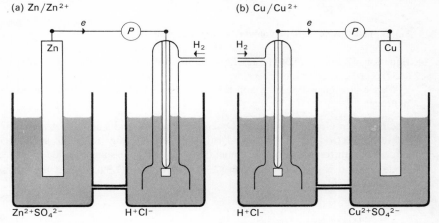

Figure 149. Comparison of electrode potentials with a standard hydrogen electrode.

electron flow with respect to the hydrogen electrode is different in (a) and (b); thus, two different processes are occurring at the hydrogen electrode, despite the fact that hydrogen gas is being passed over the platinum surface under identical conditions in both cases.

In (a) we have the two processes, equations (**7.34**) and (**7.35**):

$$Zn \rightarrow Zn^{2+} + 2e \tag{7.34}$$

$$H^+ + e \rightarrow \tfrac{1}{2}H_2. \tag{7.35}$$

In (b) the two processes, equations (**7.36**) and (**7.37**) occur:

$$\tfrac{1}{2}H_2 \rightarrow H^+ + e \tag{7.36}$$

$$Cu^{2+} + 2e \rightarrow Cu. \tag{7.37}$$

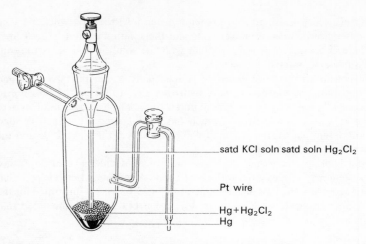

satd KCl soln satd soln Hg_2Cl_2

Pt wire

$Hg+Hg_2Cl_2$
Hg

Figure 150. A saturated calomel reference electrode.

Equations (**7.34**) and (**7.36**) represent oxidation processes, and equations (**7.35**) and (**7.37**) represent reduction processes.

We are now beginning to establish a scale of potential differences with respect to hydrogen.

The hydrogen electrode is not a very convenient practical standard. A subsidiary reference electrode is the saturated calomel electrode (fig. 150); the solution is saturated with respect to both calomel (Hg_2Cl_2) and potassium chloride. The electrode reaction is given by equation (**7.38**), followed by (**7.39**), so that the overall reaction is (**7.40**).

$$Hg \rightarrow \tfrac{1}{2}Hg_2^{2+} + e \tag{7.38}$$

$$\frac{\tfrac{1}{2}Hg_2^{2+} + Cl^- \rightarrow \tfrac{1}{2}Hg_2Cl_2}{Hg + Cl^- \rightarrow \tfrac{1}{2}Hg_2Cl_2 + e} \tag{7.39}$$
$$\tag{7.40}$$

The *standard* potential of this electrode is 0·244 volt at 25°C. and the variation of this value with temperature t is given by equation (**7.41**).

$$\pi = 0·244 - 0·0007(t - 25). \tag{7.41}$$

Another useful subsidiary reference electrode is the silver–silver chloride electrode. This is a silver wire on which silver chloride has been anodically deposited from a potassium chloride solution. The standard electrode potential is 0·223 volt; this can be evaluated from the standard electrode potentials and a consideration of the processes in equations (**7.42**) to (**7.44**).

$$Ag \rightarrow Ag^+ + e \tag{7.42}$$

$$\frac{Ag^+ + Cl^- \rightarrow AgCl}{Ag + Cl^- \rightarrow AgCl + e} \tag{7.43}$$
$$\tag{7.44}$$

The *standard* electrode potential ($a_{\pm}[Ag^+] = 1$) associated with the reaction (**7.42**) is, from Appendix D, 0·80 volt. The e.m.f. associated with reaction (**7.42**) is obtained from equation (**7.47**). Since $-\Delta G^0 = 2 \cdot 3026 RT \log_{10}(a_{\pm})^2$ and $(a_{\pm})^2$ is the thermo-dynamic solubility product (Appendix C), we may formulate equation (**7.45**):

$$E = \frac{2 \cdot 3026 RT \log_{10}(S_T)}{nF}.$$ (7.45)

From this equation, with $n = 1$, $R = 8 \cdot 314$ joule mole^{-1} deg.$^{-1}$ and $T = 298 \cdot 16°$K., E is evaluated as $-0 \cdot 578$ volt. Since the standard electrode potential for the Ag/Ag$^+$ system is 0·80 volt, the standard electrode potential for the Ag–AgCl electrode is 0·22(2) volt.

7·8·1   *Measurement of e.m.f.*

The electrical energy dissipated by a cell working in a thermodynamically reversible manner is equivalent to the free energy decrease accompanying the cell reaction. The free energy decrease accompanying the Daniell cell reaction is 50·73 kcal. mole.$^{-1}$ The cell reaction requires 2 faraday of charge per g-ion discharged or formed. If the reaction (**7.46**) occurs in the Daniell cell, the quantity of electricity passed is 2 faraday.

$$\begin{array}{cccc} \text{Zn} & + \ \text{Cu}^{2+} \ \rightarrow & \text{Zn}^{2+} \ + & \text{Cu} \\ (65 \cdot 4 \, \text{g.}) & (63 \cdot 5 \, \text{g.}) & (65 \cdot 4 \, \text{g.}) & (63 \cdot 5 \, \text{g.}) \end{array}$$ (7.46)

The maximum energy change of an electrical process is the product of charge and e.m.f. If the charge is measured in coulombs (amperes × seconds) and the e.m.f. is measured in volts, the energy is expressed in joules (watts × seconds). In the present case, the energy associated with the cell reaction is $2FE$ joule g-ion.$^{-1}$ This energy change corresponds to the free energy change of the reaction. Hence, we can equate 50730 cal. mole^{-1} to $(2 \times 96487 \times E)/J$, where J is the Joule equivalent (4·184 joule cal.$^{-1}$) leading to the value 1·1 volt for the e.m.f. In general, we can write equation (**7.47**) in which n is the number of faradays which must be passed for the chemical

$$-\Delta G = nFE$$ (7.47)

$$Ag^+ + \tfrac{1}{2}H_2 \rightarrow H^+ + Ag$$ (7.48)

reaction as written to occur. If we write reaction (**7.48**) the free energy change is $-FE$ joule gram.-ion^{-1} of silver deposited. If, however, we write the same process by equation (**7.49**), the free energy change is $-2FE$ joule mole^{-1} of hydrogen ionized;

$$2Ag^+ + H_2 \rightarrow 2H^+ + 2Ag$$ (7.49)

the value of E remains unchanged.

The measurement of cell e.m.f. must be carried out under equilibrium conditions, if the free energy change of the cell reaction is to be evaluated. Thus, as the measurement is made, unidirectional chemical reaction is not occurring; we are measuring the tendency for such a reaction to occur.

An ordinary voltmeter cannot be used to measure the e.m.f. of a cell since it draws current continuously. A potentiometer circuit is suitable and is shown in fig. 151. C is a storage battery connected through a variable resistance R to a uniform resistance wire AB. A sliding contact D connects this wire, through a galvanometer G to either a standard cell S of e.m.f. E_S or to the cell X of unknown e.m.f. E_X. Both cells are arranged so that their e.m.f. are in opposition to the e.m.f. of the storage battery.

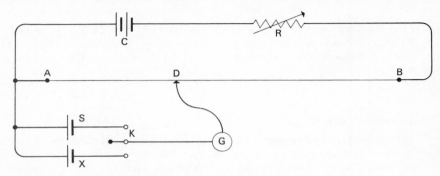

Figure 151.   A potentiometer circuit for measuring e.m.f.

With the standard cell S in the circuit, D is adjusted until no current flows through the galvanometer. Then the e.m.f. E_S is balanced by the length of wire, say AD_S. The switch K is altered to bring the cell X into the circuit, and a new balance point, say AD_X, is found. Hence, we may write $\dfrac{E_S}{E_X} = \dfrac{AD_S}{AD_X}$ and E_X may be evaluated. The variable resistance R is used to ensure that balance points can be obtained within the length of the wire AB. R remains constant while the two readings are taken.

In commercial potentiometers, a switch is first set to 'standardize', connecting the standard cell to the circuit; the standardizing resistor is adjusted for zero deflection of the galvanometer. The scale of the instrument is now calibrated directly in millivolts. The unknown e.m.f. is balanced with the switch in the 'read' position.

The standard cell employed is the Weston cell:

$$12 \cdot 5 \, \% \mathrm{Cd} \text{ in } Hg|CdSO_4 \text{ (satd), } Hg_2SO_4 \text{ (satd)} | Hg.$$

From the point of view of the current flowing in the external circuit, the negative electrode is a 12·5 per cent cadmium amalgam covered with crystals of cadmium sulphate, $3CdSO_4 . 8H_2O$; the positive electrode is mercury covered by a paste of mercury and mercurous sulphate. Electrical contact in the cell is obtained through a saturated solution of cadmium sulphate. The e.m.f. of the Weston cell is 1·0183 volt at 20°C. and the variation of e.m.f. with temperature is given by equation (7.50).

$$E_t = 1 \cdot 0183 - 4 \cdot 06 \times 10^{-5}(t-20) - 9 \cdot 5 \times 10^{-7}(t-20)^2. \tag{7.50}$$

The enthalpy of reaction for the Daniell cell process can be measured calorimetric-ally; the result is $-50\cdot13$ kcal. mole^{-1}, or only $0\cdot60$ kcal. mole^{-1} less than the value obtained by evaluating $\left(\dfrac{-nFE}{1000J}\right)$. This fact led originally to the incorrect view that the enthalpy of reaction could be equated to the term $(-nFE)$. However, measure-ments involving other cells showed that the close correspondence of the results for the Daniell cell was fortuitous. For example, the reaction

$$Pb + 2Ag^+ \rightarrow Pb^{2+} + 2Ag \tag{7.51}$$

can be studied calorimetrically, and also by setting up the cell

$$Pb|KI(m), PbI_2 \text{ (satd)}, AgI \text{ (satd)}|Ag. \tag{7.52}$$

Here, $\Delta H_{\text{calor.}} = 12\cdot2$ kcal. mole^{-1} at 25°C. but $\left(\dfrac{-nFE}{1000J}\right) = -9\cdot85$ kcal. mole^{-1} at the same temperature. Clearly, these two quantities are *not* identical.

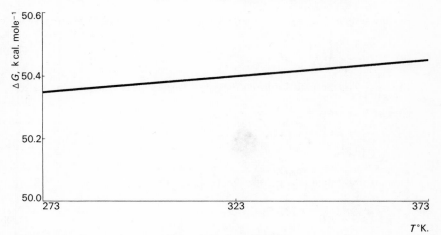

Figure 152.   The variation of ΔG with T for the Daniell cell.

It is possible to measure the e.m.f. of a cell at several temperatures; the results for the Daniell cell and for cell **(7.52)** are shown in figs. 152 and 153 respectively in terms of ΔG for the cell reaction. From a consideration of the equation of a straight line, we may write

$$\Delta G = T\left(\frac{\partial \Delta G}{\partial T}\right)_P + C. \tag{7.53}$$

The partial differential ∂ is used to indicate that ΔG is a function of more variables than temperature alone; the subscript P indicates that we are considering a constant-

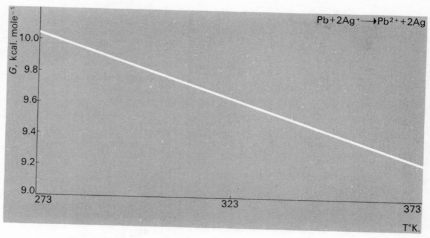

Figure 153. The variation of ΔG with T for the cell (7.52).

pressure system. Since now we equate ΔG with $-nFE$, equation (7.47), we may write

$$E = T\left(\frac{\partial E}{\partial T}\right)_P - \frac{C}{nF} \tag{7.54}$$

where $\left(\dfrac{\partial E}{\partial T}\right)_P$ is the temperature coefficient of e.m.f. of the cell, at constant pressure.
Since $nFE = -\Delta G$,

$$\left(\frac{\partial E}{\partial T}\right)_P = -\frac{1}{nF}\left(\frac{\partial \Delta G}{\partial T}\right)_P.$$

It can be shown that $\left(\dfrac{\partial \Delta G}{\partial T}\right)_P = -\Delta S$, i.e. $\left(\dfrac{\partial E}{\partial T}\right)_P = \dfrac{\Delta S}{nF}$.

$$\Delta G = \Delta H + T\left(\frac{\partial \Delta G}{\partial T}\right)_P \tag{7.55}$$

$$E = -\frac{\Delta H}{nF} + T\left(\frac{\partial E}{\partial T}\right)_P \tag{7.56}$$

From the slopes of the lines in figs. 152 and 153, we can calculate the temperature coefficients of the cells under consideration and hence also the entropy change of each cell reaction at a given temperature:

	Daniell cell	Cell (7.52)
$\left(\dfrac{\partial E}{\partial T}\right)_P$, volt deg.$^{-1}$, at 25°	$+2\cdot2 \times 10^{-5}$	$-1\cdot7 \times 10^{-4}$
ΔS_{25}, cal. mole^{-1} deg.$^{-1}$	$+0\cdot84$	$-7\cdot9$

We may *not* extrapolate the graphs to $T = 0°$ in order to obtain ΔH. In general, ΔH varies with temperature, although over the limited temperature range considered, the variation of ΔH with temperature is negligible compared with the variation of $T\Delta S$, as the graphs show.

We see now that the question of whether the electrical work is greater than or less than the enthalpy change depends upon the sign of the temperature coefficient of e.m.f. or more fundamentally, upon the sign of ΔS. It is noteworthy that a spontaneous reaction is not always accompanied by an increase in entropy of the system; it *is* always accompanied by a decrease in the free energy of the system.

If $\left(\dfrac{\partial E}{\partial T}\right)_P$ is positive, the electrical energy produced by the cell reaction will be greater than the enthalpy change of the reaction; heat is absorbed from the surroundings. Conversely, if $\left(\dfrac{\partial E}{\partial T}\right)_P$ is negative, heat is given out to the surroundings in the operation of the cell. The *heat of reaction* in an electrochemical cell operating reversibly is thus seen to be $T\Delta S$ and not ΔH. If the same reaction is performed as indicated by fig. 36 (process $3 \to 4$), then no useful work is done and the enthalpy of reaction $\Delta H (= \Delta G + T\Delta S)$ appears as heat.

We may call the free energy the *available* energy – energy available to do useful work. The energy $T\Delta S$ may be regarded as *unavailable* for useful work; it is concerned with changes in the orderliness of the system.

7·9 **Electrode potentials**

The potentials of all known electrode systems have been recorded with respect to the standard hydrogen electrode. We have already noted that the electrode potentials of zinc and copper are of different sign with respect to the hydrogen electrode, chosen as zero. We shall adopt as the sign convention for electrode potentials that the sign for the oxidation as written in equation (**7.57**) is that of the metals with respect to the

$$M \to M^{z+} + ze \tag{7.57}$$

solution. Thus, for example, zinc and copper are negative and positive respectively. Some *standard* oxidation electrode potentials are listed in table 43; a more extensive selection is given in appendix D. We note that the order of the standard electrode potentials corresponds to that in the electro-chemical series of the elements. This is the definition of the electrochemical series. It is *not* a list of elements, any one of which

Table 43 Standard Electrode Potentials π^0 Volt, at 25°C. and $a_{\pm} = 1$

	π^0		π^0		π^0
K/K^+	$-2\cdot93$	Mn/Mn^{2+}	$-1\cdot10$	H_2/H^+	$0\cdot00$
Ca/Ca^{2+}	$-2\cdot87$	Zn/Zn^{2+}	$-0\cdot76$	Cu/Cu^{2+}	$0\cdot34$
Na/Na^+	$-2\cdot71$	Fe/Fe^{2+}	$-0\cdot44$	Hg/Hg_2^{2+}	$0\cdot79$
Mg/Mg^{2+}	$-2\cdot37$	Sn/Sn^{2+}	$-0\cdot14$	Ag/Ag^+	$0\cdot80$
Al/Al^{3+}	$-1\cdot66$	Pb/Pb^{2+}	$-0\cdot13$	Cl^-/Cl_2	$1\cdot36$

replaces one below it from solution. Thus, while zinc replaces copper from copper sulphate, lithium does not replace sodium from sodium chloride solution at any concentration, nor is the reaction (**7.58**) spontaneous.

$$H_2 + Cu^{2+}(c = 1) \rightarrow 2H^+ + Cu. \tag{7.58}$$

The relative position of metal and hydrogen may be given incorrectly by the electrochemical series for a particular application. For example, zinc replaces hydrogen from acid solution, theoretically at any concentration of $H^+ > 10^{-12}$; however, hydrogen does not replace copper from copper sulphate solution, in this case because of a large *overvoltage* for hydrogen at a copper surface.

Overvoltage will not be discussed in detail here. The theoretical voltage required to decompose an aqueous solution of an acid or a base is about 1·2 volt. The voltage needed in practice is, in fact, much larger – about 1·7 volt; its value depends upon

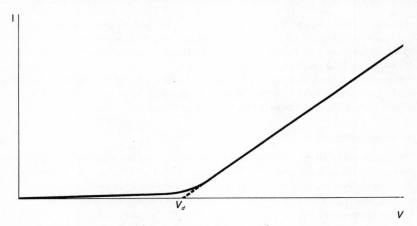

Figure 154. The decomposition voltage V_d.

the electrolyte and upon the nature of the electrodes. The voltage at which appreciable current begins to pass through an electrolyte is called the decomposition voltage (fig. 154). Some typical overvoltages are listed in table 44. It may be noted that Ohm's law applies to an electrolyte only at and above the decomposition voltage.

Table 44 Hydrogen Overvoltage in Dilute Sulphuric Acid, in Volt

Platinum (platinized)	0·005	Tin	0·53
Platinum (smooth)	0·09	Lead	0·64
Silver	0·15	Zinc	0·70
Copper	0·23	Mercury	0·78

The absolute position of an element in the electrochemical series will be altered if the ion activity is not unity. In extreme examples, the relative positions may be altered as well. Table 45 illustrates the variation of the electrode potentials of zinc

Table 45 The Variation of Electrode Potential with Activity at 25°C.

$a_{\pm}(Zn^{2+})$	$\pi(Zn/Zn^{2+})$	$a_{+}(Cu^{2+})$	$\pi(Cu/Cu^{2+})$
0·01	−0·82	0·01	0·28
0·10	−0·79	0·10	0·31
1·00	−0·76	1·00	0·34
2·00	−0·67	2·00	0·35

and of copper, with activity of the electrolytes. The need to compare electrode potentials at a fixed 'concentration' – unit activity – is readily appreciated. The variation of electrode potential with activity and with temperature is given, without proof here, by equation (7.59)

$$\pi = \pi^0 + \frac{RT}{nF} \ln a(M^+) \tag{7.59}$$

in which π^0 represents the standard electrode potential and $a(M^+)$ is the activity of the ionic species under consideration. At 25°C., this equation may be reduced to the form of (7.60). It may be noted that the electrode potential and the electrode e.m.f., of the same electrode system, are of the same magnitude but of opposite sign.

$$\pi = \pi^0 + \frac{0 \cdot 05915}{n} \log_{10} a(M^+). \tag{7.60}$$

From table 44 we see that tin, for example, has a more negative oxidation potential than lead, in the electrochemical series. This is true if the activities of their ions are equal. Consider the two systems Sn/Sn^{2+} at unit activity, or approximately unit concentration and Pb/Pb^{2+} at 10^{-2} molar, respectively. Then the electrode potential of the Sn/Sn^{2+} system remains at $-0 \cdot 14$ volt. From equation (7.60), we calculate that the electrode potential of the Pb/Pb^{2+} system is $-0 \cdot 25$ volt, and the relative positions of the two systems are interchanged.

7·9·1   *Oxidation potentials*

The Daniell cell is an electrochemical cell. We represent it symbolically by (7.61).

$$Zn|ZnSO_4 \text{ (aq.)}|CuSO_4 \text{ (aq.)}|Cu \tag{7.61}$$

A vertical bar indicates a boundary across which a potential difference exists. The potential difference $\Delta\pi$ at the junction of the two solutions introduces a complication since its magnitude cannot be evaluated readily. The e.m.f. of the cell is given by equation (7.62). Where π_{lhs} and π_{rhs} represent the electrode oxidation potentials of the systems on the left-hand side (lhs) and right-hand side (rhs) respectively of the cell written.

$$E = \pi_{rhs} - \pi_{lhs} + \Delta\pi. \tag{7.62}$$

The cell is written so that a positive e.m.f. corresponds to an electron flow from left to right in the external circuit. $\Delta\pi$ is the *liquid junction potential difference*, $(\pi_{rh\,soln.} - \pi_{lh\,soln.})$. A device intended to eliminate the liquid junction potential $\Delta\pi$ is the salt bridge. This is usually a small-bore U-tube containing a concentrated aqueous solution of potassium chloride or potassium nitrate conveniently made into a gel with agar-agar. The cation and anion have similar transport numbers in these solutions (table 37), and the high concentration of electrolyte at each junction made by the salt-bridge overrides most of the effect of the liquid junction potential between the two solutions.

Another electrochemical cell is represented by equation (7.63); the double vertical bar is used to indicate a salt-bridge junction and the comma indicates that equilibrium exists between the two components adjacent to the comma. From equation (7.62), with $\Delta\pi$ assumed to be eliminated by the salt-bridge, the e.m.f. of the cell is 0·11 volt at 25°C.

$$Ag|AgBr, KBr(a_{\pm} = 1)\|KCl\,(satd.), Hg_2Cl_2|Hg. \tag{7.63}$$
$$(0\cdot13\ v.) \qquad\qquad\qquad (0\cdot24\ v.)$$

The electron flow in the external circuit is, by convention, from the left-hand electrode system to the right-hand electrode system. Thus, the half-cell reactions are given by equations (7.64) and (7.65), and the overall reaction by (7.66).

$$Ag + Br^- \rightarrow AgBr + e \tag{7.64}$$

$$\tfrac{1}{2}Hg_2Cl_2 + e \rightarrow Hg + Cl^- \tag{7.65}$$

$$\overline{Ag + Br^- + \tfrac{1}{2}Hg_2Cl_2 \rightarrow AgBr + Hg + Cl^-} \tag{7.66}$$

The free energy change for the process as written can be evaluated from equation (7.47):

$$-\Delta G = nFE = \frac{1 \times 96487 \times 0\cdot11}{4\cdot184}$$

$$\Delta G = -25\cdot37\ kcal.\ mole^{-1}\ AgBr\ formed.$$

In the pairs of equations (7.34), (7.35) and (7.36), (7.37), the first equation in each pair represents an *oxidation* process and the second equation in each pair represents a *reduction* process. Any chemical reaction which can be envisaged as carried out in an electrochemical cell can be divided into half-cell, or partial, reactions. One of these half-cell reactions is an oxidation and the other is a reduction. Electrode potentials have been defined as oxidation process:

$$M \rightarrow M^{n+} + ne. \tag{7.67}$$

It is clear, however, that when two electrodes are combined to form an electrochemical cell, the process of oxidation takes place at one electrode and the process of reduction takes place at the other electrode. The values of the electrode (oxidation) potentials of the two systems determines their redox (oxidation–reduction) behaviour. In the Daniell cell, oxidation takes place at the zinc electrode. However, if zinc and manganese are used in the cell (**7.68**),

$$\text{Mn}|\text{MnSO}_4\,(a_\pm = 1)\|\text{ZnSO}_4\,(a_\pm = 1)|\text{Zn} \tag{7.68}$$

the spontaneous reaction, positive e.m.f., requires that oxidation takes place at the manganese electrode (table 43) in which case reduction now takes place at the zinc electrode. In general, oxidation will occur at the electrode of more negative electrode potential *in the particular circumstances obtaining*, i.e. it is not simply a question of comparing standard electrode potentials; concentrations different from unity may exist and must be considered in evaluating the electrode potentials.

The general electrode reaction (**7.69**) may be written and its oxidation potential is then given by equation (**7.70**).

$$\text{reduced state} \rightarrow \text{oxidized state} + ne \tag{7.69}$$

$$\pi = \pi^0 + \frac{RT}{nF} \ln \frac{a(\text{oxidized state})}{a(\text{reduced state})} \tag{7.70}$$

The terms in the logarithmic expression represent activities. This equation was implied by equation (**7.47**); the reduced state was there the metal and its activity is unity, since the activity of an element in its standard state is defined as unity.

Another type of reversible electrode system is that of an inert metal in contact with a solution of a metal as ions in two oxidation states: $\text{Pt}|\text{Fe}^{2+}, \text{Fe}^{3+}$. The electrode reaction is given by equation (**7.71**) and the standard potential of this system,

$$\text{Fe}^{2+} \rightarrow \text{Fe}^{3+} + e \tag{7.71}$$

i.e. for the case $a(\text{Fe}^{3+})/a(\text{Fe}^{2+}) = 1$, is 0·77 volt. Another similar system involves the ions Mn^{2+} and MnO_4^-:

$$\text{Mn}^{2+} + 4\text{H}_2\text{O} \rightarrow \text{MnO}_4^- + 8\text{H}^+ + 5e. \tag{7.72}$$

It has the standard oxidation potential $\pi^0 = 1\cdot51$ volt. It should be clear now that the terms electrode potential and oxidation potential are synonymous when the electrode potential is defined as an oxidation.

The electrochemical cell represented by equation (**7.73**) can be set up, in which Fe^{2+} is oxidized by MnO_4^- in a spontaneous chemical reaction.

$$\text{Pt}|\text{Fe}^{2+}\,(\text{aq.}),\ \text{Fe}^{3+}\,(\text{aq.})\|\text{Mn}^{2+}\,(\text{aq.}),\ \text{MnO}_4^-\,(\text{aq.}),\ \text{H}^+\,(\text{aq.})|\text{Pt} \tag{7.73}$$

The right-hand electrode accepts electrons from the left-hand electrode through the external circuit. We can represent the overall reaction by equation (**7.74**).

$$5\text{Fe}^{2+} + \text{MnO}_4^- + 8\text{H}^+ \rightarrow 5\text{Fe}^{3+} + \text{Mn}^{2+} + 4\text{H}_2\text{O} \tag{7.74}$$

The standard e.m.f. (E^0) of this cell is 0.74 volt and the variation of E with concentration is given by equations (7.75) to (7.78).

$$\pi_{lhs} = \pi^0(Fe^{2+}, Fe^{3+}) + \frac{RT}{F} \ln \frac{a(Fe^{3+})}{a(Fe^{2+})} \tag{7.75}$$

$$\pi_{rhs} = \pi^0(Mn^{2+}, MnO_4^-) + \frac{RT}{5F} \ln \frac{a(MnO_4^-)a^8(H^+)}{a(Mn^{2+})a^4(H_2O)} \tag{7.76}$$

$$E = \pi_{rhs} - \pi_{lhs} = E^0 - \frac{RT}{5F} \ln \frac{a^5(Fe^{3+})a(Mn^{2+})a^4(H_2O)}{a^5(Fe^{2+})a(MnO_4^-)a^8(H^+)} \tag{7.77}$$

If the solutions are dilute, so that $a(H_2O) = 1$, and if $a(H^+)$ remains constant, then since $E_0 = 0.740$ volt,

$$E = 0.740 - \frac{RT}{5F} \ln \frac{a^5(Fe^{3+})a(Mn^{2+})}{a^5(Fe^{2+})a(MnO_4^-)} + \frac{RT}{5F} \ln a^8(H^+). \tag{7.78}$$

We may investigate the completeness of a reaction from a knowledge of the e.m.f. of the appropriate electrochemical cell. Considering the oxidation of ferrous iron by potassium permanganate, we have seen that the standard e.m.f. for this reaction is 0.74 volt. Hence, ΔG^0 is, from equation (7.47), -85.33 kcal. per g-ion MnO_4^-. A relationship between ΔG^0 and the equilibrium constant K is given, without proof here, by equation (7.79).

$$-\Delta G^0 = RT \ln K. \tag{7.79}$$

From this equation, K is approximately 10^{63} for reaction (7.74), as written. This means that the reaction is complete for all practical purposes.

A study of half-cell reactions is useful in constructing equations for complex redox processes. As an example, we consider the oxidation of manganous ions to permanganate ions by bismuthate ions in acid solution. The partial reactions are (7.80) and (7.81):

$$Mn^{2+} + 4H_2O \rightarrow MnO_4^- + 8H^+ + 5e \tag{7.80}$$

$$BiO_3^- + 6H^+ + 2e \rightarrow Bi^{3+} + 3H_2O. \tag{7.81}$$

By multiplying (7.81) by 5 and adding to (7.80) multiplied by 2, the overall reaction is

$$5BiO_3^- + 14H^+ + 2Mn^+ \rightarrow 2MnO_4^- + 5Bi^{3+} + 7H_2O. \tag{7.82}$$

It should be noted when evaluating ΔG or K, that the integers used in balancing the cell equation with respect to both chemical species and to charge, do *not* multiply the electrode potentials. For reaction (7.82), $E = 0.2$ V, so that $K = 10^{33}$ and the oxidation is complete.

7·10 Potentiometric titrations

7·10·1 *pH determination by e.m.f. measurement*

The pH of a solution was defined first by Sørensen in 1909 as $-\log_{10}[H^+]$, where $[H^+]$ represents the hydrogen ion concentration in g-ion l.$^{-1}$ The pH is a number ranging from about 0 in a normal solution of a strong acid to about 14 in a normal solution of a strong base.

Methods of determining pH are all based, directly or indirectly, upon measurements using the hydrogen electrode. We have considered that the potential of a hydrogen electrode is controlled by the activity of the hydrogen ion in solution. Hence, a more correct definition of pH is given by equation (**7.83**). However, the

$$pH = -\log_{10} a(H^+) \tag{7.83}$$

activity of any single ionic species cannot be measured experimentally and a practical definition of pH is based upon e.m.f. measurements.

The potential of the standard hydrogen electrode is defined as 0·000 volt. At any activity of hydrogen ions and at unit partial pressure of hydrogen, the electrode potential may be written by equation (**7.84**). Hence, using equation (**7.70**), we can

$$\pi = \frac{RT}{F} \ln a(H^+). \tag{7.84}$$

deduce (**7.85**) relating the pH to electrode potential, at 25°C. When the standard

$$\pi = -0.05915 \, pH. \tag{7.85}$$

hydrogen electrode is used, a cell such as (**7.86**) is set up. The e.m.f. is measured potentiometrically and the pH may be evaluated from (**7.87**) at 25°C., or at any other

$$Pt, H_2 \ (1 \ atm.)|unknown \ soln \| KCl \ (satd), Hg_2Cl_2|Hg \tag{7.86}$$

$$pH = \frac{e.m.f. - \pi_{ref}}{0.05915} \tag{7.87}$$

temperature from equation (**7.88**). π_{ref} is the electrode potential of the calomel

$$pH = \frac{e.m.f. - \pi_{ref}}{0.0001984T} \tag{7.88}$$

reference electrode under the experimental conditions. The measuring instrument is calibrated, using the British standard of reference for pH which is a 0·05 molar solution of potassium hydrogen phthalate which is taken to have a pH of 4·00 at 15°C. The variation in pH of this solution with temperature is given by equation (**7.89**).

$$pH = 4.00 + 0.5 \left\{ \frac{t-15}{100} \right\}^2 \tag{7.89}$$

Another system which is reversible to hydrogen ion concentration is the hydroquinone (H_2Q), quinone (Q) system, equation (**7.90**):

$$\tag{7.90}$$

hydroquinone   quinone

The electrode potential is given by equation (7.91), in which π_{QH}^0 is 0·70 volt at 25°C.

$$\pi = \pi_{QH}^0 + \frac{RT}{2F}\ln\frac{a(Q)a^2(H^+)}{a(H_2Q)} \tag{7.91}$$

In practice, the ratio $a(Q)/a(H_2Q)$ is maintained constant and equal to unity by saturating the solution with 'quinhydrone' (QH) which is a 1 : 1 molecular compound of quinone and hydroquinone. The cell (7.92) is set up and the pH of the unknown

$$\text{Pt}|\text{'quinhydrone' (satd), unknown soln}\|\text{calomel ref. electrode} \tag{7.92}$$

solution is given by equation (7.93). Again, π_{ref} is the electrode potential of the calomel

$$\text{pH} = \frac{E + \pi_{QH}^0 - \pi_{ref}}{0\cdot0001984T}. \tag{7.93}$$

reference electrode system under the given experimental conditions.

If an acid–base titration is carried out potentiometrically in a cell such as (7.86), the e.m.f. change, on addition of alkali to acid in the left-hand half-cell, will follow the pH curves already illustrated in chapter 5, since, from equation (7.87), pH is directly proportional to e.m.f. $(-\pi)$.

7·10·2 *Redox titrations*

Consider the cell (7.94).

$$\text{calomel ref. electrode}\|\text{Fe}^{2+}, \text{Fe}^{3+}|\text{Pt}. \tag{7.94}$$

The e.m.f. will be dependent upon the ratio $a(\text{Fe}^{3+})/a(\text{Fe}^{2+})$, leading to equation (7.95)

$$E = \pi^0(\text{Fe}^{2+}, \text{Fe}^{3+}) + \frac{RT}{F}\ln\frac{a(\text{Fe}^{3+})}{a(\text{Fe}^{2+})} - \pi_{ref} \tag{7.95}$$

for the e.m.f. of this system. If the right-hand half-cell contains acidified ferrous sulphate, then the ratio $a(\text{Fe}^{3+})/a(\text{Fe}^{2+})$ will be small. Now suppose that potassium permanganate is added to this solution from a burette. As the oxidation of ferrous ions proceeds, the ratio of $a(\text{Fe}^{3+})/a(\text{Fe}^{2+})$ increases and the overall e.m.f. of the cell changes as the reaction (7.96) takes place:

$$5\text{Fe}^{2+} + \text{MnO}_4^- + 8\text{H}^+ \rightarrow 5\text{Fe}^{3+} + \text{Mn}^{2+} + 4\text{H}_2\text{O}. \tag{7.96}$$

The ratio $a(\text{Fe}^{3+})/a(\text{Fe}^{2+})$ reaches a maximum value, effectively, at the equivalence point of the titration, and thereafter does not change appreciably. Beyond the equivalence point, the solution is coloured pink because free permanganate ions are present; the redox system (7.97) now controls the e.m.f. of the cell [originally (7.94)].

$$\text{calomel ref. electrode}\|\text{Mn}^{2+}, \text{MnO}_4{}^-|\text{Pt} \tag{7.97}$$

Further variation in the overall e.m.f. is now governed by equation (7.98).

$$E = \pi^0(\text{Mn}^{2+}, \text{MnO}_4^-) + \frac{RT}{5F}\ln\frac{a(\text{MnO}_4^-)a^8(H^+)}{a(\text{Mn}^{2+})}. \tag{7.98}$$

Since the solutions are dilute, the activity of water is unity. As excess potassium permanganate is added, the ratio $a(MnO_4^-)/a(Mn^{2+})$ increases and the overall e.m.f. now follows this change. It has been assumed that the pH remains sensibly constant throughout the experiment.

The changes in e.m.f. during the course of such a titration can be calculated, using the equations (**7.95**) and (**7.98**) as appropriate. In the following example, titrations of 25 ml. of 0·1 N ferrous sulphate with (a) 0·1 N potassium permanganate and (b) 0·1 N

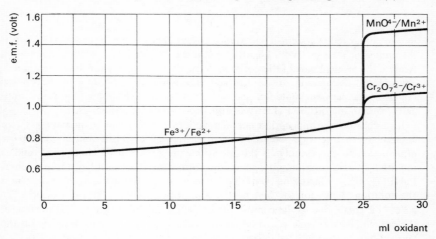

Figure 155.   Potentiometric redox titration curves.

potassium dichromate are considered; π_{ref} has been taken as 0·24 volt in computing table 46. The results are plotted in fig. 155 with respect to the hydrogen electrode, i.e. by adding π_{ref} to the values in table 46.

Table 46   Potentiometric Redox Titration Data

Volume of oxidant in ml.	$\dfrac{a(Fe^{3+})}{a(Fe^{2+})}$	E (volt)	$\dfrac{a(MnO_4^-)}{a(Mn^{2+})}$	E (volt)	$\dfrac{a(Cr_2O_7^{2-})}{a(Cr^{3+})}$	E (volt)
1·0	0·042	0·45	—	—	—	—
15·0	1·50	0·54	—	—	—	—
24·9	249	0·67	—	—	—	—
25·1	—	—	0·004	1.24	0·004	0·83
30·0	—	—	0·200	1·26	0·200	0·85

10.3   Redox indicators

A redox indicator is a substance which exhibits different colours in its oxidized and its reduced forms, for example, diphenylamine. Its partial redox reaction is given by equation (7.99);

$$2 \langle\bigcirc\rangle\text{—NH—}\langle\bigcirc\rangle \rightleftharpoons \langle\bigcirc\rangle\text{—N=}\langle\bigcirc\rangle\langle\bigcirc\rangle\text{=N—}\langle\bigcirc\rangle$$

(colourless)   (blue)

$$+4\mathrm{H}^+ +4e \qquad\qquad (7.99)$$

like any other redox system, it has a redox potential governed by equation (7.70). For this indicator π^0 is 0·76 volt. Ideally, a suitable indicator has an electrode potential lying in the vertical part of the potentiometric titrations curve for the system under consideration. Potassium permanganate is self-indicating because of the intense colour of the permanganate ion. However, potassium dichromate requires an indicator, and, in the titration of ferrous iron, diphenylamine is often used.

If we consider the appropriate curve in fig. 155, it is clear that an indicating system should have an electrode potential lying in the range 0·95 to 1·05 volt. In order to use diphenylamine successfully in this titration, the presence of phosphoric acid is required. In acid solution, phosphate ions form complexes with ferric iron, such as $\mathrm{FeHPO_4^+}$, thus reducing markedly the concentration, and activity, of ferric iron in the solution. Thus, for the first part of the titration curve, the ratio of $a(\mathrm{Fe^{3+}})/a(\mathrm{Fe^{2+}})$ is small, due to the complexing of $\mathrm{Fe^{3+}}$ ions thus lowering this portion of the curve. The electrode potential for the diphenylamine system now lies on the vertical part of the modified curve.

Problems

1. A water voltameter and a silver voltameter are connected in series. Calculate the weight of silver which is deposited during the same time as 80 ml. of hydrogen gas at 20°C. and 755 mm. pressure are liberated. (H = 1·008; Ag = 107·87; 1 l. of hydrogen weighs 0·089 g. at s.t.p.).

2. Describe the electrode mechanisms involved in the following electrolyses:

Copper sulphate with platinum electrodes
Copper sulphate with copper electrodes
Sodium chloride (dilute) with carbon electrodes
Sodium chloride (concentrated) with carbon electrodes.

3. At 25°C. the resistance of a conductivity cell containing 0·1 N potassium chloride solution is 307·62 ohm. The same cell containing 0·1 N silver nitrate has a resistance of 362·65 ohm. Refer to the text to find the specific conductance of 0·1 N potassium chloride and calculate (i) the cell constant and (ii) the equivalent conductance of the silver nitrate solution.

4. The dissociation constant of propionic acid is $1·34 \times 10^{-5}$ at 25°C. and the limiting conductances of its ions are $\lambda^0(\mathrm{H}^+) = 350·0$ ohm^{-1} cm.$^{-1}$ l. g-equiv.$^{-1}$ and

$\lambda^0(\text{Pr}^-) = 35\cdot8$ ohm^{-1} cm.$^{-1}$ l. g-equiv.$^{-1}$ Calculate the specific conductance of a $0\cdot1$ N solution of propionic acid.

5. From the following data at 18°C., determine the equivalent conductance at zero concentration, Λ_0, for sodium chloride, sodium acetate, hydrochloric acid and acetic acid:

c, milli-equiv. l.$^{-1}$	$\sqrt{c}$	Λ, ohm^{-1} cm.$^{-1}$ l. g.-equiv.$^{-1}$		
		NaCl	NaAc	HCl
2	1·414	105·6	74·5	373·6
10	3·162	102·0	71·2	368·1
36	6·000	97·6	67·1	360·4
80	8·944	93·5	63·4	353·0
100	10·00	92·0	62·1	350·6

6. The specific conductances of saturated barium sulphate solution and of the conductivity water are $3\cdot590 \times 10^{-6}$ ohm^{-1} cm.$^{-1}$ and $0\cdot618 \times 10^{-6}$ ohm^{-1} cm.$^{-1}$ respectively, at 25°C. Using the limiting conductances of the ions,

$$\lambda^0(\text{Ba}^{2+}) = 65\cdot0 \text{ ohm}^{-1} \text{ cm.}^{-1} \text{ l. g-equiv.}^{-1}$$

and

$$\lambda^0(\text{SO}_4^{2-}) = 79\cdot0 \text{ ohm}^{-1} \text{ cm.}^{-1} \text{ l. g-equiv.}^{-1},$$

calculate the solubility product of barium sulphate at 25°C. Evaluate $f_\pm$ for saturated barium sulphate solution, using the Debye–Hückel limiting equation (5.56) and comment upon its effect on the calculated solubility product.

7. A solution containing 10·85 g. of silver nitrate in 1000 g. of water was electrolysed between silver electrodes in a Hittorf apparatus. After electrolysis, the solutions in the anode compartment and the centre compartment were removed and the following data were obtained:

Mass of anode compartment	54·90 g.
Mass of silver nitrate in anode compartment	0·7217 g.
Mass of centre compartment	46·20 g.
Mass of silver nitrate in centre compartment	0·4959 g.

A copper coulometer connected in series with the transport cell showed a gain in weight at the cathode of 0·04672 g., during the above experiment. Calculate the transport numbers for the silver and the nitrate ions.

8. Using the data

Zn/Zn^{2+}	$\pi^0 = -0\cdot76$ volt
$\frac{1}{2}$H$_2$/H$^+$	$\pi^0 = 0\cdot00$ volt
Ag/Ag$^+$	$\pi^0 = +0\cdot80$ volt

set up three standard electrochemical cells, observing the sign conventions. For each cell write down (i) the electrode reactions (ii) the overall reaction (iii) the standard e.m.f. of the cell (iv) the standard free energy change for the spontaneous reaction (v) the direction of electron flow in an external circuit.

9. At 25°C. the cell

$$Pb|PbCl_2 \text{ (satd)}, KCl(m)\|KCl(m), AgCl \text{ (satd)}|Ag$$

has a standard e.m.f. of 0·490 volt and $10^4 \dfrac{dE}{dT}$ is $-1·86$ volt deg.$^{-1}$, and the cell

$$Pb|PbI_2 \text{ (satd)}, KI(m)\|KI(m), AgI \text{ (satd)}|Ag$$

has a standard e.m.f. of 0·211 volt and $10^4 \dfrac{dE}{dT}$ is $-1·27$ volt deg.$^{-1}$

Calculate the values of ΔG^0, ΔH^0 and ΔS^0 for the reaction

$$PbI_2 + 2AgCl \rightarrow PbCl_2 + 2AgI.$$

10. Calculate the standard e.m.f. and its temperature coefficient for the following cell:

$$Pt, H_2(1 \text{ atm.})|HCl(m), AgCl \text{ (satd)}|Ag.$$

The standard free energies of formation and enthalpies of formation are as follows:

	ΔG_f^0, kcal. mole^{-1}	ΔH_f^0, kcal. mole^{-1}
AgCl	$-30·4$	$-26·2$
HCl(aq)	$-40·0$	$-31·4$

11. The e.m.f. of the cell

$$Hg|HgCl_2 \text{ (satd)}, KCl \text{ (satd)}\|HA(m), \text{ quinhydrone (satd)}|Pt$$

is 219 millivolt at 25°C. Calculate the pH of the solution of HA, given that the oxidation potential of the saturated calomel electrode is 0·244 volt and the standard oxidation potential of the quinhydrone electrode is 0·70 volt, both at 25°C.

12. If the Avogadro constant is $6·023 \times 10^{23}$ ions g-ion^{-1} and the Faraday is 96,487 coulomb g-equiv.$^{-1}$, calculate the charge in coulomb, on each of the ions Cl^- and Sr^{2+}.

13. The e.m.f. of the cell

$$Ag|HCl(m), AgCl \text{ (satd)}, Hg_2Cl_2 \text{ (satd)}|Hg$$

is 0·0455 volt at 25°C. If the temperature coefficient of e.m.f. is $3·4 \times 10^{-4}$ volt deg.$^{-1}$, calculate the enthalpy of reaction at 25°.

Chapter 8
Kinetics of chemical reactions

8·1   **Kinetics**

The usual stoichiometric chemical equation gives no indication of how, or how fast, the represented reaction occurs. For example, the equations

$$H_2 + Cl_2 \rightarrow 2HCl$$
$$H_2 + Br_2 \rightarrow 2HBr$$
$$H_2 + I_2 \ \ \rightarrow 2HI$$

are formally similar; yet the details of the reactions are quite different, as is shown by their very different rates of reaction under comparable conditions. A detailed account is called the *mechanism* of the reaction; the purpose of studying the *rate* of a chemical reaction, and the variation of rate with change of conditions, is to obtain as much information as possible concerning its mechanism. This study enables us to carry out reactions under favourable conditions – so that we obtain rapidly a high yield of the products required, with little interference from side reactions.

There are a number of factors which determine the rate of a chemical reaction. In this introduction to chemical kinetics we shall consider three: the concentrations of the reactants, the temperature, and the influence of a catalyst. All reactions, with about three known exceptions, show considerable increases in rate with rise of temperature; the effects of changes in reactant concentration are less uniform.

In deducing the law of mass action, it is often assumed that, for the reaction

$$aA + bB + \ldots \rightarrow \text{products}$$

the rate is proportional to $[A]^a$, to $[B]^b$ etc., so that

$$\text{rate} = k[A]^a[B]^b \ldots . \tag{8.1}$$

where k is the *rate constant* of the reaction. Now this is sometimes true; for example, in the reaction

$$H_2 + I_2 \rightarrow 2HI,$$

the rate of formation of hydrogen iodide, which we can express in the form: rate of change of concentration of HI with respect to time, or $\dfrac{d}{dt}[HI]$, is given by

$$\frac{d}{dt}[HI] = k[H_2][I_2] \tag{8.2}$$

the *rate equation* for the reaction. But we cannot *infer* this from the stoichiometric equation; the rates of formation of hydrogen chloride and hydrogen bromide are *not* given by analogous expressions, but by very much more complex rate equations.

Again, we might expect, from the equation

$$2N_2O_5 \rightarrow 4NO_2 + O_2$$

that the rate of decomposition of dinitrogen pentoxide would be given by

$$-\frac{d}{dt}[N_2O_5] = k[N_2O_5]^2 \tag{8.3}$$

the negative sign indicating that the concentration of N_2O_5 *decreases* as the reaction proceeds. In fact, the correct form of the rate equation is

$$-\frac{d}{dt}[N_2O_5] = k[N_2O_5]. \tag{8.4}$$

The rate equation must be determined *by experiment*, under well-defined conditions. In the first case, we must show that increase of concentration of *either* hydrogen *or* iodine causes a proportionate increase in the rate of reaction; in the second case, that the rate increases as the *first power*, not as the *square*, of the concentration of dinitrogen pentoxide.

To give a further example, the nitration of an aromatic compound requires both the aromatic molecule and nitric acid as reactants; for example

$$C_6H_5CH_3 + HNO_3 \rightarrow C_6H_4CH_3NO_2 + H_2O.$$

Yet, under certain conditions, the concentration of the organic molecule may be increased fourfold without any appreciable change in the rate of its nitration. Clearly the rate equation

$$\frac{d}{dt}[C_6H_4CH_3NO_2] = k[HNO_3][C_6H_5CH_3]$$

does *not* apply under these conditions.

8·1·1   *Order of reaction*

The dependence of the rate upon a particular reactant is expressed by the *order* of the reaction with respect to that component.

This is the power to which the concentration of that reactant is present in the rate equation, as found by experiment. Thus, in the formation of hydrogen iodide, the reaction is *first-order* with respect to both hydrogen and iodine; the decomposition of dinitrogen pentoxide is *first-order* with respect to this reactant; and the nitration of toluene is, within a certain range, *zero-order* with respect to (i.e. independent of) the concentration of toluene.

In the thermal decomposition of hydrogen iodide, the rate equation is

$$-\frac{d}{dt}[\text{HI}] = k[\text{HI}]^2 \tag{8.5}$$

and the reaction is *second-order* with respect to this reagent.

A few reactions of nitric oxide are of the form

$$2\text{NO} + \text{X}_2 = 2\text{NOX}, \qquad \text{X}_2 = \text{Cl}_2 \text{ or } \text{Br}_2.$$

$$\frac{d}{dt}[\text{NOX}] = k[\text{NO}]^2[\text{X}_2] \tag{8.6}$$

and the reaction is *second-order* with respect to nitric oxide, and *first-order* with respect to the halogen X_2.

In simple reactions, no order higher than two with respect to a single component is met with, and the sum of the orders with respect to all components never exceeds three.*

It is convenient to group reactions according to their *molecularities*. The molecularity is the number of molecules of all species which are involved in the rate-determining step of a reaction. Thus, the decomposition of dinitrogen pentoxide is a *unimolecular* process, equation (**8.4**); that of hydrogen iodide is *bimolecular*, equation (**8.5**). The formation of a nitrosyl compound is one of the very few examples of a *termolecular* reaction, as in equation (**8.6**). In a number of nitration reactions, the rate-determining step is:

$$2\,\text{HNO}_3 \rightarrow \text{NO}_2^+ + \text{NO}_3^- + \text{H}_2\text{O} \tag{8.7}$$

and this followed by a rapid reaction:

$$\text{NO}_2^+ + \text{C}_6\text{H}_5\text{CH}_3 \rightarrow \text{C}_6\text{H}_4\text{CH}_3\text{NO}_2 + \text{H}^+. \tag{8.8}$$

The reaction is therefore bimolecular, from equation (**8.7**).

The rate equation for the decomposition of dinitrogen pentoxide is given by equation (**8.4**). The total order is 1, so that this is a *first-order* rate equation.

The rate of a reaction is expressed as the change in concentration per unit time, e.g. mole l.^{-1} sec.$^{-1}$ The concentration term on the r.h.s. of equation (**8.4**) is in mole l.^{-1}, so that the units of k, for a *first-order* reaction, are those of (time)$^{-1}$, e.g. seconds^{-1}. The rate of reaction *decreases* as the reaction proceeds; this is seen in fig. 156a, where the concentration of N_2O_5 is plotted as a function of time. The rate is given by the tangent to the curve, and decreases along the series of increasing times $t_1, t_2, t_3 \ldots$. Suppose the initial concentration of dinitrogen pentoxide is a mole l.^{-1} If we found the concentration of dinitrogen pentoxide present at times $t = t_1, t = t_2$, etc. we could

* The more complex equations which one meets in elementary textbooks, e.g.

$$4\text{Zn} + 10\text{HNO}_3 = 4\text{Zn(NO}_3)_2 + 5\text{H}_2\text{O} + \text{N}_2\text{O}$$

actually take place by a series of *simple* steps, one of which is comparatively *slow*: this determines the overall rate of reaction, and is called the *rate-determining* step.

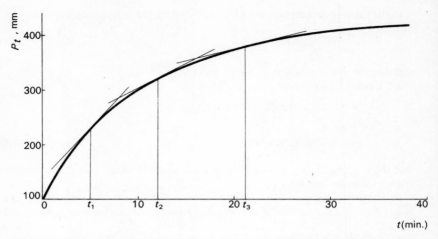

Figure 156(a). Variation of total pressure with time during thermal decomposition of dinitrogen pentoxide at 329°K.

determine the rate-constant k. If x_1 mole of N_2O_5 has been decomposed at time t_1, x_2 mole at time t_2, etc., then $\dfrac{dx_1}{dt} = k(a-x_1)$, the rate at time t_1, $\dfrac{dx_2}{dt} = k(a-x_2)$, the rate at time t_2, etc.

Now these forms of the rate equation are particular examples of the general expression

$$\frac{dx}{dt} = k(a-x). \tag{8.9}$$

Equation (8.9) can be integrated:

$$\int \frac{dx}{(a-x)} = k \int dt$$

$$-\ln(a-x) = kt + \text{an arbitrary constant, } \alpha.$$

Now, at time $t = 0$, $x = 0$. Therefore

$$-\ln a = \alpha$$

and $\qquad -\ln(a-x) = kt - \ln a$

or $\qquad \ln \dfrac{a}{(a-x)} = kt. \tag{8.10}$

This is the *integrated form* of the rate equation (8.9) for a first-order reaction. Since $(\log_e a)$ is a constant, we can obtain the rate-constant k by plotting $\log_e(a-x)$ against time t; the slope of this line is $-k$. If, as is more usual, we convert to logarithms to the base ten, then since

$$\ln z = 2 \cdot 303 \log_{10} z,$$

the slope of the graph of $\log_{10}(a-x)$ against t is $\dfrac{-k}{2 \cdot 303}$. Notice that, once again, the units of k, in equation (8.10), are reciprocal time (e.g. seconds^{-1}) since the l.h.s. of this equation is dimensionless, and that the reaction is only completed (i.e. $x = a$) when $t = \infty$. However, the reaction is about 99 per cent complete after seven half-lives.

Suppose that x, the amount of dinitrogen pentoxide decomposed after time t, is some definite fraction β of a.
Then

$$\ln \frac{a}{a(1-\beta)} = kt,$$

$$t_\beta = \frac{\ln \dfrac{1}{(1-\beta)}}{k} \tag{8.11}$$

where t_β is the time required for the fraction β to be decomposed.

In particular, if $\beta = \tfrac{1}{2}$,

$$t_{\frac{1}{2}} = \frac{\ln 2}{k} = \frac{0 \cdot 693}{k}. \tag{8.12}$$

$t_{\frac{1}{2}}$ is called the *half-life* or *half-time* of the reaction; it is independent of a, so that for example it requires the same period of time, $t_{\frac{1}{2}}$, for one kg. of N_2O_5 to become $0 \cdot 5$ kg. as for 1 g. to become $0 \cdot 5$ g.

In general, the half-life of a reaction is inversely proportional to the initial concentration a of reactant to the power $(n-1)$, where n is the order of the reaction; for a reaction of rate equation:

$$A^n \rightarrow \text{products}$$

$$t_{\frac{1}{2}} \propto \frac{1}{a^{n-1}}. \tag{8.13}$$

For a first-order process, $n = 1$, and $t_{\frac{1}{2}}$ is *independent* of a, as we have seen, equation (8.12).

The decay of a radioactive isotope provides an example of a truly first-order process. From the rate equation

$$k = \frac{1}{t} \ln \frac{a}{a-x}$$

$$= \frac{1}{t} \ln \frac{a}{a_t}$$

$$\therefore \quad a_t = ae^{-kt}$$

where k is the *decay constant* for the isotope. At time $t_{\frac{1}{2}}$, $a_t = \dfrac{a}{2}$, so that

$$0{\cdot}5 = e^{-kt_{\frac{1}{2}}},$$

$$\therefore \quad -kt_{\frac{1}{2}} = \ln_e 0{\cdot}5$$

or $$t_{\frac{1}{2}} = \frac{0{\cdot}693}{k}, \text{ as before.}$$

It is often convenient to follow the course of a reaction by studying the change in some physical property of the reacting system. In the decomposition of N_2O_5 there is an increase in pressure:

$$2N_2O_5 \rightarrow 4NO_2 + O_2$$

and thus the reaction may be followed by the indications of a manometer. Suppose the initial pressure of dinitrogen pentoxide (or its initial *partial pressure*, if there is some other gas present, e.g. air) is p_0, the pressure after time t is p_t, and the final pressure after complete reaction is p_∞. Then the initial concentration of N_2O_5 is proportional to the total change in pressure, $(p_\infty - p_0)$, and the concentration of N_2O_5 present after time t is proportional to the further change in pressure, $(p_\infty - p_t)$. Substituting these expressions for the concentration terms in equation (**8.4**):

$$\ln \frac{p_\infty - p_0}{p_\infty - p_t} = kt,$$

and the plot of $\log_{10}(p_\infty - p_t)$ against time gives a straight line of slope $\dfrac{-k}{2{\cdot}303}$.

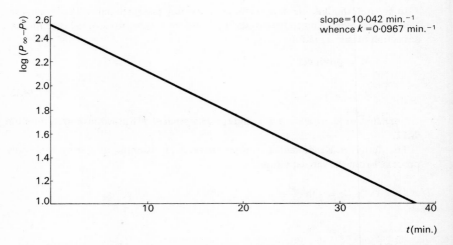

slope = $10{\cdot}042$ min.$^{-1}$
whence $k = 0{\cdot}0967$ min.$^{-1}$

Figure 156(b). Evaluation of the rate constant for the thermal decomposition of dinitrogen pentoxide at 329°K.

From the data in table 47, plotted in fig. 156b, k is determined.

Table 47 Kinetics of Decomposition of Dinitrogen Pentoxide at 329°K.

t, min.	p_t, mm.	$p_\infty - p_t$, mm.
0	100	331
3	178	253
5	220	211
10	297	134
15	345	86
20	377	54
30	409	22
40	421	10
∞	431	0

From the value of k, the half-time of the reaction at this temperature is $\dfrac{0\cdot693}{0\cdot0967}$, or 7·17 minutes. The thermal decompositions (pyrolyses) of a number of organic compounds in the gas phase proceed by a similar unimolecular process.

A reaction such as ester hydrolysis:

$$RCO_2R' + H_2O \rightarrow RCO_2H + R'OH$$

is often bimolecular, and is represented by a second-order rate equation:

$$-\frac{d}{dt}[RCO_2R'] = k[RCO_2R'][H_2O]. \tag{8.14}$$

If, however, one reactant, usually water, is present in large excess, its change in concentration during the reaction is negligible, and its constant concentration may be included in k, i.e. equation (**8.13**) may be written:

$$-\frac{d}{dt}[RCO_2R'] = k'[RCO_2R'], \tag{8.15}$$

where $k' = k[H_2O]$.

Equation (**8.14**) is now of first-order form; under these conditions of excess of one reagent, the reaction is said to be *pseudo* first-order.

Second-order rate equations are of two kinds; for the decomposition of hydrogen iodide,

$$-\frac{d}{dt}[HI] = k[HI]^2$$

and for the hydrolysis of an ester by hydroxide ions,

$$RCO_2R' + OH^- \rightarrow RCO_2^- + R'OH$$

$$-\frac{d}{dt}[RCO_2R'] = k[RCO_2R'][OH^-]. \tag{8.16}$$

Integration of equation (8.15) gives:

$$kt = \frac{x}{a(a-x)} \tag{8.17}$$

where x is the number of moles of hydrogen iodide decomposed after time t.

If $x = \frac{a}{2}$,

$$kt_{\frac{1}{2}} = \frac{1}{a} \tag{8.18}$$

i.e. $t_{\frac{1}{2}} = \frac{1}{ak}$, so that the half-time is *inversely* proportional to a [cf. (8.13)].

The dimensions of k, for a *second-order* reaction, are concentration^{-1} time^{-1}, e.g. litres mole^{-1} second^{-1}.

In terms of some physical property, e.g. pressure p,

$$kt = \frac{(p_t - p_0)}{(p_\infty - p_0)(p_\infty - p_t)} \tag{8.19}$$

since, if the amount of hydrogen iodide left after time t is proportional to $(p_\infty - p_t)$, the amount dissociated is proportional to $[(p_\infty - p_0) - (p_\infty - p_t)]$, i.e. to $(p_t - p_0)$.

Integration of equation (8.16) in the form:

$$\frac{-dA}{dt} = k[A][B]$$

leads (Appendix F) to:

$$kt = \frac{1}{(a-b)} \ln \frac{a(b-x)}{b(a-x)} \tag{8.20}$$

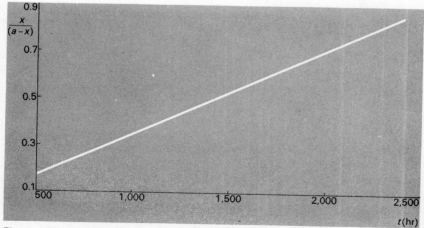

Figure 157. Kinetics of hydrolysis of the tetrachlorosuccinate ion at 25°C.

where a and b are the initial concentrations of reactions A and B, respectively, and x is the amount of A, and of B, which has reacted after time t.

There is no unique half-life of this reaction, unless $a = b$, in which case equations **(8.15)** and **(8.18)** are applicable. The dimensions of k, from equation **(8.20)** are again (time^{-1} concentration^{-1}).

For example, the hydrolysis of the tetrachlorsuccinate ion

$$\begin{matrix} CHCl_2CO_2^- \\ | \\ CHCl_2CO_2^- \end{matrix} + OH^- \rightarrow \begin{matrix} CHCl(OH)CO_2^- \\ | \\ CHCl_2CO_2^- \end{matrix} + Cl^-$$

is second-order. Data for this reaction are given in table 48.

Table 48 Kinetics of Alkaline Hydrolysis of the Tetrachlorosuccinate Ion at 25°C.

$a = b = 0.0214$ mole litre^{-1}		
t (hr)	$10^2 x$	$\dfrac{x}{(a-x)}$
500	0·311	0·170
1000	0·543	0·340
1500	0·723	0·510
2000	0·866	0·682
2500	0·983	0·851

The graph of $\dfrac{x}{(a-x)}$ against t is shown in fig. 157. The slope is (ak), so that $k = 0.0160$ l. mole^{-1} hr^{-1}, and the half-life is 2920 hours.

8·2   **Equilibrium reactions**

As we have seen in chapter 5, many chemical reactions reach a position of equilibrium, after which there is no further change in composition of the reacting system. We consider now the kinetics of such a reaction.

Suppose that both the forward and reverse reactions are first-order processes, as represented by

$$A \underset{k_{-1}}{\overset{k_1}{\rightleftharpoons}} B \qquad (8.21)$$

where k_1 is the rate-constant for the forward reaction (A $\rightarrow$ B), and k_{-1} the rate constant for the reverse reaction (B $\rightarrow$ A). From the law of mass action, equation **(5.8)**

$$\frac{k_1}{k_{-1}} = \left(\frac{[B]}{[A]} \right)_{t=\infty} = K \qquad (8.22)$$

where K is the equilibrium constant for equation **(8.21)**

If the initial numbers of moles at time $t = 0$, are $[A]_{t=0} = a$, $[B]_{t=0} = b$, then after time t,

$$[A]_t = (a-x), \qquad [B]_t = (b+x),$$

where x is the number of moles of A reacted, and hence the number of moles of B formed. The rate equation is thus:

$$\frac{dx}{dt} = k_1(a-x) + k_{-1}(b+x) \tag{8.23}$$

Integration of this equation (Appendix F) leads to the form

$$(k_1 + k_{-1}) = \frac{1}{t} \ln \frac{a - a_\infty}{a_t - a_\infty}. \tag{8.24}$$

This is a first-order integrated rate equation, from which the *sum* of the rate constants can be found. In order to determine k_1 and k_{-1} individually, their ratio (i.e. K, equation **8.22**) may be determined; alternatively, by studying the rate of reaction of pure component A in the initial stages, when the concentration of B is insufficient for the back reaction ($B \rightarrow A$) to be of importance, k_1 is determined.

For example, an optically active ketone A slowly changes from the pure form A to an equilibrium mixture of A and its isomer B. The reaction can be followed by observing the change in optical rotation with time of a solution of the ketone. The results in table 49 were obtained at 25°C.; α_t is the optical rotation after time t hours.

Table 49 Mutarotation of the Ketone A, at 25°C.

t(hr)	α_t^0	$(\alpha_t - \alpha_\infty)^0$
0	189·0	157·7
3	169·3	138·0
5	156·2	124·9
7	145·9	114·6
11	124·6	93·3
15	110·4	79·1
24	84·5	53·2
∞	31·3	0

We can substitute the optical rotations in equation (**8.24**), from the relationships:

$$(a - a_\infty) \propto (\alpha_0 - \alpha_\infty)$$

$$(a_t - a_\infty) \propto (\alpha_t - \alpha_\infty).$$

The plot of $\log(\alpha_t - \alpha_\infty)$ against time is shown in fig. 158. From the slope $\left(= \dfrac{-k}{2·303} \right)$, we obtain

$$(k_1 + k_{-1}) = 3·05 \times 10^{-2} \ \text{hr}^{-1}.$$

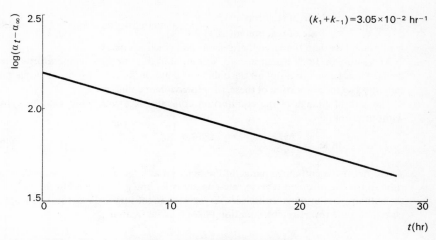

$(k_1 + k_{-1}) = 3.05 \times 10^{-2}$ hr^{-1}

Figure 158. Kinetics of mutarotation of ketone A at 25°C.

From equation (8.20),

$$\frac{k_1}{k_{-1}} = \left\{ \frac{b+x}{a-x} \right\}_{t=\infty}$$

Now $b = 0$, and x_∞ (the amount of A converted to B, at equilibrium) $= (a - a_\infty)$. Hence

$$\frac{k_1}{k_{-1}} = \frac{(\alpha_0 - \alpha_\infty)}{\alpha_\infty} = \frac{157 \cdot 7}{31 \cdot 3} = 5 \cdot 04.$$

Solving for the rate-constants k_1 and k_{-1}:

$$k_1 = 2 \cdot 55 \times 10^{-2} \text{ hour}^{-1}$$

$$k_{-1} = 0 \cdot 504 \times 10^{-2} \text{ hour}^{-1}.$$

8·3   **Dependence of rate of reaction upon temperature**

The rates of most chemical reactions are very sensitive to changes in temperature; frequently the rate increases by a factor of two or three if the temperature is raised from 25°C. to 35°C.

It seems reasonable to postulate that, in order for the molecules A and B to react, as in equation (8.25), A must 'collide with' B:

$$A + B \rightarrow \text{products.} \tag{8.25}$$

The number of collisions which occur per second between A and B can be calculated from the kinetic theory. It is found that this number increases with increasing temperature – but only proportionally to the square root of the absolute temperature.

Thus, the ratio $\dfrac{\text{(rate of reaction at 35°C.)}}{\text{(rate of reaction at 25°C.)}}$ is calculated to be about $\sqrt{\dfrac{308}{298}}$, or $1\cdot03$, very much less than the large increase in rate which is observed.

Arrhenius, in 1889, attempted to account for this marked temperature-dependence. He assumed that not all the collisions between A and B produced a reaction, but only a small proportion of these, the more violent collisions.

The rate of change of the equilibrium constant, K_p, with temperature is given without proof here by

$$\frac{d}{dT}\ln K_p = \frac{\Delta H}{RT^2} \tag{8.26}$$

where ΔH is the enthalpy change of the reaction at a temperature T. Now K_p is the ratio of the forward and reverse rate-constants, k_1 and k_{-1}; if in addition we divide the enthalpy ΔH into two enthalpies, E_1 (specific to the forward reaction step) and E_2 (specific to the reverse step), equation (8.26) may be written:

$$\frac{d}{dT}\ln k_1 - \frac{d}{dT}\ln k_2 = \frac{E_1}{RT^2} - \frac{E_2}{RT^2}$$

i.e. $\qquad \dfrac{d}{dT}\ln k_1 = \dfrac{E_1}{RT^2}, \quad$ and $\quad \dfrac{d}{dT}\ln k_2 = \dfrac{E_2}{RT^2}.$

Integration gives

$$\ln k_1 = \frac{-E_1}{RT} + (\text{constant}) \quad\text{and}\quad \ln k_2 = \frac{-E_2}{RT} + (\text{constant}) \tag{8.27}$$

so that a graph of $\log_{10} k_1$ (or $\log_{10} k_2$) against $\left(\dfrac{1}{T}\right)$ should be linear and of slope $\dfrac{-E_1}{2\cdot303R}\left(\text{or } \dfrac{-E_2}{2\cdot303R}\right).$

8·3·1 *Activation energies*

The relationship between E_1, E_2 and ΔH is illustrated in fig. 159, where the path of reaction for the equilibrium

$$H_2 + I_2 \underset{k_{-1}}{\overset{k_1}{\rightleftharpoons}} 2HI \tag{8.28}$$

is traced. For the forward reaction $\Delta H = -5\cdot0$ kcal. mole^{-1} at 670°K. From the variation with temperature of the rate-constants k_1 and k_{-1}, equation (8.27), the enthalpies E_1 and E_2 have the values 39·0 kcal. mole^{-1} and 44·0 kcal. mole^{-1} respectively.

E_1 and E_2 are called the *activation enthalpies* of the forward and reverse reactions, (8.28). The activation enthalpy is often called the *activation energy*. E_1 may be considered to indicate minimum kinetic energy which the two molecules, H_2 and I_2,

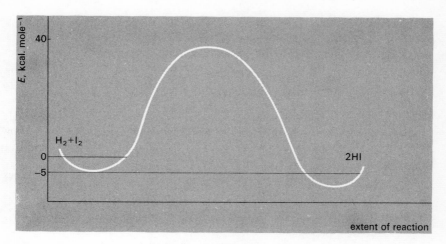

Figure 159. Activation and reaction enthalpies for equilibrium (8.28), at 670°K., assuming the mechanism in section (8.3.1).

must possess before, upon collision, the atoms re-form to produce two HI molecules; E_2 applies similarly to the collision process

$$HI + HI \overset{k}{\rightleftharpoons} H_2 + I_2 .$$

The probability that a molecule possesses enthalpy per mole in excess of E_1 is given by $\exp\left(-\dfrac{E_1}{RT}\right)$, where R is the gas constant per mole and T is the absolute temperature. If A_1 represents the total collision frequency of reactant molecules H_2 and I_2 whatever their energy, then the rate of reaction depends upon the product of A_1 and the factor $-\dfrac{E_1}{RT}$, or specifically

$$k_1 = A_1 \exp\left(-\frac{E_1}{RT}\right)$$

Thus $$\ln k_1 = -\frac{E_1}{RT} + \ln A_1, \tag{8.29}$$

a similar equation to (8.27).

Since, as previously stated, A_1 varies as $\sqrt{T}$ only, the exponential factor $\exp\left(-\dfrac{E_1}{RT}\right)$ clearly accounts for the large variation of k_1 with T, which implies that E_1 is quite large. For example, if $E_1 = 14$ kcal. $mole^{-1}$, at $T = 300°K.$,

$$k_{300} = A_1 \exp\left(\frac{-14000}{1 \cdot 98 \times 300}\right)$$

and at $T = 310°K.$,

$$k_{310} = A_1 \exp\left(\frac{-14000}{1\cdot98 \times 310}\right)$$

i.e.
$$\frac{k_{310}}{k_{300}} = \exp\left[\frac{14000}{1\cdot98}\left(\frac{1}{300} - \frac{1}{310}\right)\right]$$

It should be noted that the exponential factor is very small, and that therefore only a very small fraction of the collisions, A_1 per second, lead to reaction. In the present example, $\exp\left(-\frac{E_1}{RT}\right)$ at $300°K.$ has the value $7\cdot5 \times 10^{-11}$.

The data in table 50 refer to the decomposition of dibromosuccinic acid in aqueous solution.

Table 50 The Decomposition of Dibromosuccinic Acid in Aqueous Solution

$t°C.$	k	$T°K.$	$\frac{1}{T}$	$\log k_1$
15°C.	$9\cdot67 \times 10^{-6}$	288	0·00347	−5·015
35°C.	$7\cdot08 \times 10^{-5}$	308	0·00325	−4·150
60°C.	$6\cdot54 \times 10^{-4}$	333	0·00300	−3·184

In fig. 160 the graph of $\log_{10} k$ against $\left(\frac{1}{T°K.}\right)$ is shown; the slope $\left(\frac{-E}{2\cdot303R}\right)$ is $-4,400$, and the activation energy $20\cdot14$ kcal. mole^{-1}.

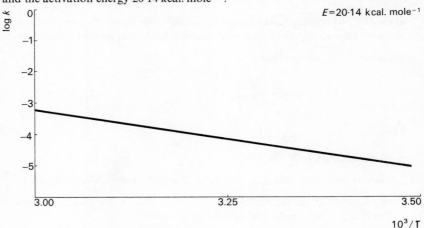

Figure 160. Hydrolysis of dibromosuccinic acid in aqueous solution: variation of rate constant with temperature.

The rates of nearly all chemical reactions *increase* with increase in temperature, but not by the same amount. Returning to the reaction of equation (**8.28**), the rates of both the forward and backward reactions will increase with temperature, but not to the same extent. Thus the equilibrium constant K, equation (**8.22**) is dependent upon the temperature: for example in an exothermic reaction K decreases with an increase in temperature.

The rates of reactions are controlled largely by their activation energies. Thus, the reaction between hydrogen and chlorine, *in the dark*, is very slow – slower than that between hydrogen and iodine at the same temperature; both reactions proceed by the bimolecular collision process:

$$H_2 + Cl_2 \text{ (or } I_2) \to 2\,HCl \text{ (or } 2\,HI)$$

the activation energies are 50 kcal. mole^{-1} and 41 kcal. mole^{-1} respectively (see section 1·2). If a chain reaction is initiated (page 258) the first reaction becomes very fast, because its effective activation energy is decreased considerably.

Where a number of parallel reactions can occur, the activation energy may determine the main product of reaction. Suppose a compound A may decompose in two ways, with the enthalpies shown:

$$A \begin{cases} \nearrow B, & \Delta H = b \\ \searrow C, & \Delta H = c \end{cases}$$

If $b < c$, the decomposition to form B is *thermodynamically* favoured. But suppose

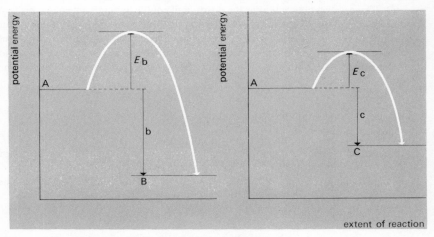

Figure 161. Energy levels for the parallel reactions

that the reaction paths are as shown in fig. 161. The activation energy for the formation of C is less than that of the alternative reaction, so that the formation of C is *kinetically* favoured. This is often the case in organic processes, where a number of different products could be formed; that produced in greatest yield, under particular conditions, is often determined kinetically rather than thermodynamically.

8·4   Catalysis

The rate of a reaction may be altered by the presence of small quantities of certain substances which are foreign to the reacting system, and which are called *catalysts.* The reaction-rate may be increased, an example of *positive* catalysis (or just *catalysis*) or decreased, which is *negative* catalysis.

Catalysed systems may be either homogeneous or heterogeneous, but certain characteristics are common to both:

(1) The catalyst is unchanged chemically (i.e. in *nature* and *amount*) at the end of the reaction. For example, platinum gauze is used as a heterogeneous catalyst in the oxidation of ammonia; the gauze is eventually roughened after use, so that the platinum is involved in the mechanism of the reaction. The granular manganese dioxide added to catalyse the thermal decomposition of potassium chlorate may be recovered at the end of the reaction, but in a much more finely-divided state.

(2) A small amount of the catalyst affects a relatively enormous extent of reaction. For example, colloidal platinum, at a concentration of 10^{-6} g. l.$^{-1}$, catalyses the decomposition of hydrogen peroxide in alkaline solution.

(3) The catalyst does not alter the position of equilibrium in a reversible reaction. Since it is unchanged chemically at the end of the reaction, the catalyst contributes nothing to the energy of the system, so that the same position of equilibrium should be obtained with or without a catalyst, at *constant temperature.* Thus, if reaction **(8.21)** is catalysed, both k_1 and k_{-1} must be increased (or decreased) to the same extent.

8·4·1   *Homogeneous catalysis*

This term implies that the catalyst is in the same phase as the reactants; for example, the gaseous catalyst nitric oxide is used to promote the reaction between the gases sulphur dioxide and oxygen in the sulphuric acid Chamber process, to give sulphur trioxide:

$$NO + \tfrac{1}{2}O_2 \rightarrow NO_2$$

$$NO_2 + SO_2 \rightarrow NO + SO_3.$$

The *mutarotation* (change in optical activity) of an aqueous solution of glucose is catalysed by acids and bases; this is an example of *acid–base* catalysis. The varying efficiencies of different catalysts are revealed by the values of the rate constants in table 51.

Table 51 Efficiencies of Catalysts in the Mutarotation of Glucose at 18°C.

Acid	$k\ \text{sec.}^{-1}$	Base	$k\ \text{sec.}^{-1}$
H_2O	$9{\cdot}5 \times 10^{-5}$	H_2O	$9{\cdot}5 \times 10^{-5}$
Acetic acid	$2{\cdot}0 \times 10^{-3}$	Mandelate	$6{\cdot}1 \times 10^{-2}$
Mandelic acid	$6{\cdot}0 \times 10^{-3}$	Acetate	$2{\cdot}7 \times 10^{-2}$
H_3O^+	$1{\cdot}4 \times 10^{-1}$	OH^-	$6{\cdot}0 \times 10^3$

The hydroxyl ion is clearly a very effective catalyst for this reaction.

The homogeneous catalyst provides an alternative path or mechanism for the reaction; in the case of a positive catalyst, a path of lower activation enthalpy. Thus, if C is a catalyst for the unimolecular decomposition of A, we can represent the two reaction paths

$$A \overset{k_1}{\to} \text{products} \tag{8.30}$$

$$A + C \overset{k_c}{\to} \text{products} + C \tag{8.31}$$

where equation (**8.30**) represents the uncatalysed reaction, and equation (**8.31**) the catalysed reaction. The rates are given by

$$-\frac{d}{dt}[A] = k_1[A] \tag{8.32}$$

and
$$-\frac{d}{dt}[A] = k_c[A][C] \tag{8.33}$$

respectively. Now, since C is a catalyst for this reaction, [C] does not change with time. Hence equation (**8.33**) may be written

$$-\frac{d}{dt}[A] = k'_c[A]$$

where $\quad k'_c = k_c[C]$

$$k'_c = k_c[C]$$

and the total rate is therefore

$$-\frac{d}{dt}[A] = (k_1 + k'_c[A]. \tag{8.34}$$

Now if $k'_c \gg k_1$, equation (**8.34**) becomes approximately

$$-\frac{d}{dt}[A] = k'_c[A]. \tag{8.35}$$

Notice that, if equation (**8.35**) is obeyed, then the rate increases proportionately to the concentration of homogeneous catalyst C, since $k'_c = k_c[C]$. If [C] is varied, in a series of experiments, then k_c, and not k'_c, will remain constant (table 52).

Table 52 Acid-Catalysed Hydrolysis of Diazoacetic Ester

pH	$10^3[H^+], = C$	k'_c	$\dfrac{k'_c}{C}$ (min.$^{-1}$)
2·50	3·25	20·8	6·40
2·74	1·82	11·7	6·45
3·05	0·90	5·8	6·33
3·44	0·36	2·7	6·38

The reaction is: $N_2CHCO_2C_2H_5 + H_2O \overset{H^+}{\rightarrow} HOCH_2CO_2C_2H_5 + N_2$.

8·4·2 *Heterogeneous catalysis*

In this case the catalyst is present in a different phase from that of the reactants. For example, finely divided platinum catalyses the reaction between hydrogen and oxygen. The gases may be mixed at room temperature and will remain unreacted indefinitely; if the platinum catalyst is introduced, combination takes place at the surface of the metal and water is formed. Platinum is also a positive catalyst for the decomposition of hydrogen peroxide:

$$2\,H_2O_2 \overset{Pt}{\rightarrow} 2\,H_2O + O_2.$$

However, this decomposition can be retarded by the addition of small quantities of glycol or acetanilide; these substances are negative catalysts, or *inhibitors*, for this reaction. Platinum catalysts are very susceptible to poisoning by traces of impurities in the reactants, so that catalysts which are less easily poisoned are frequently used, although they may be of lower efficiency. For example, vanadium pentoxide is nowadays preferred to platinum as a catalyst for the formation of sulphur trioxide in the sulphuric acid contact process.

The heterogeneous catalyst also provides a reaction path of lower activation energy than that of the uncatalysed reaction. The reactants are first *adsorbed* on the surface of the catalyst; in this state they are able to react more readily. If equation **(8.36)** refers to the uncatalysed reaction, and equation **(8.37)** to that predominating when the heterogeneous catalyst is present, then E_u is greater than E_c:

$$A(gas) + B(gas) \rightarrow product, \text{ activation enthalpy } = E_u \qquad \textbf{(8.36)}$$

$$A(ads.) + B(ads.) \rightarrow product, \text{ activation enthalpy } = E_c. \qquad \textbf{(8.37)}$$

8·5 Chain reactions

Many chemical reactions occur by a series of simple steps, some of which are repeated many times. In these cases stoichiometry differs from the order of reaction.

For example, the decomposition of acetaldehyde vapour

$$CH_3CHO \rightarrow CH_4 + CO \qquad \textbf{(8.38)}$$

proceeds by the following series of reactions:

$$CH_3CHO \rightarrow CH_3 \cdot + CHO \cdot \tag{8.39}$$

$$CH_3 \cdot + CH_3CHO \rightarrow CH_4 + CH_3CO \cdot \tag{8.40}$$

$$CH_3CO \cdot \rightarrow CH_3 + CO \cdot \tag{8.41}$$

$$2CH_3 \cdot \rightarrow C_2H_6 \tag{8.42}$$

The complete series constitutes a *chain reaction* process. Reaction (**8.39**) is called the *initiation step*, because it must occur first for the process to be established. It is a relatively difficult step, with a high activation energy, because a strong carbon–carbon bond must be broken in this process. As a result a few pairs of 'free radicals' – fragments of molecules with incomplete electron shells – are formed. The $CHO \cdot$ fragment plays no further part in the reaction; but the methyl radical $CH_3 \cdot$ reacts *readily* (and therefore rapidly, i.e. at almost every collision) with aldehyde molecules, as shown by equation (**8.40**). One of the products of this reaction is methane; the other decomposes to form carbon monoxide and a *new* methyl radical. This methyl radical reacts with a further acetaldehyde molecule, so that the reactions (**8.40**) and (**8.41**) are repeated many times over, for each methyl radical formed in the initiation step. These two stages constitute the *propagation steps* of the reaction, and virtually all the acetaldehyde is decomposed by equation (**8.40**). The methyl radical is called the *chain carrier*. The rate of the process is limited by the fact that methyl radicals are sometimes lost to the system by such processes as equation (**8.42**); these are called *chain terminating steps*.

An overall rate-equation may be derived for this reaction:

$$\frac{d}{dt}[CH_4] = k \cdot [CH_3CHO]^{\frac{3}{2}}$$

so that the order of the reaction is 1·5, and not unity, as might have been inferred from the stoichiometric equation (**8.38**). Fractional orders frequently arise as a result of such chain-processes.

The reaction proceeds by this rather complex mechanism because it requires less energy than decomposition by collisions between acetaldehyde molecules. Stage (**8.39**) is a difficult process, but it need not occur very often in order for large numbers of acetaldehyde molecules to decompose.

Many gas-phase decompositions of organic compounds – *pyrolytic reactions* – occur by similar mechanisms. In the reactions between hydrogen and chlorine, and hydrogen and oxygen, *chain branching* may occur, in which the number of chain carriers is multiplied during the propagation series of reactions. In such cases the rate of reaction increases very rapidly, and if the enthalpy of reaction cannot be removed sufficiently rapidly, an explosion will result. Thus, in the case of the hydrogen–chlorine reaction we can imagine that a few chlorine *atoms* are formed by the irradiation of chlorine molecules by sunlight, or by the light emitted by burning magnesium ribbon. Both of these sources provide quanta (hv) of ultra violet radiation:

$$Cl_2 + hv \rightarrow Cl \cdot + Cl \cdot$$

These atoms are the chain-carriers in a series of propagation steps:

$$Cl + H_2 \rightarrow HCl + H \cdot$$

$$H + Cl_2 \rightarrow HCl + Cl \cdot \quad , \quad etc.,$$

which are both facile reactions. As we have seen, hydrogen and iodine do not, in general, react in this way; from equation (8.2), they favour a bimolecular collision process.

Problems

1. The kinetics of the hydrolysis of methyl acetate

$$CH_3CO_2CH_3 + H_2O \overset{H^+}{\rightarrow} CH_3CO_2H + CH_3OH$$

in excess dilute hydrochloric acid at 25°C. were followed by withdrawing 2 ml. portions of the reaction mixture at intervals of time t adding to 50 ml. of ice-cold water and titrating against baryta water. The following results were obtained:

t (min.)	0	10	21	40	115	∞
baryta (ml.)	18·5	19·1	19·7	20·7	23·6	34·8

Determine the velocity constant and the half-life of the hydrolysis.

2. (a) The half-life of krypton, ^{85}Kr, is 10·6 years. How long will it take for 99 per cent of ^{85}Kr to disintegrate?

(b) Calculate the mass of radon which is in equilibrium with 1 g. of radium if the half-lives are

$$^{222}Rn: 3\cdot83 \text{ days} \qquad ^{226}Ra: 1622 \text{ years.}$$

3. The conversion of sucrose into glucose and fructose, in the presence of dilute hydrochloric acid, is a first-order reaction, and leads to a reversal of optical rotation (inversion).

The following polarimeter readings (α) were obtained at times (t) shown:

t, min.	5	20	44	90	140	175	∞
α^0	12·2	9·95	6·95	2·70	0·10	−1·30	−4·00

Determine the first-order rate constant, and the half-life, for this reaction.

4. The following results refer to the decomposition of ammonia on a heated tungsten surface:

$$2NH_3 \rightarrow N_2 + 3H_2$$

initial pressure (mm.)	65	105	150	185
half-life (sec.)	290	460	670	820

Deduce the order of the reaction and determine the velocity constant.

5. In the homogeneous decomposition of nitrous oxide, it is found that, at a constant temperature, the time needed for half the reaction to be completed, $t_{\frac{1}{2}}$, is inversely proportional to the initial pressure, p_0. On varying the temperature, the following results were obtained:

temperature (deg. C.)	694	757	812
p_0 (mm.)	294	360	345
$t_{\frac{1}{2}}$ (sec.)	1,520	212	53

Deduce the order of reaction and calculate (i) the velocity constant at 694°C. and (ii) the activation energy of the reaction.

6. The rearrangement of N-chloroacetanilide to p-chloroacetanilide is catalysed by hydrochloric acid:

$$C_6H_5N(Cl)COCH_3 \xrightarrow{H^+} ClC_6H_4N(H)COCH_3.$$

N-chloroacetanilide liberates iodine from potassium iodide solution, and the reaction can be followed readily. From the following data deduce the order of the reaction and determine the rate constant at the temperature of the experiment.

t (min.)	0	15	30	45	60	75
$Na_2S_2O_3$ (ml.)	24·5	18·1	13·3	9·7	7·1	5·2

Appendix A
Selected fundamental units

c.g.s. units

N	Avogadro constant	$6 \cdot 023 \times 10^{23}$ molecules mole^{-1}
c	Velocity of light (in vacuo)	$2 \cdot 998 \times 10^{10}$ cm. sec.$^{-1}$
e	Electronic charge	$4 \cdot 803 \times 10^{-10}$ e.s.u.
m	Electron rest mass	$9 \cdot 109 \times 10^{-28}$ g.
h	Planck constant	$6 \cdot 626 \times 10^{-27}$ erg sec.
F	Faraday	$9 \cdot 6487 \times 10^{4}$ coulomb g. equiv.$^{-1}$
a_0	1st Bohr radius	$5 \cdot 292 \times 10^{-9}$ cm.
m_{H^+}	Atomic weight of proton	$1 \cdot 0073$ a.m.u.
k	Boltzmann constant	$1 \cdot 381 \times 10^{-16}$ erg (deg. K.)$^{-1}$
R	Gas constant	$8 \cdot 314 \times 10^{7}$ erg mole^{-1} (deg. K.)$^{-1}$
J	Joule constant	$4 \cdot 184$ joule cal.$^{-1}$
R_H	Rydberg constant for hydrogen	$109677 \cdot 58$ cm.$^{-1}$

S.I. units*

N	$6 \cdot 023 \times 10^{23}$ molecules mole^{-1}
c	$2 \cdot 998 \times 10^{8}$ m. s.$^{-1}$
e	$1 \cdot 601 \times 10^{-7}$ pC.
m	$9 \cdot 109 \times 10^{-16}$ pg.
h	$6 \cdot 626 \times 10^{-34}$ J. s.
F	$9 \cdot 6487 \times 10^{4}$ C. g-equiv.$^{-1}$
a_0	$5 \cdot 292 \times 10^{-2}$ nm.
m_{H^+}	$1 \cdot 0073$ amu.
k	$1 \cdot 381 \times 10^{-23}$ J. (deg. K.)$^{-1}$
R	$8 \cdot 314$ J. mol.$^{-1}$ (deg. K.)$^{-1}$
J	$- - -$
R_H	$10 \cdot 967758$ μm.$^{-1}$

* See B.S.I. publication PD 5686 (1967).

Atomic weights

The atomic weights listed in this appendix are based upon the 1961 standard, $^{12}C = 12.0000$. All known elements are included; the atomic weights for some of the more recently discovered elements are represented by the mass number of the most stable isotope, in parentheses.

Name	Symbol	Atomic number	International atomic weight
Actinium	Ac	89	(227)
Aluminium	Al	13	26·9815
Americium	Am	95	(243)
Antimony	Sb	51	121·75
Argon	Ar	18	39·948
Arsenic	As	33	74·9216
Astatine	At	85	(210)
Barium	Ba	56	137·34
Berkelium	Bk	97	(249)
Beryllium	Be	4	9·0122
Bismuth	Bi	83	208·980
Boron	B	5	10·811
Bromine	Br	35	79·909
Cadmium	Cd	48	112·40
Caesium	Cs	55	132·905
Calcium	Ca	20	40·08
Californium	Cf	98	(251)
Carbon	C	6	12·0112
Cerium	Ce	58	140·12
Chlorine	Cl	17	35·453
Chromium	Cr	24	51·996
Cobalt	Co	27	58·9332
Copper	Cu	29	63·54
Curium	Cm	96	(247)
Dysprosium	Dy	66	162·50
Einsteinium	Es	99	(254)
Erbium	Er	68	167·26
Europium	Eu	63	151·96
Fermium	Fm	100	(253)
Fluorine	F	9	18·9984
Francium	Fr	87	(223)

Name	Symbol	Atomic number	International atomic weight
Gadolinium	Gd	64	157·25
Gallium	Ga	31	69·72
Germanium	Ge	32	72·59
Gold	Au	79	196·967
Hafnium	Hf	72	178·49
Helium	He	2	4·0026
Holmium	Ho	67	164·930
Hydrogen	H	1	1·00797
Indium	In	49	114·82
Iodine	I	53	126·9044
Iridium	Ir	77	192·2
Iron	Fe	26	55·847
Krypton	Kr	36	83·80
Lanthanum	La	57	138·91
Lawrencium	Lw	103	(257)
Lead	Pb	82	207·19
Lithium	Li	3	6·939
Lutetium	Lu	71	174·97
Magnesium	Mg	12	24·312
Manganese	Mn	25	54·9380
Mendelevium	Md	101	(256)
Mercury	Hg	80	200·59
Molybdenum	Mo	42	95·94
Neodymium	Nd	60	144·24
Neon	Ne	10	20·183
Neptunium	Np	93	(237)
Nickel	Ni	28	58·71
Niobium	Nb	41	92·906
Nitrogen	N	7	14·0067
Nobelium	No	102	(254)
Osmium	Os	76	190·2
Oxygen	O	8	15·9994
Palladium	Pd	46	106·4
Phosphorus	P	15	30·9738
Platinum	Pt	78	195·09
Plutonium	Pu	94	(242)
Polonium	Po	84	(210)
Potassium	K	19	39·102
Praseodymium	Pr	59	140·907
Promethium	Pm	61	(147)
Protactinium	Pa	91	(231)
Radium	Ra	88	(226)
Radon	Rn	86	(222)

Atomic weights – *continued*

Name	Symbol	Atomic number	International atomic weight
Rhenium	Re	75	186·2
Rhodium	Rh	45	102·905
Rubidium	Rb	37	85·47
Ruthenium	Ru	44	101·07
Samarium	Sm	62	150·35
Scandium	Sc	21	44·956
Selenium	Se	34	78·96
Silicon	Si	14	28·086
Silver	Ag	47	107·870
Sodium	Na	11	22·9898
Strontium	Sr	38	87·62
Sulphur	S	16	32·064*
Tantalum	Ta	73	180·948
Technetium	Tc	43	(99)
Tellurium	Te	52	127·60
Terbium	Tb	65	158·924
Thallium	Tl	81	204·37
Thorium	Th	90	232·038
Thulium	Tm	69	168·934
Tin	Sn	50	118·69
Titanium	Ti	22	47·90
Tungsten	W	74	183·85
Uranium	U	92	238·03
Vanadium	V	23	50·942
Xenon	Xe	54	131·30
Ytterbium	Yb	70	173·04
Yttrium	Y	39	88·905
Zinc	Zn	30	65·37
Zirconium	Zr	40	91·22

* Because of natural variations in the relative abundances of the isotopes of sulphur the atomic weight of this element has a range of $\pm 0 \cdot 003$.

Electron configurations of the elements of atomic numbers 1 to 38

Atomic number	Element	K	L		M			N				O				P				Q			
		1	2		3			4				5				6				7			
		s	s	p	s	p	d	s	p	d	f	s	p	d	f	s	p	d	f	s	p	d	f
1	H	1																					
2	He	2																					
3	Li	2	1																				
4	Be	2	2																				
5	B	2	2	1																			
6	C	2	2	2																			
7	N	2	2	3																			
8	O	2	2	4																			
9	F	2	2	5																			
10	Ne	2	2	6																			
11	Na	2	2	6	1																		
12	Mg	2	2	6	2																		
13	Al	2	2	6	2	1																	
14	Si	2	2	6	2	2																	
15	P	2	2	6	2	3																	
16	S	2	2	6	2	4																	
17	Cl	2	2	6	2	5																	
18	Ar	2	2	6	2	6																	
19	K	2	2	6	2	6		1															
20	Ca	2	2	6	2	6		2															
21	Sc	2	2	6	2	6	1	2															
22	Ti	2	2	6	2	6	2	2															
23	V	2	2	6	2	6	3	2															
24	Cr	2	2	6	2	6	5*	1															
25	Mn	2	2	6	2	6	5	2															
26	Fe	2	2	6	2	6	6	2															
27	Co	2	2	6	2	6	7	2															
28	Ni	2	2	6	2	6	8	2															
29	Cu	2	2	6	2	6	10*	1															
30	Zn	2	2	6	2	6	10	2															
31	Ga	2	2	6	2	6	10	2	1														
32	Ge	2	2	6	2	6	10	2	2														
33	As	2	2	6	2	6	10	2	3														
34	Se	2	2	6	2	6	10	2	4														
35	Br	2	2	6	2	6	10	2	5														
36	Kr	2	2	6	2	6	10	2	6														
37	Rb	2	2	6	2	6	10	2	6			1											
38	Sr	2	2	6	2	6	10	2	6			2											

* Note irregularity

Appendix B
Selected ionization energies

The ionization energies are expressed in kcal. g-atom^{-1}. Each value of I_z represents the energy change of the corresponding process:

$$X^{(z-1)+} \rightarrow X^{z-} + e.$$

In this appendix, the values of z range from 1 to 5. For $z = 1$, $X^{(z-1)+}$ is the unionized atom.

	Atomic Number	I_1	I_2	I_3	I_4	I_5
H	1	313·5				
He	2	566·8	1254			
Li	3	124·3	1744	2823		
Be	4	214·9	419·9	3542	5019	
B	5	191·3	349·4	870·5	5979	7843
C	6	259·7	562·1	1090	1556	9039
N	7	335·3	682·6	1094	1786	2257
O	8	314·5	810·5	1267	1785	2626
F	9	401·7	806·6	1445	1988	2634
Ne	10	497·2	947·1	1476	2241	2915
Na	11	118·5	1091·	1652	2280	3196
Mg	12	176·3	346·6	1848	2520	3256
Al	13	138·0	434·0	655·8	2767	3547
Si	14	195·8	376·8	771·6	1041	3844
P	15	253·7	453·1	695·5	1183	1499
S	16	238·9	539·6	796·7	1091	1672
Cl	17	300·0	548·8	920·1	1234	1494
Ar	18	363·4	636·9	943·2	1333	1730
K	19	100·1	733·3	1061	1404	1914
Ca	20	140·9	273·7	1181	1538	1946
Sc	21	151·2	297·2	570·7	1704	2122
Ti	22	157·5	312·9	648·9	999·4	2301
V	23	155·4	327·5	684·9	1116	1485
Cr	24	156·0	380·3	714·9	1158	1704
Mn	25	171·4	360·7	776·9	1222	1753
Fe	26	182·2	373·1	706·6	1291	1822
Co	27	181·3	393·2	772·3	1222	1891
Ni	28	176·0	418·5	833·8	1291	1822
Cu	29	178·1	467·9	876·3	1361	1914
Zn	30	216·6	414·2	914·6	1430	1983

	Atomic Number	I_1	I_2	I_3	I_4	I_5
Se	34	224·9	496·0	693·6	989·3	1686
Br	35	273·0	497·6	827·6	1158	2760
Kr	36	322·6	566·6	851·8	1199	1522
Rb	37	96·3	634·2	915·0	1222	1637
Sr	38	131·3	254·3	991·6	1314	1660
Ag	47	174·7	495·3	832·5	1199	1614
Cd	48	207·3	389·7	807·1	1268	1683
In	49	133·7	435·1	646·6	1337	1776
Sn	50	169·1	337·4	707·0	940·8	1863
Sb	51	199·2	415·3	546·5	1013	1280
Te	52	207·8	496·9	705·9	872·1	1391
I	53	240·7	438·4	714·9	968·5	1199
Xe	54	279·7	489·1	740·9	1075	1753
Cs	55	89·8	541·0	807·1	1176	1337
Ba	56	134·0	230·1	853·2	1130	1430
La	57	129·4	263·6	442·1	1199	1522
Ce	58	159·3	283·6	463·5	846·3	1614
Hg	80	240·6	432·4	791·0	1660	1891
Tl	81	140·8	470·8	687·2	1165	1476
Pb	82	171·0	346·6	739·8	974·3	1607
Bi	83	168·0	445·1	590·3	1047	1294
Rn	84	247·9	461·2	691·8	1015	1268

Selected electron affinities

The electron affinities are expressed in kcal. g-atom^{-1}. Each value of $E(X^{z-})$ represents the energy change of the corresponding process:

$$X + ze \rightarrow X^{z-}$$

	$z = 1$	$z = 2$
H	-17	
F	-80	
Cl	-86	
Br	-81	
I	-74	
At	-61	
O	-34	179
S	-48	99
Se	-51	117
Te	-53	97
CN	-81	
OH	-65	

Selected bond lengths and bond energies

This appendix lists interatomic distances in Å. for pairs of atoms in differing environments and, where appropriate, the corresponding bond energies, in kcal. mole^{-1}. In the third column, (c) denotes the crystalline state and (g) denotes the gaseous state, of the corresponding substance. In the case of a homonuclear compound, one-half of the interatomic distance may be identified with the corresponding atomic radius.

Bonds not involving carbon

			Bond lengths	Bond energies
Ag—Ag	Ag	(c)	2·89	
Ag—O	Ag$_2$O	(c)	2·05	
Ag—F	AgF	(c)	2·46	
Ag—Cl	AgCl	(c)	2·77	
Ag—Br	AgBr	(c)	2·88	
Ag—I	AgI	(c)	2·80	
Al—Al	Al	(c)	2·89	
Al—Cl	Al$_2$Cl$_6$	(c)	2·06, 2·21	
As—As	As	(c)	2·50	
Au—Au	Au	(c)	2·88	
Au—Cl	Au$_2$Cl$_6$	(c)	2·24, 2·34	
Ba—Ba	Ba	(c)	4·35	
Ba—O	BaO	(c)	2·76	
Be—Be	Be	(c)	2·23	
Be—O	BeO	(c)	1·64	
Bi—Bi	Bi	(c)	3·10	
Br—Br	Br$_2$	(g)	2·28	46·1
Br—H	HBr	(g)	1·41	87·4
Br—Cl	BrCl	(g)	2·14	53·0
Ca—Ca	Ca	(c)	3·95	
Ca—O	CaO	(c)	2·40	
Cd—Cd	Cd	(c)	2·98	
Cl—Cl	Cl$_2$	(g)	1·99	57·9
Cl—H	HCl	(g)	1·27	103·1
Co—Co	Co	(c)	2·51	
Cr—Cr	Cr	(c)	2·50	

			Bond lengths	Bond energies
Cr—O	CrO$_2$Cl$_2$	(g)	1·57	
Cr—Cl	CrO$_2$Cl$_2$	(g)	2·12	
Cs—Cs	Cs	(c)	5·31	
Cs—F	CsF	(c)	3·00	
Cs—F	CsF	(g)	2·35	122
Cs—Cl	CsCl	(c)	3·57	
Cs—Cl	CsCl	(g)	2·91	102
Cs—Br	CsBr	(c)	3·71	
Cs—Br	CsBr	(g)	3·07	93
Cs—I	CsI	(c)	3·95	
Cs—I	CsI	(g)	3·32	76
Cu—Cu	Cu	(c)	2·56	
Cu—Cl	Cs$_2$CuCl$_4$	(c)	2·22	
F—F	F$_2$	(g)	1·42	37
F—H	HF	(g)	0·92	135
F—H	F···H···F in liquid HF		2·55	
F—H	F···H···F in KHF$_2$	(c)	2·26	
Fe—Fe	Fe	(c), α	2·48	
H—H	H$_2$	(g)	0·74	104·2
Hg—Hg	Hg	(c)	3·01	
Hg—Cl	HgCl$_2$	(c)	2·25	
Hg—Br	HgBr$_2$	(c)	2·50	
Hg—I	HgI$_2$	(c)	2·78	
I—I	I$_2$	(c)	2·67	
I—I	I$_3^-$	(ion)	2·83, 3·04	
I—H	HI	(g)	1·61	71·4
I—Cl	ICl	(g)	3·32	50·5
K—K	K	(c)	4·54	
K—F	KF	(c)	2·66	
K—F	KF	(g)	2·55	119
K—Cl	KCl	(c)	3·14	
K—Cl	KCl	(g)	2·67	102
K—Br	KBr	(c)	3·29	
K—Br	KBr	(g)	2·82	92
K—I	KI	(c)	3·57	
K—I	KI	(g)	3·05	78
La—La	La	(c)	3·74	
Li—Li	Li	(c)	3·04	
Li—Li	Li$_2$	(g)	2·67	
Li—F	LiF	(c)	2·01	
Li—Cl	LiCl	(c)	2·57	
Li—Br	LiBr	(c)	2·75	
Li—I	LiI	(c)	3·00	
Lu—Lu	Lu	(c)	3·44	

Bonds not involving carbon – *continued*

			Bond lengths	Bond energies
Mg—Mg	Mg	(c)	3·20	
Mg—O	MgO	(c)	2·10	
N—N	N_2	(g)	1·10	171·1
N—N	N_3^-	(ion)	1·12	
N—H	NH_3	(g)	1·02	84·3
N—O	N_2O	(g)	1·19	
N—O	NO	(g)	1·15	
N—O	NO_2	(g)	1·19	
Na—Na	Na	(c)	3·72	
Na—Na	Na_2	(g)	3·08	
Na—F	NaF	(c)	2·31	
Na—Cl	NaCl	(c)	2·81	
Na—Cl	NaCl	(g)	2·36	99
Na—Br	NaBr	(c)	2·98	
Na—Br	NaBr	(g)	2·50	89
Na—I	NaI	(c)	3·23	
Na—I	NaI	(g)	2·71	72
Ni—Ni	Ni	(c)	2·49	
O—O	O_2	(g)	1·21	118·9
O—O	O_3	(g)	1·28	
O—O	H_2O_2	(c)	1·49	
O—H	H_2O	(c)	0·96	
O—H	H_2O_2	(c)	0·97	
Os—F	OsF_8	(g)	2·5	
P—P	P_4	(c)	2·21	
P—H	PH_3	(g)	1·42	77
P—Cl	PCl_5	(g)	2·04, 2·19	
P—Cl	PCl_4^+ } PCl_5	(c)	1·98	
P—Cl	PCl_6^- }		2·07	
Pb—Pb	Pb	(c)	3·50	
Pb—O	PbO	(c)	2·30	
Pb—O	PbO	(g)	1·92	
Rb—Rb	Rb	(c)	3·03	
Rb—F	RbF	(c)	2·82	
Rb—Cl	RbCl	(c)	3·27	
Rb—Br	RbBr	(c)	3·42	
Rb—I	RbI	(c)	3·66	
S—S	S_2	(g)	1·89	84
S—S	S_8	(c)	2·04	
S—H	H_2S	(g)	1·35	87·7
S—O	SO_2	(g)	1·43	128
S—O	SO_3	(g)	1·43	113
S—F	SF_6	(g)	1·57	
Sb—Sb	Sb	(c)	2·90	
Se—Se	Se	(c)	2·32	

Bonds not involving carbon – *continued*

			Bond lengths	Bond energies
Se—H	H_2Se	(g)	1·47	66
Si—Si	Si	(c)	2·35	
Si—H	SiH_4	(g)	1·48	76
Si—O	SiO_2, α-quartz	(c)	1·61	
Si—F	SiF_4	(g)	1·55	
Si—F	SiF_4	(c)	1·56	
Si—Cl	$SiCl_4$	(g)	2·01	
Si—Br	$SiBr_4$	(g)	2·15	
Si—I	SiI_4	(g)	2·43	
Si—I	SiI_4	(c)	2·45	
Sn—Sn	Sn	(c), α	2·81	
Sn—Sn	Sn	(c), β	3·02, 3·18	
Sn—O	SnO	(c)	2·57	
Te—Te	Te	(c)	2·86	
Te—H	H_2Te	(g)	1·67	
Tl—Tl	Tl	(c)	3·41	
Tl—Cl	TlCl	(c)	2·48	
Tl—Br	TlBr	(c)	2·62	
U—U	U	(c)	2·77	
Zn—Zn	Zn	(c)	2·67	
Zn—O	ZnO	(c)	1·95	

Bonds involving carbon

The data listed below represent general values for bond lengths and bond energies, averaged over several structures.

C—C	$\diagdown$C—C$\diagup$, Paraffinic	1·54	66·2
C—C	C=C , Ethylenic	1·33	112·9
C—C	—C≡C—, Acetylenic	1·20	150·3
C—C	Aromatic	1·40	
C—H	Paraffinic	1·09	91·1
C—H	Ethylenic	1·07	91
C—H	Acetylenic	1·06	91
C—H	Aromatic	1·08	
C—Cl	Paraffinic	1·77	70
C—Cl	Ethylenic	1·72	72
C—Cl	Acetylenic	1·64	
C—Cl	Aromatic	1·70	
C—N	Amines	1·47	51
C—N	Nitriles	1·16	161
C—O	Alcohols, aliphatic	1·43	72
C—O	Phenols	1·36	
C—O	Aldehydes, ketones	1·23	160
C—O	Acyl halides	1·17	
C—O	CO_2(g)	1·16	175
C—S	Thiols, aliphatic	1·81	59
C—S	Thioethers, aliphatic	1·81	61

Ionic radii

Element	Charge	Atomic number	Radius in Å.
Ac	+3	89	1·18
Ag	+1	47	1·26
Al	+3	13	0·51
Am	+3	95	1·07
Ar	+1	18	1·54
As	−3	33	2·22
	+3		0·58
Au	+1	79	1·37
	+3		0·85
B	+1	5	0·35
	+3		0·23
Ba	+2	56	1·34
Be	+2	4	0·35
Bi	+3	83	0·96
Br	−1	35	1·96
Ca	+2	20	0·99
Cd	+2	48	0·97
Ce	+3	58	1·07
	+4		0·94
Cl	−1	17	1·81
Co	+2	27	0·72
	+3		0·63
Cr	+2	24	0·89
	+3		0·63
Cs	+1	55	1·67
Cu	+1	29	0·96
	+2		0·72
Dy	+3	66	0·92
Er	+3	68	0·89
Eu	+3	63	0·98
F	−1	9	1·33
Fe	+2	26	0·74
	+3		0·64
Fr	+1	87	1·80
Ga	+1	31	0·81
	+3		0·62
Gd	+3	64	0·62
Ge	−4	32	2·72
	+2		0·73
	+4		0·53

Element	Charge	Atomic number	Radius in Å.
H	−1	1	1·54
Hf	+4	72	0·78
Hg	+1	80	1·27
	+2		1·10
Ho	+3	67	0·91
I	−1	53	2·20
In	+3	49	0·81
Ir	+4	77	0·68
K	+1	19	1·33
La	+1	57	1·39
	+3		1·14
Li	+1	3	0·68
Lu	+3	71	0·85
Mg	+1	12	0·82
	+2		0·66
Mn	+2	25	0·80
	+3		0·66
	+4		0·60
Mo	+1	42	0·93
	+4		0·70
	+6		0·62
N	−3	7	1·71
	+1		0·25
NH_4	+1		1·43
Na	+1	11	0·97
Nb	+1	41	1·00
	+4		0·74
Nd	+3	60	1·04
Ne	+1	10	1·12
Ni	+2	28	0·69
Np	+3	93	1·10
	+4		0·95
O	−2	8	1·32
	−1		1·76
Os	+4	76	0·88
P	−3	15	2·12
	+3		0·44
Pa	+3	91	1·13
	+4		0·98

Ionic radii – *continued*

Element	Charge	Atomic number	Radius in Å.
Pb	+2	82	1·20
	+4		0·84
Pd	+2	46	0·80
	+4		0·65
Pm	+3	61	1·06
Pr	+3	59	1·06
	+4		0·92
Pt	+2	78	0·80
	+4		0·65
Pu	+3	94	1·08
	+4		0·93
Ra	+2	88	1·43
Rb	+1	37	1·47
Re	+4	75	0·72
Rh	+3	45	0·68
Ru	+4	44	0·67
S	−2	16	1·84
	−1		2·19
Sb	−3	51	2·45
	+3		0·76
Sc	+3	21	0·81
Se	−2	34	1·91
	−1		2·32
Si	−4	14	2·71
	−1		1·84
Sm	+3	62	1·00
Sn	+2	50	0·93
	+4		0·71
Sr	+2	38	1·12
Tb	+3	65	0·93
	+4		0·81
Te	−2	52	2·11
	−1		2·50
Th	+4	90	1·02
Ti	+2	22	0·94
	+3		0·76
	+4		0·68
Tl	+1	81	1·47
	+3		0·95
Tm	+3	69	0·87
U	+4	92	0·97
V	+2	23	0·88
	+3		0·74
	+4		0·63
W	+4	74	0·70
Y	+3	39	0·92
Yb	+3	70	0·86
Zn	+2	30	0·74
Zr	+4	40	0·79

Appendix C
Solubility products

The data listed in this table are true thermodynamic solubility products at 25°C. They are tabulated in the form α, β, where β is the exponent of 10 which multiplies α. Thus $1\cdot7, -10$ must be interpreted as $1\cdot7 \times 10^{-10}$.

	α	β		α	β
AgCl	1·7	−10	$Fe(OH)_2$	1·8	−15
AgBr	5·0	−13	$Fe(OH)_3$	6·0	−38
AgI	8·5	−17	FeS	4·0	−19
AgCN	1·6	−14	Fe_2S_3	1·0	−88
AgCNS	1·0	−12	$FeCO_3$	2·1	−11
Ag_2CrO_4	1·9	−12	$FePO_4$	1·5	−18
$Al(OH)_3$	5·0	−33			
			Hg_2Cl_2	1·1	−18
$Ba(OH)_2$	5·0	−3	Hg_2Br_2	1·3	−22
BaF_2	2·4	−5	Hg_2I_2	4·5	−29
$BaCO_3$	1·6	−9	Hg_2S	1·0	−45
$BaSO_4$	1·5	−9	HgS	1·6	−54
$BaCrO_4$	8·5	−11	$Hg_2(CNS)_2$	3·0	−20
BaC_2O_4	1·5	−8			
			$KClO_4$	8·9	−3
$Ca(OH)_2$	1·3	−6			
CaF_2	1·7	−10	$La(OH)_3$	1·0	−19
$CaCO_3$	4·7	−9	$Lu(OH)_3$	2·5	−24
$CaSO_4$	2·4	−5			
$Ca_3(PO_4)_2$	1·3	−32	$Mg(OH)_2$	8·9	−12
CaC_2O_4	1·3	−9	MgF_2	8·0	−8
$Cd(OH)_2$	2·0	−14	$MgCO_3$	8·0	−9
CdS	1·0	−28	MgC_2O_4	8·6	−5
$CdCO_3$	5·2	−12	$Mn(OH)_2$	2·0	−13
$Co(OH)_2$	2·5	−16	MnS	7·0	−16
CoS, α	5·0	−22	$MnCO_3$	8·8	−11
CoS, β	1·9	−27			
$CoCO_3$	8·0	−13	$Ni(OH)_2$	1·6	−16
$CsClO_4$	3·2	−3	NiS, α	3·0	−21
$Cu(OH)_2$	1·6	−19	NiS, β	1·0	−26
CuCl	3·2	−7	$NiCO_3$	1·4	−7
CuBr	5·9	−9			
CuI	1·1	−12	$Pb(OH)_2$	4·2	−15
Cu_2S	1·2	−45	PbF_2	4·0	−8
CuS	8·0	−37	$PbCl_2$	1·6	−5
$CuCO_3$	2·5	−10			
CuCNS	4·0	−14			

Solubility products – *continued*

	α	β
$PbBr_2$	4·6	− 6
PbI_2	8·3	− 9
PbS	7·0	− 29
$PbCO_3$	1·5	− 13
$PbSO_4$	1·3	− 8
$Pb_3(PO_4)_2$	1·0	− 54
$PbCrO_4$	2·0	− 16
$RbClO_4$	3·8	− 3
$Sc(OH)_3$	1·0	− 27
$Sn(OH)_2$	3·0	− 27
SnS	1·0	− 26
$Sr(OH)_2$	3·2	− 4
SrF_2	7·9	− 10
$SrCO_3$	7·0	− 10
$SrSO_4$	7·6	− 7
$SrCrO_4$	3·6	− 5
SrC_2O_4	5·6	− 8
$Th(OH)_4$	1·0	− 39
ThF_4	7·0	− 12
TlCl	1·9	− 4
TlBr	3·6	− 6
TlI	8·9	− 8
Tl_2S	1·2	− 24
$Y(OH)_3$	8·1	− 23
$Zn(OH)_2$	4·5	− 17
ZnS	7·0	− 26
$ZnCO_3$	2·0	− 10

Selected constant boiling point (azeotropic) binary mixtures at 760 mm.

1. Minimum boiling point systems

A	B	Mole % A	Wt % A	b.p. (°C.)
H_2O	C_2H_5OH	10·6	4·43	78·2
	$(C_2H_5)_2O$	5·0	1·26	84·2
	C_6H_6	44·4	15·6	69·4
CH_3OH	$(CH_3)_2CO$	20·0	12·2	55·7
	C_6H_6	61·4	39·5	58·3
CH_3CO_2H	C_6H_6	97·5	96·8	80·1
C_2H_5OH	C_6H_6	44·8	32·4	68·2
	C_6H_{12}	33·2	21·4	58·7

2. Maximum boiling point systems

A	B	Mole % A	Wt % A	b.p. (°C.)
H_2O	HF	65·4	62·9	111·4
	HCl	88·9	79·8	108·6
	HBr	83·1	96·7	126·0
	HI	84·3	43·1	127·0
	$HClO_4$	32·0	7·79	203·0
	HNO_3 (735 mm.)	62·2	32·0	120·5
	HCO_2H	43·3	15·6	107·1
HCl	$(CH_3)_2O$	65·0	59·5	−1·5
$CHCl_3$	$(CH_3)_2CO$	65·5	79·6	105·4
HCO_2H	$(C_2H_5)_2CO$	48·0	33·0	64·5
C_6H_5OH	$C_6H_5CH_2OH$	8·0	7·04	206·0
	C_6H_5CHO	54·0	51·0	185·6

Selected cryoscopic and ebullioscopic constants

These have the units deg. C. mole kg.$^{-1}$ Their values must be determined from measurements on *dilute* solutions. Usually the units are given simply as deg. C.

Molal freezing point depression constants

Acetic acid	3·90
Benzene	5·11
Bromoform	14·3
Camphene	35
*Camphor	40
Cyclohexane	20·2
Naphthalene	6·9
Nitrobenzene	6·9
Water	1·86

* Commercial camphor is not usually a pure chemical compound. The cryoscopic constant should be determined for the given sample by means of a solute of known molecular weight.

Molal boiling point elevation constants

Acetic acid	3·07
Acetone	1·71
Benzene	2·65
Carbon tetrachloride	5·0
Ethanol	1·2
Water	0·52

Selected dissociation constants for acids and bases

The data in this appendix are true thermodynamic dissociation constants at 25°C. They are tabulated in the form described in the table of solubility products; K_1, K_2 and K_3 represent the first, second and third dissociation constants respectively.

		K_1		K_2		K_3	
		α	β	α	β	α	β
Acids							
Boric acid	H_3BO_3	7·3	-10	1·8	-13	1·6	-14
Carbonic acid	H_2CO_3	4·3	-7	5·6	-11		
Hydrofluoric acid	HF	3·5	-4				
Phosphoric acid	H_3PO_4	7·5	-3	6·2	-8	2·2	-13
Water	H_2O	1·0	-14				
Acetic acid	CH_3CO_2H	1·8	-5				
Benzoic acid	$C_6H_5CO_2H$	6·5	-5				
Monochloracetic acid	$ClCH_2CO_2H$	1·4	-3				
Dichloracetic acid	Cl_2CHCO_2H	3·3	-2				
Trichloracetic acid	Cl_3CCO_2H	2·0	-1				
Formic acid	HCO_2H	1·8	-4				
Malonic acid	$CH_2(CO_2H)_2$	1·5	-3	2·0	-6		
Oxalic acid	$(CO_2H)_2$	5·9	-2	6·4	-5		
Phenol	C_6H_5OH	1·3	-10				
Bases							
Ammonia	$NH_3 . H_2O$	1·8	-5				
Water	H_2O	1·0	-14				
Aniline	$C_6H_5NH_2$	3·8	-10				
Ethylamine	$C_2H_5NH_2$	5·6	-4				
Diethylamine	$(C_2H_5)_2NH$	9·6	-4				
Triethylamine	$(C_2H_5)_3N$	5·7	-4				
Para-phenylenediamine	$C_6H_4(NH_2)_2$	1·1	-8				
Piperidine	$(CH_2)_5NH$	1·6	-3				
Pyridine	C_5H_5N	1·7	-9				
Hydrazine*	NH_2NH_2	1·7	-6				
Hydroxylamine*	NH_2OH	1·1	-8				

* At 20°C.

Appendix D
Selected equivalent conductances of ions (at 18°C. and 25°C.)

	$\lambda*(18°C.)$	$\lambda*(25°C.)$
H^+	314	350
K^+	64·6	74·5
Na^+	43·5	50·9
NH_4^+	64·5	74·5
Ag^+	54·3	63·5
$\frac{1}{2}Ba^{2+}$	55	65
$\frac{1}{2}Ca^{2+}$	51	60
$\frac{1}{3}La^{3+}$	61	72
OH^-	172	192
Cl^-	65·5	75·5
NO_3^-	61·7	70·6
$CH_3CO_2^-$	34·6	40·8
$\frac{1}{2}SO_4^{2-}$	68	79
$\frac{1}{2}C_2O_4^{2-}$	63	73
$\frac{1}{3}Fe(CN)_6^{3-}$		101
$\frac{1}{4}Fe(CN)_6^{4-}$	95	111

* The units of λ are $ohm^{-1} cm.^{-1} l. g\text{-}equiv.^{-1}$

Selected electrode potentials

This appendix lists the standard oxidation potentials of couples (π_0 at 25°C. and unit activity). All couples are to be written as oxidations and with electrons on the right hand side of the equation, for example:

$$Zn \rightarrow Zn^{2+} + 2e \qquad \pi_0 = -0.76 \text{ V}.$$

$$Cu \rightarrow Cu^{2+} + 2e \qquad \pi_0 = 0.34 \text{ V}.$$

A negative value for π_0 means that the reduced form (Zn) of the couple is a better reducing agent than hydrogen (H_2). Further, a positive value for π_0 indicates that the oxidized form (Cu^{2+}) of the couple is a better oxidizing agent than hydrogen ion (H^+). By convention, the standard electrode potential for the reaction $\frac{1}{2}H_2 \rightarrow H^+ + e$ is taken as zero $\pi_0 = 0.00 \text{ V}$.

Standard oxidation potentials (volt)

Li/Li^+	-3.05	$\frac{1}{2}H_2/H^+$	0.00
K/K^+	-2.93	Cu^+/Cu^{2+}	$+0.15$
Rb/Rb^+	-2.93	Cu/Cu^{2+}	$+0.34$
Ba/Ba^{2+}	-2.90	$I^-/\frac{1}{2}I_2$	$+0.54$
Sr/Sr^{2+}	-2.89	Fe^{2+}/Fe^{3+}	$+0.77$
		$Hg/\frac{1}{2}Hg_2^{2+}$	$+0.79$
		Ag/Ag^+	$+0.80$
La/La^{3+}	-2.52	$\frac{1}{2}Hg_2^{2+}/Hg^{2+}$	$+0.92$
Mg/Mg^{2+}	-2.37	$Br^-/\frac{1}{2}Br_2$(liq.)	$+1.07$
$H^-/\frac{1}{2}H_2$	-2.25	$Cr^{3+}/Cr_2O_7^{2-}$	$+1.33$
Be/Be^{2+}	-1.85	$Cl^-/\frac{1}{2}Cl_2$	$+1.36$
Al/Al^{3+}	-1.66	Mn^{2+}/Mn^{3+}	$+1.51$
Mn/Mn^{2+}	-1.18	Mn^{2+}/MnO_4^-	$+1.51$
S^{2-}/S	-0.92	$F^-/\frac{1}{2}F_2$	$+2.85$
Se^{2-}/Se	-0.78		
Zn/Zn^{2+}	-0.76		
Te^{2-}/Te	-0.51		
Fe/Fe^{2+}	-0.44		
Cd/Cd^{2+}	-0.40		
Tl/Tl^+	-0.34		
Co/Co^{2+}	-0.28		
Ni/Ni^{2+}	-0.25		
Sn/Sn^{2+}	-0.14		
Pb/Pb^{2+}	-0.13		
$\frac{1}{2}H_2/H^+$	0.00		

Appendix E
Selected enthalpies of atomization

1. Enthalpies of sublimation of solids

The standard state for solids is the crystalline state at 25°C.; for gases it is 25°C. and 1 atmosphere pressure corrected for non-ideality. This section lists the standard enthalpy changes for the process:

$$X \text{ (cryst.)} \rightarrow X \text{ (gaseous atom).}$$

For crystalline solids, this is usually referred to as the sublimation enthalpy, S_m, and is measured in kcal. g-atom^{-1}.

Element	Atomic number	S_m
Li	3	38·4
Be	4	77·9
B	5	97·2
C	6	171·7
Na	11	25·9
Mg	12	35·6
Al	13	77·5
Si	14	88·0
S(S_8)	16	24·1
K	19	21·4
Ca	20	42·2
Sc	21	82·0
Ti	22	112·6
V	23	122·8
Cr	24	95·0
Mn	25	66·7
Fe	26	99·8
Co	27	101·6
Ni	28	101·3
Cu	29	81·1
Zn	30	31·2
Se	34	55·6
Rb	37	19·6
Sr	38	39·1
Ag	47	68·4
Cd	48	26·8
In	49	58·2
Sn	50	72·0

Selected enthalpies of atomization – *continued*

Element	Atomic number	S_m
Sb	51	60·8
Te	52	47·6
Cs	55	18·7
Ba	56	41·7
La	57	99·6
Hg	80	14·5
Tl	81	43·0
Pb	82	46·8
Bi	83	47·5
U	92	117·2

2. Dissociation enthalpies

The dissociation enthalpy $D(X_p)$ corresponds to the process:

$$X_p \text{ (standard state)} \rightarrow pX \text{ (gaseous atoms).}$$

The values are listed in kcal. mole^{-1}.

Element	Atomic number	Standard state		$D(X_p)$
H	1	H_2	(g)	103·2
O	8	O_2	(g)	117·1
F	9	F_2	(g)	36
S	16	S_8	(c)	415
Cl	17	Cl_2	(g)	57·1
Br	35	Br_2	(l)	52·8
I	53	I_2	(c)	50·4

Selected enthalpies of formation, free energies of formation and entropies

The standard enthalpies of formation, ΔH_f, and standard free energies of formation, ΔG_f, are listed in kcal. mole^{-1} and correspond to the process (at 25°C.):

$$aX(\text{standard state}) + bY(\text{standard state}) + \ldots \rightarrow X_a Y_b \ldots (\text{standard state}).$$

The standard entropy S^0 of $X_a Y_b \ldots$ is measured in cal. mole^{-1} deg.$^{-1}$ By convention, both the standard enthalpy of formation and the standard free energy of formation of elements in their standard states are taken to be zero. The standard entropy of $X_a Y_b \ldots$ is equal to the integral of the molar heat capacity divided by the temperature, with respect to temperature, over the temperature range -273°C. to 25°C.*

Species		$-\Delta H_f^0$	$-\Delta G_f^0$	S^0
Al	(c)	0·0	0·0	6·8
Al_2O_3, α	(c)	399·1	376·8	12·2
Al_2Cl_6	(c)	332·4	304·4	80·0
$Al(NH_4)(SO_4)_2 12H_2O$	(c)	1419	1179	166·6
Sb	(c)	0·0	0·0	10·8
$SbCl_3$	(c)	91·3	77·6	44·5
Ba	(c)	0·0	0·0	16·0
BaO	(c)	150·5	135·8	15·7
BaCl	(c)	111·0	105·3	23·4
$BaCl_2$	(c)	205·6	193·8	30·0
$BaCl_2 H_2O$	(c)	278·4	253·1	40·0
$BaCl_2 2H_2O$	(c)	349·4	309·8	48·5
$BaCO_3$	(c)	291·3	272·2	26·8
$BaSO_4$	(c)	350·2	323·4	31·6
Bi	(c)	0·0	0·0	13·6
$BiCl_3$	(c)	90·6	76·2	45·3
BiOCl	(c)	87·3	77·0	20·6
B	(c)	0·0	0·0	1·6
H_3BO_3	(c)	260·2	230·2	21·4
Br_2	(l)	0·0	0·0	36·4
HBr	(g)	8·7	12·7	47·4
BrCl	(g)	$-3·5$	0·2	57·3
Cd	(c)	0·0	0·0	12·3
CdS	(c)	34·5	33·6	17·0

* i.e. $\displaystyle\int_0^{298} \frac{C_p}{T} dT$

**Selected enthalpies of formation, free energies of
formation and entropies** – *continued*

Species		$-\Delta H_f^0$	$-\Delta G_f^0$	S^0
$CdCl_2$	(c)	93·0	81·9	28·3
$Cd(CN)_2$	(c)	$-39·0$	$-49·7$	24·9
Ca	(c)	0·0	0·0	10·0
CaO	(c)	151·9	144·4	9·5
$CaCO_3$	(c)	288·5	269·8	22·2
$CaSO_4$	(c)	342·4	315·6	25·5
C, graphite	(c)	0·0	0·0	1·4
C, diamond	(c)	$-0·5$	$-0·7$	0·6
CO	(g)	26·4	32·8	47·3
CO_2	(g)	94·1	94·3	51·1
HCO_2H	(l)	97·8	82·7	30·8
CH_3CO_2H	(l)	116·4	93·8	38·2
C_2N_2	(g)	$-73·6$	$-70·8$	57·9
CCl_4	(g)	25·5	15·4	74·0
$CHCl_3$	(g)	24·0	16·0	70·9
CH_2Cl_2	(g)	21·0	15·0	64·7
CH_3Cl	(g)	19·6	14·0	56·0
CH_4	(g)	17·9	12·1	44·5
Cl_2	(g)	0·0	0·0	53·3
HCl	(g)	22·1	22·8	44·6
Cr	(c)	0·0	0·0	5·7
$CrCl_3$	(c)	134·6	118·0	30·0
CrO_2Cl_2	(l)	143·1	125·4	50·0
Co	(c)	0·0	0·0	6·8
$CoCl_2$	(c)	75·8	65·5	25·4
Cu	(c)	0·0	0·0	8·0
Cu_2O	(c)	39·8	35·0	24·1
CuO	(c)	37·1	30·4	10·4
CuCl	(c)	32·5	28·2	20·2
$CuCl_2$	(c)	52·3	42·0	26·8
$CuSO_4 5H_2O$	(c)	544·5	449·3	73·0
F_2	(g)	0·0	0·0	48·6
HF	(g)	64·2	64·7	41·5
H_2	(g)	0·0	0·0	31·2
I_2	(c)	0·0	0·0	27·9
HI	(g)	$-6·2$	$-0·3$	49·3
ICl	(g)	$-4·2$	1·3	59·1
ICl	(c)	8·0	3·2	24·5
Fe, α	(c)	0·0	0·0	6·5
$FeCl_2$	(c)	81·5	72·2	28·6
$FeCl_3$	(c)	96·8	80·4	31·1
La	(c)	0·0	0·0	13·7
LaI_3	(c)	167·4	166·1	51·3
Pb	(c)	0·0	0·0	15·5
PbS	(c)	22·5	22·2	21·8
$PbCl_2$	(c)	85·9	75·0	32·6
Li	(c)	0·0	0·0	6·7
Li_2O	(c)	142·4	133·9	9·1
LiOH	(c)	116·5	105·9	10·2

Selected enthalpies of formation, free energies of formation and entropies – *continued*

Species		$-\Delta H_f^0$	$-\Delta G_f^0$	S^0
LiF	(c)	146·3	139·6	8·6
LiCl	(c)	97·7	91·7	13·2
LiBr	(c)	83·7	81·2	16·5
LiI	(c)	64·8	64·0	18·1
$LiNO_3$	(c)	115·3	93·1	25·2
Li_2CO_3	(c)	290·5	270·1	21·6
Li_2SO_4	(c)	342·8	316·6	27·0
Lu	(c)	0·0	0·0	14·5
LuI_3	(c)	133·2	131·0	51·3
Mg	(c)	0·0	0·0	7·8
MgO	(c)	143·8	136·1	6·4
MgCl	(c)	53·0	46·5	17·3
$MgCl_2$	(c)	153·4	141·6	21·4
$MgCO_3$	(c)	266·0	246·0	15·7
Mn	(c)	0·0	0·0	7·6
$MnCl_2$	(c)	115·3	105·5	28·0
MnO_2	(c)	124·2	111·1	12·7
Hg	(l)	0·0	0·0	18·5
HgO	(c)	21·7	14·0	17·2
Hg_2Cl_2	(c)	63·3	50·4	46·8
$HgCl_2$	(c)	55·0	44·4	34·5
Ni	(c)	0·0	0·0	7·2
$NiCl_2$	(c)	75·5	65·1	25·6
N_2	(g)	0·0	0·0	45·8
N_2O	(g)	− 19·5	− 24·8	52·6
NO	(g)	− 21·6	− 20·7	50·3
NO_2	(g)	− 8·1	− 12·4	57·5
O_2	(g)	0·0	0·0	49·0
O_3	(g)	− 34·0	− 39·0	56·8
H_2O	(g)	57·8	54·6	45·1
H_2O	(l)	68·3	56·7	16·7
H_2O_2	(l)	44·8	27·2	22·0
P, white P_4	(c)	0·0	0·0	10·6
PH_3	(g)	− 2·2	− 4·4	50·2
PCl_5	(g)	95·4	77·6	84·3
PCl_5	(c)	110·7		
K	(c)	0·0	0·0	15·2
K_2O	(c)	86·4	76·2	20·8
KOH	(c)	101·8	89·5	14·2
KF	(c)	134·5	127·4	15·9
$KF . 2H_2O$	(c)	277·0	242·7	36·0
KCl	(c)	104·1	97·6	19·8
KBr	(c)	93·7	90·6	23·1
KI	(c)	78·3	77·0	24·9
KNO_3	(c)	117·8	94·0	31·8
K_2CO_3	(c)	273·9	255·5	33·6
K_2SO_4	(c)	342·7	314·6	42·0
Sc	(c)	0·0	0·0	8·0

Selected enthalpies of formation, free energies of formation and entropies – *continued*

Species		$-\Delta H_f^0$	$-\Delta G_f^0$	S^0
$ScCl_3$	(c)	220·8	205·7	30·4
Se	(c)	0·0	0·0	10·0
SeO_2	(c)	55·0	41·5	13·6
H_2Se	(g)	$-20·5$	$-17·0$	52·9
Si	(c)	0·0	0·0	4·5
SiO_2, quartz	(c)	205·4	192·4	10·0
SiO_2, cristobalite	(c)	205·0	192·1	10·2
SiF_4	(g)	370·0	360·0	68·0
$SiCl_4$	(g)	145·7	136·2	79·2
Ag	(c)	0·0	0·0	10·2
AgF	(c)	48·5	44·2	20·0
AgCl	(c)	30·4	26·2	23·0
AgBr	(c)	23·8	22·9	25·6
AgI	(c)	14·9	15·9	27·3
AgCN	(c)	$-34·9$	$-39·2$	20·0
Na	(c)	0·0	0·0	12·2
Na_2O	(c)	99·4	90·0	17·4
NaOH	(c)	102·0	90·1	12·5
NaF	(c)	136·0	129·3	14·0
NaCl	(c)	98·2	91·8	17·3
NaBr	(c)	86·0	83·1	20·5
NaI	(c)	68·8	56·7	22·1
$NaNO_3$	(c)	101·5	87·5	27·8
Na_2CO_3	(c)	270·3	250·4	32·5
Na_2SO_4	(c)	330·9	302·8	35·7
Sr	(c)	0·0	0·0	13·0
SrO	(c)	141·1	133·8	13·0
$SrCO_3$	(c)	291·9	271·9	23·2
$SrSO_4$	(c)	345·3	318·9	29·1
S, rhombic S_8	(c)	0·0	0·0	7·6
S_2	(g)	$-29·9$		
SO_2	(g)	70·8	71·8	59·4
SO_3	(g)	94·5	88·5	61·2
H_2S	(g)	4·8	7·9	49·2
SF_6	(g)	262·0	237·0	69·5
Te	(c)	0·0	0·0	11·9
TeO_2	(c)	77·7	64·6	17·0
H_2Te	(g)	$-36·9$	$-33·1$	56·0
Tl	(c)	0·0	0·0	15·4
TlCl	(c)	49·0	44·2	25·9
TlBr	(c)	41·2	39·7	28·6
Sn, α	(c)	0·0	0·0	12·3
SnS	(c)	18·6	19·7	23·6
$SnCl_2$	(c)	83·6	72·2	29·3
Ti	(c)	0·0	0·0	7·2
$TiCl_3$	(c)	165·0	148·0	30·5
V	(c)	0·0	0·0	7·1
VCl_3	(c)	137·0	120·0	31·3

**Selected enthalpies of formation, free energies of
formation and entropies** – *continued*

Species		$-\Delta H_f^0$	$-\Delta G_f^0$	S^0
Zn	(c)	0·0	0·0	10·0
ZnS, zinc blende	(c)	48·5	47·4	13·8
ZnS, wurtzite	(c)	45·3	44·2	13·8
$ZnCl_2$	(c)	99·4	82·3	25·9
$Zn(CN)_2$	(c)	− 18·4	− 29·0	22·9

Appendix F
Integrated rate equations

1. Second order rate equation

$$\frac{dx}{dt} = k(a-x)(b-x)$$

$$\int \frac{dx}{(a-x)(b-x)} = k \int dt.$$

From partial fractions,

$$\frac{1}{(a-x)(b-x)} = \frac{\frac{1}{(b-a)}}{(a-x)} - \frac{\frac{1}{(b-a)}}{(b-x)}$$

$$\therefore \quad \int \frac{dx}{(a-x)(b-x)} = \frac{1}{(b-a)} \int \frac{dx}{(a-x)} - \frac{1}{(b-a)} \int \frac{dx}{(b-x)},$$

i.e. $$kt = \frac{1}{(b-a)}[-\ln(a-x)+\ln(b-x)]+\text{constant}$$

$$= \frac{1}{(b-a)}\left\{\ln\frac{(b-x)}{(a-x)}\right\}+\text{constant}.$$

At $t = 0, x = 0$, i.e.

$$0 = \frac{1}{(b-a)}\ln\left(\frac{b}{a}\right)+\text{constant},$$

hence $$kt = \frac{1}{(b-a)}\ln\frac{a(b-x)}{b(a-x)}.$$

2. Equilibrium reactions (both reactions of first order)

$$\frac{dx}{dt} = k_1(a-x)-k_{-1}(b+x)$$

$$= k_1 a - k_{-1}b - (k_1+k_{-1})x$$

$$= (k_1+k_{-1})\left\{\frac{k_1 a - k_{-1}b}{k_1+k_{-1}} - x\right\}$$

$$= (k_1+k_{-1})(A-x),$$

where $\quad A = \dfrac{k_1 a - k_{-1} b}{k_1 + k_{-1}}$

$$\therefore \quad \int \frac{dx}{(A-x)} = (k_1 + k_{-1}) \int dt$$

$$-\ln(A-x) = (k_1 + k_{-1})t + \text{constant}$$

At $t = 0, x = 0$,

$$(k_1 + k_{-1})t = \ln \frac{A}{(A-x)}, = \ln \frac{a - a_\infty}{a_t - a_\infty}.$$

At equilibrium, $\dfrac{k_1}{k_{-1}} =$ equilibrium constant K

$$K = \left\{ \frac{(b+x)}{(a-x)} \right\}_{t=\infty}.$$

If b (i.e. [B] at $t = 0$) is zero,

$$K = \frac{x_\infty}{(a-x_\infty)}.$$

Answers to Problems

Chapter 2

  1. Consider the ionic radii
  2. -89.5 kcal g-atom^{-1} (average)

Chapter 3

  4. -56.1 kcal. mole^{-1}
  5. -23.1 kcal. mole^{-1}
  6. -12.4 kcal. mole^{-1}
  7. -340.5 kcal. mole^{-1}

Chapter 4

1.

	t_c°C.	P_c (atm.)		t_c°C.	P_c(atm.)
He	-269	1·93	N_2	-144	34·1
H_2	-240	12·8	CO_2	29	72·1
O_2	-122	50·1	NH_3	128	114

  2. 0.321°C. atm.$^{-1}$; -2°C.
  3. Assign R cal. to each of the three modes of vibration, per mole of water.
  4. (i) $(21\bar{3})$, (ii) (104), (iii) $(00\bar{1})$, (iv) $(1\bar{2}0)$, (v) $(\bar{3}\bar{1}2)$, (vi) $(12, 3\bar{4})$

  5. $1:\dfrac{2}{\sqrt{2}}:\dfrac{1}{\sqrt{3}}:3\dfrac{1}{\sqrt{13}}$

  7. 5.84 Å; 4.12 Å.
  8. 21.2 kcal. mole^{-1} deg.$^{-1}$, 22.5 kcal. mole^{-1} deg.$^{-1}$, 26.0 kcal. mole^{-1} deg.$^{-1}$.

Chapter 5

1. Assume constant volume conditions; then $\alpha = \dfrac{(P-p_0)}{p_0}$, where p_0 is the initial

pressure of N_2O_4, and is given by: $p_0 = cRT(c = $ mole l.$^{-1}$ $N_2O_4)$
$$K_p = 0.141, 0.305; \Delta H = 14.1 \text{ kcal. mole}^{-1}.$$

2. 43.2 kcal. mole^{-1}, 41.3 kcal. mole^{-1}, 40.0 kcal. mole^{-1}, 39.2 kcal. mole^{-1}, 38.9 kcal. mole^{-1}, 40.5 kcal. mole^{-1}

$$a = 78.60, b = 6.447 \times 10^{-2}, c = 2.643 \times 10^{-5}$$

5. (i) 4.13×10^{-5} g. l.$^{-1}$, (ii) 3.83×10^{-3} g. l.$^{-1}$

6. 1.6051 or -124.6051.

7. (i) 12·0, (ii) 2·30, (iii) 2·40, (iv) 7·01
8. 7·46, 7·00, 6·51; 12·8 kcal. mole^{-1}
9. (i) 3·52, (ii) 8·77, (iii) 5·13, (iv) 7·00, (v) 9·18, (vi) 9·09
10. 4·05, +0·14.
11. 1·8
12. See figure 104.

Chapter 6

2. 246·8 mm.; 20·79 mm.
3. 44·1
4. 45·9
6. 60·7
7. 5·09°C.; 5·0°C.; 4·90°C.
8. 0·0816 l. atm. mole^{-1} deg.$^{-1}$, 0·0819 l. atm. mole^{-1} deg.$^{-1}$, 0·0839 l. atm. mole^{-1} deg.$^{-1}$, 0·0852 l. atm. mole^{-1} deg.$^{-1}$, 0·0874 l. atm. mole^{-1} deg.$^{-1}$, 0·0894 l. atm. mole^{-1} deg.$^{-1}$, 0·0806 l. atm. mole^{-1} deg.$^{-1}$ at $c = 0$
9. −0·153°C.
10. (i) 0·069°C., (ii) 0·245 atm.
11. 0·047; 0·890
12. (i) 1·333 g., (ii) 1·440 g.
13. 59·5%
14. (i) 4, (ii) 337±2

Chapter 7

1. 0·705(3) g.
3. (i) 3·695, (ii) 109·3 ohm^{-1} cm.$^{-1}$ l. g-equiv.$^{-1}$
4. 4·47 × 10^{-4} ohm^{-1} cm.$^{-1}$
5. 378·2 ohm^{-1} cm.$^{-1}$ l. g-equiv.$^{-1}$;   108·5 ohm^{-1} cm.$^{-1}$ l. g-equiv.$^{-1}$; 76·5 ohm^{-1} cm.$^{-1}$ l. g-equiv.$^{-1}$: 346·2 ohm^{-1} cm.$^{-1}$ l. g-equiv.$^{-1}$; 1·12 × 10^{-10} ohm^{-1} cm.$^{-1}$ l. g-equiv.$^{-1}$
6. 1·06 × 10^{-10}; 0·971.
7. $t_+ = 0·462$; $t_- = 0·538$
8. (iii) 0·76 V., 0·80 V., 1·56 V.
   (iv) −35·09 kcal. mole^{-1}, −36·94 kcal. mole^{-1}, −72·03 kcal. g-atom^{-1}
9. −12·87 kcal. mole^{-1}; −13·68 kcal. mole^{-1}; 2·72 cal. mole^{-1} deg.$^{-1}$
10. 0·225 V.; −6·28 × 10^{-4} V. deg.$^{-1}$
11. 4·02
12. −1·602 × 10^{-19} coloumb, +3·204 × 10^{-19} coulomb
13. −4·06 kcal. mole^{-1} Hg_2Cl_2

Chapter 8

1. 0·00335 min.$^{-1}$; 20·9 min.
2. (a) 70·3 year, (b) 6·47 × 10^{-6} g.
3. 0·01036 min^{-1}; 66·9 min.

4. In general, the half-life for a reaction of order n is proportional to $\dfrac{1}{a^{n-1}}$, where a is the initial concentration. In this example, plot $\log t_{1/2}$ against a and determine n from the slope.

Zero order; 0.133 mm. sec^{-1}

5. 2nd order; (i) 0.133 l. mole^{-1} sec.$^{-1}$, (ii) 55.8 kcal. mole^{-1}

6. 1st order; 0.0206 min.$^{-1}$

Four-figure logarithm tables

	0	1	2	3	4	5	6	7	8	9	1	2	3	4	5	6	7	8	9
10	0000	0043	0086	0128	0170	0212	0253	0294	0334	0374	4	8	13	17	21	25	29	33	37
11	0414	0453	0492	0531	0569	0607	0645	0682	0719	0755	4	8	11	15	19	23	27	30	34
12	0792	0828	0864	0899	0934	0969	1004	1038	1072	1106	4	7	10	14	17	21	24	28	31
13	1139	1173	1206	1239	1271	1303	1335	1367	1399	1430	3	6	10	13	16	19	23	26	29
14	1461	1492	1523	1553	1584	1614	1644	1673	1703	1732	3	6	9	12	15	18	21	24	27
15	1761	1790	1818	1847	1875	1903	1931	1959	1987	2014	3	6	8	11	14	17	20	23	25
16	2041	2068	2095	2122	2148	2175	2201	2227	2253	2279	3	5	8	11	13	16	18	21	24
17	2304	2330	2355	2380	2405	2430	2455	2480	2504	2529	2	5	7	10	12	15	17	20	22
18	2553	2577	2601	2625	2648	2672	2695	2718	2742	2765	2	5	7	9	12	14	16	19	21
19	2788	2810	2833	2856	2878	2900	2923	2945	2967	2989	2	4	7	9	11	13	16	18	20
20	3010	3032	3054	3075	3096	3118	3139	3160	3181	3201	2	4	6	9	11	13	15	17	19
21	3222	3243	3263	3284	3304	3324	3345	3365	3385	3404	2	4	6	8	10	12	14	16	18
22	3424	3444	3464	3483	3502	3522	3541	3560	3579	3598	2	4	6	8	10	12	14	15	17
23	3617	3636	3655	3674	3692	3711	3729	3747	3766	3784	2	4	6	7	9	11	13	15	17
24	3802	3820	3838	3856	3874	3892	3909	3927	3945	3962	2	4	5	7	9	11	12	14	16
25	3979	3997	4014	4031	4048	4065	4082	4099	4116	4133	2	3	5	7	9	10	12	14	15
26	4150	4166	4183	4200	4216	4232	4249	4265	4281	4298	2	3	5	7	8	10	12	13	15
27	4314	4330	4346	4362	4378	4393	4409	4425	4440	4456	2	3	5	6	8	9	11	13	14
28	4472	4487	4502	4518	4533	4548	4564	4579	4594	4609	2	3	5	6	8	9	11	12	14
29	4624	4639	4654	4669	4683	4698	4713	4728	4742	4757	1	3	4	6	7	9	10	12	13
30	4771	4786	4800	4814	4829	4843	4857	4871	4886	4900	1	3	4	6	7	9	10	11	13
31	4914	4928	4942	4955	4969	4983	4997	5011	5024	5038	1	3	4	6	7	8	10	11	12
32	5052	5065	5079	5092	5105	5119	5132	5145	5159	5172	1	3	4	5	7	8	9	11	12
33	5185	5198	5211	5224	5237	5250	5263	5276	5289	5302	1	3	4	5	6	8	9	10	12
34	5315	5328	5340	5353	5366	5378	5391	5403	5416	5428	1	3	4	5	6	8	9	10	11
35	5441	5453	5465	5478	5490	5502	5514	5527	5539	5551	1	2	4	5	6	7	9	10	11
36	5563	5575	5587	5599	5611	5623	5635	5647	5658	5670	1	2	4	5	6	7	8	10	11
37	5682	5694	5705	5717	5729	5740	5752	5763	5775	5786	1	2	3	5	6	7	8	9	10
38	5798	5809	5821	5832	5843	5855	5866	5877	5888	5899	1	2	3	5	6	7	8	9	10
39	5911	5922	5933	5944	5955	5966	5977	5988	5999	6010	1	2	3	4	6	7	8	9	10
40	6021	6031	6042	6053	6064	6075	6085	6096	6107	6117	1	2	3	4	5	6	8	9	10
41	6128	6138	6149	6160	6170	6180	6191	6201	6212	6222	1	2	3	4	5	6	7	8	9
42	6232	6243	6253	6263	6274	6284	6294	6304	6314	6325	1	2	3	4	5	6	7	8	9
43	6335	6345	6355	6365	6375	6385	6395	6405	6415	6425	1	2	3	4	5	6	7	8	9
44	6435	6444	6454	6464	6474	6484	6493	6503	6513	6522	1	2	3	4	5	6	7	8	9
45	6532	6542	6551	6561	6571	6580	6590	6599	6609	6618	1	2	3	4	5	6	7	8	9
46	6628	6637	6646	6656	6665	6675	6684	6693	6702	6712	1	2	3	4	5	6	7	7	8
47	6721	6730	6739	6749	6758	6767	6776	6785	6794	6803	1	2	3	4	5	5	6	7	8
48	6812	6821	6830	6839	6848	6857	6866	6875	6884	6893	1	2	3	4	4	5	6	7	8
49	6902	6911	6920	6928	6937	6946	6955	6964	6972	6981	1	2	3	4	4	5	6	7	8
50	6990	6998	7007	7016	7024	7033	7042	7050	7059	7067	1	2	3	3	4	5	6	7	8
51	7076	7084	7093	7101	7110	7118	7126	7135	7143	7152	1	2	3	3	4	5	6	7	8
52	7160	7168	7177	7185	7193	7202	7210	7218	7226	7235	1	2	2	3	4	5	6	7	7
53	7243	7251	7259	7267	7275	7284	7292	7300	7308	7316	1	2	2	3	4	5	6	7	7
54	7324	7332	7340	7348	7356	7364	7372	7380	7388	7396	1	2	2	3	4	5	6	6	7

Reproduced from *The Penguin–Honeywell Book of Tables* (ed. F. W. Kellaway), Penguin Books, 1968.

	0	1	2	3	4	5	6	7	8	9	1	2	3	4	5	6	7	8	9
														Mean differences					
55	7404	7412	7419	7427	7435	7443	7451	7459	7466	7474	1	2	2	3	4	5	5	6	7
56	7482	7490	7497	7505	7513	7520	7528	7536	7543	7551	1	2	2	3	4	5	5	6	7
57	7559	7566	7574	7582	7589	7597	7604	7612	7619	7627	1	2	2	3	4	5	5	6	7
58	7634	7642	7649	7657	7664	7672	7679	7686	7694	7701	1	1	2	3	4	4	5	6	7
59	7709	7716	7723	7731	7738	7745	7752	7760	7767	7774	1	1	2	3	4	4	5	6	7
60	7782	7789	7796	7803	7810	7818	7825	7832	7839	7846	1	1	2	3	4	4	5	6	6
61	7853	7860	7868	7875	7882	7889	7896	7903	7910	7917	1	1	2	3	4	4	5	6	6
62	7924	7931	7938	7945	7952	7959	7966	7973	7980	7987	1	1	2	3	3	4	5	6	6
63	7993	8000	8007	8014	8021	8028	8035	8041	8048	8055	1	1	2	3	3	4	5	5	6
64	8062	8069	8075	8082	8089	8096	8102	8109	8116	8122	1	1	2	3	3	4	5	5	6
65	8129	8136	8142	8149	8156	8162	8169	8176	8182	8189	1	1	2	3	3	4	5	5	6
66	8195	8202	8209	8215	8222	8228	8235	8241	8248	8254	1	1	2	3	3	4	5	5	6
67	8261	8267	8274	8280	8287	8293	8299	8306	8312	8319	1	1	2	3	3	4	5	5	6
68	8325	8331	8338	8344	8351	8357	8363	8370	8376	8382	1	1	2	3	3	4	4	5	6
69	8388	8395	8401	8407	8414	8420	8426	8432	8439	8445	1	1	2	3	3	4	4	5	6
70	8451	8457	8463	8470	8476	8482	8488	8494	8500	8506	1	1	2	2	3	4	4	5	6
71	8513	8519	8525	8531	8537	8543	8549	8555	8561	8567	1	1	2	2	3	4	4	5	5
72	8573	8579	8585	8591	8597	8603	8609	8615	8621	8627	1	1	2	2	3	4	4	5	5
73	8633	8639	8645	8651	8657	8663	8669	8675	8681	8686	1	1	2	2	3	4	4	5	5
74	8692	8698	8704	8710	8716	8722	8727	8733	8739	8745	1	1	2	2	3	4	4	5	5
75	8751	8756	8762	8768	8774	8779	8785	8791	8797	8802	1	1	2	2	3	3	4	5	5
76	8808	8814	8820	8825	8831	8837	8842	8848	8854	8859	1	1	2	2	3	3	4	5	5
77	8865	8871	8876	8882	8887	8893	8899	8904	8910	8915	1	1	2	2	3	3	4	4	5
78	8921	8927	8932	8938	8943	8949	8954	8960	8965	8971	1	1	2	2	3	3	4	4	5
79	8976	8982	8987	8993	8998	9004	9009	9015	9020	9025	1	1	2	2	3	3	4	4	5
80	9031	9036	9042	9047	9053	9058	9063	9069	9074	9079	1	1	2	2	3	3	4	4	5
81	9085	9090	9096	9101	9106	9112	9117	9122	9128	9133	1	1	2	2	3	3	4	4	5
82	9138	9143	9149	9154	9159	9165	9170	9175	9180	9186	1	1	2	2	3	3	4	4	5
83	9191	9196	9201	9206	9212	9217	9222	9227	9232	9238	1	1	2	2	3	3	4	4	5
84	9243	9248	9253	9258	9263	9269	9274	9279	9284	9289	1	1	2	2	3	3	4	4	5
85	9294	9299	9304	9309	9315	9320	9325	9330	9335	9340	1	1	2	2	3	3	4	4	5
86	9345	9350	9355	9360	9365	9370	9375	9380	9385	9390	1	1	2	2	3	3	4	4	5
87	9395	9400	9405	9410	9415	9420	9425	9430	9435	9440	0	1	1	2	2	3	3	4	4
88	9445	9450	9455	9460	9465	9469	9474	9479	9484	9489	0	1	1	2	2	3	3	4	4
89	9494	9499	9504	9509	9513	9518	9523	9528	9533	9538	0	1	1	2	2	3	3	4	4
90	9542	9547	9552	9557	9562	9566	9571	9576	9581	9586	0	1	1	2	2	3	3	4	4
91	9590	9595	9600	9605	9609	9614	9619	9624	9628	9633	0	1	1	2	2	3	3	4	4
92	9638	9643	9647	9652	9657	9661	9666	9671	9675	9680	0	1	1	2	2	3	3	4	4
93	9685	9689	9694	9699	9703	9708	9713	9717	9722	9727	0	1	1	2	2	3	3	4	4
94	9731	9736	9741	9745	9750	9754	9759	9763	9768	9773	0	1	1	2	2	3	3	4	4
95	9777	9782	9786	9791	9795	9800	9805	9809	9814	9818	0	1	1	2	2	3	3	4	4
96	9823	9827	9832	9836	9841	9845	9850	9854	9859	9863	0	1	1	2	2	3	3	4	4
97	9868	9872	9877	9881	9886	9890	9894	9899	9903	9908	0	1	1	2	2	3	3	4	4
98	9912	9917	9921	9926	9930	9934	9939	9943	9948	9952	0	1	1	2	2	3	3	4	4
99	9956	9961	9965	9969	9974	9978	9983	9987	9991	9996	0	1	1	2	2	3	3	3	4

Index

Periodic table

3 **Li**	4 **Be**	

11 **Na**	12 **Mg**	

19 **K**	20 **Ca**	21 Sc

37 **Rb**	38 **Sr**	39 Y

55 **Cs**	56 **Ba**	57 La	58 *Ce*	59 *Pr*	60 *Nd*	61 *Pm*	62 *Sm*	63 *Eu*	64 *Gd*	65 *Tb*	66 *Dy*	67 *Ho*	68 *Er*	69 *Tm*
87 **Fr**	88 **Ra**	89 Ac	90 *Th*	91 *Pa*	92 *U*	93 *Np*	94 *Pu*	95 *Am*	96 *Cm*	97 *Bk*	98 *Cf*	99 *Es*	100 *Fm*	101 *Md*